ELEMENTARY
DIFFERENTIAL
EQUATIONS

This book is in the
ADDISON-WESLEY SERIES IN MATHEMATICS

ELEMENTARY
DIFFERENTIAL
EQUATIONS

by

WILLIAM TED MARTIN *and* ERIC REISSNER

Department of Mathematics
Massachusetts Institute of Technology

SECOND EDITION

ADDISON-WESLEY PUBLISHING COMPANY, INC.

READING, MASSACHUSETTS · PALO ALTO · LONDON

To Henry Bayard Phillips

PREFACE

It has been the authors' aim to write an introductory book on differential equations which is of particular interest to students who need to know mathematics rather well because of their work in science and engineering. Our selection of material and method of presentation are intended to give students of this kind as much of a working knowledge and understanding of the subject as can be accomplished on the introductory level. However, it is our hope that mathematics majors as well will find our approach of interest.

We think that it is possible to see two major aspects to a study of differential equations. One of these aspects is concerned with the translation of problems from the fields of science and engineering into mathematical equation form. The other has to do with ways of solving the mathematical equations, so as to extract information of interest from them.

We have, as is customary, included many relatively simple examples of how to formulate scientific and engineering problems as differential equations. We are, however, inclined to feel that it is a present-day trend to delegate this task more and more to the teacher of physics, mechanics, engineering, chemistry, and even economics. Consequently, we have arranged the material in such a manner that it is possible to omit material on "setting up" of differential equations without affecting the continuity of the text.

Concerning the contents of our book, we may make the following remarks. We begin with a chapter on geometrical and physical problems. This chapter may be omitted or portions of it may be inserted at suitable places throughout the text.

Our second chapter deals with the first-order equation. We introduce the notions of unique solution and of general and particular solution and then discuss some of the equations which can be solved in closed form. We next take up power-series solutions, first for linear and then for nonlinear problems. Part of what we are doing here is for the purpose of facilitating subsequent work on higher-order equations. We have included sections, which we think will generally be left for further reading by interested students, on convergence of series solutions and on the possibility of somewhat unusual power-series expansions.

Chapter 3 deals with the second-order equation. Again we talk about unique, general, and particular solution, and about the significance of initial conditions. After treating the important equation $y'' = f(y, y')$ in the conventional way, we concentrate on the linear equation and stress the notions of the superposition principle and of the general solution.

This is followed by a detailed treatment of the equation with constant coefficients and of the equidimensional equation. After this we turn to the method of variation of parameters and from there we proceed to power-series methods. We begin with Taylor series expansions and the notion of the ordinary point. We go on to more general power-series expansions and to the notion of the regular singular point. (Some of this material need not be taken up during a first study.) The chapter concludes with an explicit treatment of Bessel's differential equation.

Chapter 4 is on the nth-order equation. In it we amplify some of the work on the second-order equation. We also introduce the Laplace transform method for the initial value problem of the nth-order equation with constant coefficients.

Chapter 5 is the final chapter on the theory of ordinary differential equations. In it we discuss systems of simultaneous first-order equations. Renewed discussion is given to the notions of general solution, of initial conditions, and of the superposition principle. Systems with constant coefficients are treated in the traditional way and also by means of the Laplace transform. Of interest should be the treatment of the method of variation of parameters which becomes particularly simple for first-order systems.

Chapter 6 begins with a discussion on how to find numerical values for the solution of a differential equation. We discuss application of the trapezoidal rule and of Simpson's rule to the step-by-step solution of first-order equations. This leads us to equation solving by iteration, and from there we go to Picard's method as a device for obtaining approximate solutions. The remainder of the chapter is devoted to the existence and uniqueness proof by means of Picard's method. To simplify the treatment the work is in two steps, first on equations for which we can prove existence and uniqueness for all values of the independent variable, and then for the larger class of problems where we are dealing with a finite interval.

Chapter 7, which is motivated in part by the work on numerical procedures, contains a brief treatment of finite difference equations. We consider first-order equations and higher-order equations with constant coefficients, including the method of variation of parameters. In conclusion we illustrate some of the possible difficulties in connection with approximating differential equations by difference equations.

In the final chapter, Chapter 8, we attempt an introduction to the subject of partial differential equations. Starting with equations such as $\partial z(x, y)/\partial x = 0$, we introduce the notion of arbitrary function and from this we go on to the quasi-linear first-order equation with two independent variables. For this equation we discuss the solution by means of the characteristic equations and, by way of the notion of characteristic curves, look into what may happen in regard to prescribed initial conditions.

Going on to second-order equations, we elected to concentrate on the separation-of-variables method, illustrated by various problems concerning the conduction of heat. The basic notions are brought home by considering in succession different versions of the way in which they occur. We introduce Fourier series, in action as it were, leaving a detailed treatment to more advanced courses. Finally, by considering an axisymmetrical problem, we exemplify the use of Bessel functions and give an inkling of orthogonal series other than Fourier series.

It should be apparent from the foregoing description that one of our aims has been to establish a number of fundamental notions rather firmly in the reader's mind, by considering them not just once but by returning to them on several occasions, each time in a slightly different context. We have also attempted to motivate the individual developments in this book in as natural a way as we knew how. We hope that we may in this way contribute not only to the reader's knowledge of differential equations but also to his ability to think about problems of mathematical analysis in general.

As for the use of this book as a text, we have found that about two-thirds of it can be covered in a one-semester, three-hour course. Our own selection of material for such a course would be as follows: Chapter 2, Sections 2–1 through 2–7, 2–9 through 2–12; Chapter 3, Sections 3–1 through 3–13, 3–15, 3–16; Chapter 4, Sections 4–1 through 4–8; Chapter 5, Sections 5–1, 5–2, 5–4 through 5–6; and 8 to 10 lessons selected from one of the Chapters 6, 7, and 8. We like the idea of having extra material for voluntary reading by some of the students.

The present second edition of the book differs from the first edition in a number of ways which include a larger number of exercises in the individual sections; newly introduced miscellaneous exercises at the end of each chapter; additional work on linear motion with variable mass (including a discussion of the principle of one- and two-stage rockets) and two new sections on plane motion (including plane motion with variable mass); a new section on differential operator methods; a revised treatment of the idea of general solution; additional work in Fourier series; various minor improvements, simplifications, and extensions, in particular, on the subjects of Bessel's equation, Laplace transform solutions, and first-order partial differential equations.

W. T. M., E. R.

Cambridge, Mass.

CONTENTS

CHAPTER 1

NATURE AND ORIGIN OF DIFFERENTIAL EQUATIONS

1-1 Introduction. Many of the basic laws of physics are formulated quantitatively by mathematical relations involving certain functions of space and time and various derivatives of these quantities. Mathematical relations of this kind are called *differential equations*.

There are at least two aspects to a study of differential equations. One of them is to learn how to describe a phenomenon in terms of differential equations. To illustrate, we may know that Newton's Law for the motion of a particle of fixed mass is mass times acceleration equals force, but it is a long way from this to the differential equations governing the behavior of missiles in flight. A problem of this sort is so complex that it must be broken down into many parts. A part of the problem has to do with the flow of fluids, another part with thermodynamics, and still another part with the deformability of the structure of the missile, to mention just a few of the questions which arise. Each part of the problem must be simplified as far as possible by elimination of unimportant effects in order not to lose sight of its essential features. In this process of simplification experimental evidence and past experience with related problems play an important role.

Once differential equations describing a phenomenon have been formulated the next step is their solution, so as to obtain information on the behavior of the system under investigation. This is the second aspect of the study of differential equations.

There are many facets to this second aspect of the study of differential equations. We may be interested in obtaining explicit analytical solutions of problems. We may be interested in proving existence and uniqueness (or non-uniqueness) of the solutions of a class of differential equations. We may be interested in devising methods for obtaining numerical values of the solution of certain classes of differential equations, or we may be interested in using a specific method of this nature for the solution of a specific differential equation problem.

While thinking of the practical values of a study of differential equations, we should not overlook that here, as in all other mathematics, the human mind may go on and extend the scope of the subject in unexpected ways beyond what would seem to be of interest from the point of view of simple and even of sophisticated applications of the subject.

1

1–2 Examples of differential equations. One of the basic problems of calculus is the determination of a function $y = f(x)$ when its derivative dy/dx is a given function of x. The solution of this problem is effected through the process of integration. Given the relation

$$\frac{dy}{dx} = g(x), \tag{1}$$

the function y is obtained in the form

$$y = \int g(x)\, dx + c. \tag{2}$$

In some cases the integral on the right of (2) can be expressed in terms of a finite number of known functions ("in closed form"), for instance when $g(x) = x$, or $g(x) = 2 \sin 3x$, or $g(x) = x^{-1} \ln x + 3 \tan 2x + \sqrt{x^2 - 1}$. In other cases this is not possible and the integral must be evaluated by the use of infinite series or by application of numerical procedures such as Simpson's rule.

Equation (1) is a particularly simple case of what is called a differential equation. The theory of differential equations is concerned with relations which are more general than Eq. (1) and with methods of solution which take the place of the step from Eq. (1) to Eq. (2).

In some instances this generalization offers no particular difficulties. For example, the differential equation

$$\frac{dy}{dx} = \frac{g(x)}{y} \tag{3}$$

may be written in the form

$$\frac{d}{dx}\left(\frac{y^2}{2}\right) = g(x), \tag{4}$$

and consequently its solution is

$$\tfrac{1}{2}y^2 = \int g(x)\, dx + c \tag{5}$$

or

$$y = \pm\sqrt{2\int g(x)\, dx + 2c}. \tag{6}$$

A fairly general class of equations which includes (1) and (3) as special cases is the following:

$$f\left(x, y, \frac{dy}{dx}, \dots, \frac{d^n y}{dx^n}\right) = 0. \tag{7}$$

In Eq. (7) a relation is specified between an *independent variable, x,* a *dependent variable, y,* and the derivatives of this dependent variable. Since the highest derivative in (7) is the nth derivative, Eq. (7) is called a *differential equation of the nth order.*

A *solution* of the differential equation (7) is a relation of the form

$$g(x, y) = 0, \tag{8}$$

which has the property that whenever x and y are related in this form then x, y, and the first n derivatives of y obtained from (8) by differentiation satisfy (7) identically. In speaking of the solution of a differential equation it will often be desirable to make statements concerning the domain or interval of the variables for which this solution is applicable.

To give a simple illustration of the foregoing statement, the second-order differential equation

$$f(x, y, y', y'') \equiv y'' - x = 0$$

has the solution

$$g(x, y) \equiv y - \tfrac{1}{6}x^3 + c_1 x + c_2 = 0,$$

where c_1 and c_2 are arbitrary constants, and this solution is valid for all values of x.

The following are some further specific examples of nth-order differential equations:

$$\frac{dy}{dx} + y + x^2 = 0 \qquad (n = 1), \tag{9}$$

$$\left(\frac{dy}{dx}\right)^3 + \sin\left(y\frac{dy}{dx}\right) + x^2\frac{dy}{dx} + 1 = 0 \qquad (n = 1), \tag{10}$$

$$\frac{d^2y}{dx^2} + 2\frac{dy}{dx} + 3y - 4 = 0 \qquad (n = 2), \tag{11}$$

$$\frac{d^4y}{dx^4} + x\frac{d^2y}{dx^2} + y - 1 - x^2 = 0 \qquad (n = 4). \tag{12}$$

We shall see later that certain of these equations can be solved quite easily, while others are difficult indeed.

Equations (2) and (6) are examples of solutions of simple differential equations of first order. In a sense, we may say that solving these first-order equations means reducing their order from first to zeroth order. Analogous steps are often possible in connection with higher-order differential equations. For example, the second-order equation

$$\frac{d^2y}{dx^2} = \frac{dy}{dx} + 1$$

may be reduced, by simple integration, to the first-order equation

$$\frac{dy}{dx} = y + x + c,$$

where c is an arbitrary constant. While such a reduction of order is not by itself a solution, it represents a step in the direction toward obtaining the solution and as such is often of great importance.

We have so far discussed functions y of one independent variable x and differential equations for such functions. We may also consider functions depending on several independent variables. As an example, we may have a function z depending on the two independent variables x and y. The function z has two first-order *partial* derivatives, $\partial z/\partial x$ and $\partial z/\partial y$. A relation of the form

$$f\left(x, y, z, \frac{\partial z}{\partial x}, \frac{\partial z}{\partial y}\right) = 0 \tag{13}$$

is called a *partial differential equation*. Because (13) contains first derivatives and no higher derivatives it is a partial differential equation of the first order.*

A celebrated partial differential equation of the second order is the following:

$$\frac{\partial^2 z}{\partial x^2} + \frac{\partial^2 z}{\partial y^2} = 0. \tag{14}$$

It happens that there is a close connection between this equation and the theory of functions of a complex variable $x + iy$. Due to this circumstance, a great deal more is known about the solutions of this partial differential equation than about the solution of other equations which on the surface appear to be no more difficult than (14).

Exercises

1. Verify that

   (a) $y = x^2 + c$ (b) $y^2 = e^x + c$ (c) $yx - c = 0$ (d) $y = cx^2$

are solutions of the differential equations

   (a) $y' - 2x = 0$ (b) $2y'y = e^x$ (c) $y'x + y = 0$ (d) $xy' = 2y$

---

* A differential equation which does *not* involve partial derivatives is often called an *ordinary* differential equation. Equations (9) through (12) are examples of ordinary differential equations in this sense.

2. Solve

(a) $y' = 2$ (b) $y' = 2e^{3x}$ (c) $y' = 2(1 - x^2)^{-1/2}$

(d) $y' = e^{x^2}$ (e) $y' = xe^{x^2}$ (f) $y' = \sin^{-1} x$

3. Solve

(a) $y' = yx$ (b) $y' = y^2x^2$ (c) $y' = -xe^y$

(d) $y' \sin y = x^2$ (e) $xy' = (1 - y^2)^{1/2}$ (f) $(y')^2 - y^2 = 0$

(g) $(y')^2 - 3y' + 2 = 0$

(h) $(1 + x^2)y' = 1$ (i) $y' \sin x = 1$

4. By direct integration, reduce the order of each of the following differential equations as far as possible.

(a) $y'' - y' + 1 = 0$ (b) $y'' + 1 = 0$ (c) $y'' + 2y' = x$

(d) $y''' + 2 = 0$ (e) $y^{iv} + 2y'' = 1$ (f) $y^{iv} - y' = x$

1–3 Geometrical problems. Many questions of a geometrical nature require for their answer the solution of a differential equation.

We know that for a plane curve with equation $y = f(x)$ the angle ϕ which the tangent to the curve at a point (x, y) makes with the x-axis is given by the relation

$$\tan \phi = \frac{dy}{dx}. \tag{1}$$

The radius of curvature R at a point (x, y) of the curve $y = f(x)$ is given by

$$\frac{1}{R} = \frac{d^2y/dx^2}{[1 + (dy/dx)^2]^{3/2}}. \tag{2}$$

If we now ask for the equation of all curves with the property that the slope or the radius of curvature of these curves bears some specified relation to the coordinates of points on the curves we are led to a differential equation. The solutions of this differential equation give us the required curves.

EXAMPLE 1. Determine all plane curves for which the part of every tangent between the x-axis and the point of tangency is bisected by the y-axis.

Since the y-axis bisects the part of the tangent between the x-axis and the point $P(x, y)$ of tangency (Fig. 1–1), the point at which the tangent crosses the y-axis must have the coordinates $(0, \frac{1}{2}y)$. The slope of the tangent is then given by

$$\tan \phi = \frac{dy}{dx} = \frac{y - \frac{1}{2}y}{x - 0} \tag{3}$$

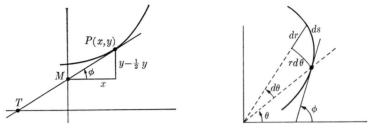

FIGURE 1–1   FIGURE 1–2

and the differential equation of the problem has the form

$$\frac{dy}{dx} = \frac{y}{2x}.$$ (4)

If we write (4) in the form

$$\frac{1}{y}\frac{dy}{dx} = \frac{d\ln|y|}{dx} = \frac{1}{2x},$$ (5)

its solution is obtained by ordinary integration:

$$\ln|y| = \tfrac{1}{2}\ln|x| + c.$$ (6)

An alternate form of the solution (6) is

$$y^2 = C|x|,$$ (7)

where $C = e^{2c}$.

The constant of integration C can be determined by the requirement that the curve $y^2 = C|x|$ pass through some specified point (x_0, y_0). For instance, if we ask that it pass through the point (2, 3) we find $C = \tfrac{9}{2}$.

EXAMPLE 2. Determine all plane curves such that their radius of curvature at a point x, y is equal to k-times the distance of this point from the origin.

We have

$$R = k\sqrt{x^2 + y^2}.$$ (8)

The differential equation of the curves follows by combination of (8) and (2):

$$\left[1 + \left(\frac{dy}{dx}\right)^2\right]^{3/2} = k(x^2 + y^2)^{1/2}\frac{d^2y}{dx^2}.$$ (9)

There is no such simple direct way of solving this differential equation as for the differential equation of Example 1.

Sometimes it is more convenient for the formulation of problems to use coordinates other than cartesian coordinates, for instance polar coordinates r and θ. The expressions for sloping angle ϕ and radius of curvature R in polar coordinates are (Fig. 1–2)

$$\tan(\phi - \theta) = r\frac{d\theta}{dr}, \tag{10}$$

$$\frac{1}{R} = \frac{d\phi}{ds} = \frac{r^2 - r\,(d^2r/d\theta^2) + 2\,(dr/d\theta)^2}{\{r^2 + (dr/d\theta)^2\}^{3/2}}. \tag{11}$$

EXAMPLE 3. Determine all plane curves with the property that at each point the tangent angle ϕ is k-times the polar angle θ.

We have $\phi = k\theta$ and this together with Eq. (10) gives the differential equation

$$\tan[(k - 1)\theta] = r\frac{d\theta}{dr}. \tag{12}$$

The differential equation (12) is again simple enough to be solved by direct integration. When $k \neq 1$ we write (12) in the form

$$\frac{1}{r}\frac{dr}{d\theta} = \frac{d\ln|r|}{d\theta} = \cot[(k - 1)\theta]. \tag{13}$$

From this we obtain as the polar equation of the required curves

$$\ln|r| = \frac{1}{k - 1}\ln|\sin[(k - 1)\theta]| + c,$$

or

$$|r| = C\,|\sin[(k - 1)\theta]|^{1/(k-1)}, \qquad k \neq 1, \tag{14a}$$

where $C = e^c$. When $k = 1$, the differential equation (12) reduces to $d\theta/dr = 0$ and from this

$$\theta = c, \qquad k = 1. \tag{14b}$$

EXAMPLE 4. Obtain the differential equation of Example 2 in polar coordinates r, θ.

We write Eq. (8) in the form $R = kr$ and combine this with (11). The resulting differential equation is

$$\left[r^2 + \left(\frac{dr}{d\theta}\right)^2\right]^{3/2} = kr\left[r^2 - r\frac{d^2r}{d\theta^2} + 2\left(\frac{dr}{d\theta}\right)^2\right]. \tag{15}$$

At first sight this seems to be little simpler than (9). Equation (15) does, however, have one important advantage over (9) which we shall appreciate later on. While (9) contains the independent variable x as well as the dependent variable y explicitly, Eq. (15) does *not* contain the independent variable θ explicitly.

A slightly different situation exists when the area under a curve is required to be in some prescribed relation to other geometrical properties of the curve. The following example will illustrate this.

EXAMPLE 5.   Determine plane curves, above the x-axis and passing through the point (a, b), with $b > 0$, such that at any station $x > a$ the area under the curve in the interval (a, x) is proportional to the difference between the final and initial ordinates.

The curves which are defined in this way must be obtained from the relation

$$\int_a^x y \, dx = k(y - b). \tag{16}$$

To determine y as a function of x we can differentiate (16) with respect to x. This leads to the differential equation

$$y = k \frac{dy}{dx}, \tag{17}$$

which has the solution

$$k \ln y = x + c \tag{18}$$

or

$$y = C e^{x/k}, \tag{19}$$

where $C = e^{c/k}$. The value of the constant C follows from the condition that $y(a) = b$, giving $C = b e^{-a/k}$ and

$$\frac{y}{b} = e^{(x-a)/k}. \tag{20}$$

EXERCISES

In Exercises 1 and 2 reduce the geometric problem to a differential equation of the form $f(x, y, dy/dx) = 0$. (Do not solve the resulting differential equations.)

1. Determine all plane curves for which the normal between the point (x, y) and the x-axis is of constant length a.

2. Determine all plane curves with the property that the radius vector from the origin to a point (x, y) of the curve is twice as long as the portion of the tangent between this point and the x-axis.

3. Determine the differential equation which has as solution curves all circles of fixed radius R with (a) centers on the x-axis, (b) centers on the line $y = x$.

In Exercises 4 and 5 reduce the geometric problems to differential equations of the form $f(r, \theta, dr/d\theta) = 0$.

4. Determine all plane curves which intersect all lines through the origin at the same angle α.

5. Determine all plane curves with arc proportional to the difference of the radii from the origin to its ends.

6. Determine all plane curves such that the tangent line at each point of any one of them and the line joining that point with the origin form an isosceles triangle when the x-axis is taken as the base of the triangle.

7. Determine all plane curves such that the part of every tangent between the coordinate axes is bisected at the point of tangency.

8. Determine all plane curves for which the projection of the ordinate on the normal is of constant length a.

9. Prove that the catenary $y = \cosh x$ has the property that its radius of curvature at any point (x, y) is equal to the length of the normal from this point to the x-axis.

1–4 Examples of physical problems leading to one first-order differential equation.

Among the simplest physical problems expressible in mathematical terms are those for which the *rate of change* of a quantity depends in a specified way on the *instantaneous value* of this quantity.

The rate of change of a quantity q which is a function of time t is given by the derivative

$$\frac{dq}{dt}.$$

A relation between the rate of change of q and the instantaneous value of q is of the form

$$f\left(q, \frac{dq}{dt}\right) = 0. \tag{1}$$

This is a first-order differential equation in which the independent variable t does not occur explicitly. Often the form of the relation between q and dq/dt also depends on time t. In that case we have a differential equation of the form

$$f\left(t, q, \frac{dq}{dt}\right) = 0. \tag{2}$$

Initial conditions. Usually the formulation of a physical problem involving rates of change requires more than the derivation of appropriate differential equations. Additional information must be supplied concerning the state of the system at the *beginning* of the process. Information of this kind provides the *initial conditions* for the solutions of the differential equations.

The following examples are simple illustrations of how to derive a differential equation and initial conditions for a physical problem.

EXAMPLE 1. A radioactive substance decomposes at a rate proportional to the amount present. Starting with a given amount of the substance at time $t = t_0$, what can be said about the available amount at a later time?

Let q be the amount of the substance still present at time t and let q_0 be the initial amount at time t_0. The rate of change dq/dt is negative and proportional to q, and this we express in equation form by writing

$$\frac{dq}{dt} = -kq, \tag{3}$$

where k is a positive constant of proportionality.

The solution of the differential equation (3) is

$$q = ce^{-kt}, \tag{4}$$

where c is a constant of integration.

The initial condition $q(t_0) = q_0$ gives us

$$q_0 = ce^{-kt_0}, \tag{5}$$

and this we may use to eliminate the constant of integration c from (4). The result is

$$q = q_0 e^{-k(t-t_0)}. \tag{6}$$

To determine the value of the constant of proportionality k in the differential equation we evidently need further information. Suppose it is known that one-half the original amount q_0 is decomposed in n years. This means that

$$q = \tfrac{1}{2}q_0 \quad \text{when } t - t_0 = n, \tag{7}$$

and consequently

$$\tfrac{1}{2}q_0 = q_0 e^{-kn} \tag{8}$$

or

$$k = \frac{\ln 2}{n}. \tag{9}$$

EXAMPLE 2. Water flowing from the orifice of a container at depth h below the surface has the velocity

$$v = c\sqrt{2gh}, \tag{10}$$

where g is the acceleration due to gravity and c is a constant the value of which depends on the shape of the orifice. For circular orifices under normal conditions c may be taken as 0.6. On the basis of this formula we may solve the following problem.

Assuming that the water level at time $t = t_0$ is at $h = h_0$, determine the water level at any time $t > t_0$.

Let A_{or} be the area of the cross section of the orifice. In time dt an amount of water given by $A_{or} v \, dt$ leaves the container.* Let $A(h)$ be the area of the water surface a distance h from the orifice. In time dt the water level changes by an amount dh and the volume of water by $A(h) \, dh$. Since the change in water volume must equal the amount which has flowed out, we have

$$A(h) \, dh = -A_{or} v \, dt$$

or, with v given by (10),

$$\frac{dh}{dt} = -A_{or} c\sqrt{2g} \, \frac{\sqrt{h}}{A(h)} . \tag{11}$$

The differential equation (11) is to be solved subject to the initial condition $h = h_0$ when $t = t_0$. Before we can solve (11) we must know the shape of the container or, in other words, the form of the function $A(h)$.†

EXAMPLE 3. In a tank are V gallons of brine containing initially x_0 pounds of dissolved salt. Water runs into the tank at the rate of v gallons per minute and the uniform mixture runs out at the same rate. How much salt is in the tank at the end of t minutes?

Let x be the number of pounds of salt in the tank at time t and let c be the concentration, defined as

$$c = \frac{x}{V} . \tag{12}$$

Each gallon of brine contains c pounds of salt. In time dt, $v \, dt$ gallons of water come in and $v \, dt$ gallons of brine go out, taking along $cv \, dt$ pounds of salt. The amount of salt going out in time dt is alternatively given by $-dx$. Equating these two expressions, we have

$$-dx = cv \, dt. \tag{13}$$

---

* The statement "In time dt an amount of water given by $A_{or} v \, dt$ leaves the container" may be stated in a mathematically precise form as follows: "At time t the rate of change of the volume of water with respect to time is $-A_{or} v(t)$." (The minus sign enters because the volume of water is decreasing.) The other terminology is, however, frequently employed.

† We remark that the formulas (10) and (11) apply not only to water but also to other liquids of low viscosity.

With the concentration c given by (12), we obtain the simple differential equation

$$\frac{dx}{dt} = -\frac{v}{V}x, \tag{14}$$

where the factor v/V is a given constant.

The initial condition is

$$t = 0: \quad x = x_0, \tag{15}$$

and with this the solution of (14) becomes

$$x = x_0 e^{-(v/V)t}. \tag{16}$$

EXERCISES

1. Assuming that radium decomposes at a rate proportional to the amount present, and that one-half of a given quantity of radium decomposes in 1600 years, what percentage of the original amount is left at the end of 100 years?

2. An amount of money is invested at the rate of (a) 2%, (b) 3%, (c) 4%, per annum, compounded continuously. After how many years will the amount be doubled?

3. A cylindrical tank of radius R and length L is initially full of water. Find the time required to empty this tank through a small orifice in its bottom (a) when the axis of the tank is vertical, (b) when the axis of the tank is horizontal.

4. Assuming that the rate of increase of population of a country is proportional to the number of inhabitants, determine the number of inhabitants at any time t, given that for $t = t_0$ this number is N_0 and for $t = t_1$ it is N_1.

5. Many chemicals dissolve in water at a rate which is jointly proportional to the amount undissolved and to the difference between the concentration in the saturated solution and the concentration in the actual solution. For a chemical of this nature determine the amount x undissolved at time t, given that at initial time $t = t_0$ we have $x = x_0$ and at time $t = t_1$ we have $x = x_1$, and that the solution when saturated contains an amount M of the chemical.

6. It is often assumed for the purposes of a simple mathematical model that the rate of increase of population of a country is jointly proportional to the number of inhabitants and to the difference between the maximum population which can be supported and the actual population. Let M be the maximum population which can be supported. Let $N = N_0$ be the population at time $t = t_0$ and $N = N_1$ the population at some later time $t = t_1$. Determine the population at any time $t > t_0$.

1–5 One-dimensional steady flow of heat. We consider a slab of solid material of face area A and thickness h. Let the temperature on one face of the slab be T_i and on the other T_o. The slab may represent the wall of a house, or a glass pane, T_i the inside temperature and T_o the outside temperature. The questions which arise naturally are (a) assuming that T_i is greater than T_o, what amount of heat is lost in unit time across the slab, and (b) how does the temperature vary across the thickness of the slab?

Experiment indicates that if the material of the slab is *homogeneous* then the temperature variation across its thickness is linear and the amount of heat Q lost in unit time is jointly proportional to the area A and to the temperature difference $T_i - T_o$, and inversely proportional to the thickness h of the slab:

$$Q = kA \frac{(T_i - T_o)}{h}. \tag{1}$$

The constant of proportionality k is a property of the material called *thermal conductivity*. If T is measured in degrees centigrade, h in centimeters, A in square centimeters, and Q in calories per second, then the units of k are cal/sec·cm°C. With these units the following are values of k for some materials:

copper	0.92
iron	0.74
aluminum	0.50
window glass	0.0025
concrete	0.0022
brick	0.0012
magnesia	0.00017

Let x be the distance in the direction of the thickness of the slab measured from the "inner" face toward the outer face, and T the temperature at distance x; then

$$T = T_i + \frac{T_o - T_i}{h} x \tag{2}$$

and

$$\frac{dT}{dx} = \frac{T_o - T_i}{h}. \tag{3}$$

Consequently, Eq. (1) for the flow of heat across a homogeneous slab may also be written in the form

$$Q = -kA \frac{dT}{dx}. \tag{4}$$

Equation (4) may be used to determine the flow of heat not only through homogeneous slabs but also through bodies of other shapes and through nonhomogeneous solids, so long as the temperature may be considered to be a function of a single coordinate.

EXAMPLE 1. Determine the variation of temperature and the heat flow through the walls of a homogeneous spherical shell of inner radius r_i and outer radius r_o if the values of the temperature $T(r)$ are given for r_i and r_o.

We have $A = 4\pi r^2$ and therewith

$$Q = -k4\pi r^2 \frac{dT}{dr}.$$ (5)

From this,

$$T = \frac{Q}{4\pi k} \frac{1}{r} + c.$$

Now

$$T(r_i) = \frac{Q}{4\pi k} \frac{1}{r_i} + c = T_i,$$

$$T(r_o) = \frac{Q}{4\pi k} \frac{1}{r_o} + c = T_o,$$

and from this we find for the unknown quantities c and Q,

$$c(r_i - r_o) = r_i T_i - r_o T_o$$

and

$$\frac{Q}{4\pi k} \left(\frac{1}{r_i} - \frac{1}{r_o} \right) = T_i - T_o.$$

The last equation indicates that the amount of heat Q flowing through the walls of the shell in unit time is given by

$$Q = 4\pi k \frac{r_o r_i}{r_o - r_i} (T_i - T_o).$$ (6a)

Let us note that this relation may be written in the form

$$Q = k\sqrt{A_o A_i} \frac{T_i - T_o}{h},$$ (6b)

where h is the wall thickness of the shell. In this form the result is analogous to Eq. (1) for the flow of heat through a slab of constant area A.

The temperature distribution across the wall is

$$T = \frac{T_i - T_o}{(1/r_i) - (1/r_o)} \frac{1}{r} + \frac{r_i T_i - r_o T_o}{r_i - r_o}$$

or, written in more symmetrical form,

$$T = \frac{T_i r_i}{r_o - r_i} \left(\frac{r_o}{r} - 1 \right) + \frac{T_o r_o}{r_i - r_o} \left(\frac{r_i}{r} - 1 \right).$$ (7)

EXAMPLE 2. Determine the temperature distribution and the flow of heat across the thickness h of a slab with temperature T_i at $x = 0$ and T_o at $x = h$ if the thermal conductivity k varies linearly from a value k_i to a value k_o.

We have

$$k = k_i + \frac{k_o - k_i}{h} x \tag{8}$$

and therewith

$$Q = -A \left(k_i + \frac{k_o - k_i}{h} x \right) \frac{dT}{dx} \tag{9}$$

or

$$\frac{dT}{dx} = -\frac{Q}{A} \frac{1}{k_i + (k_o - k_i)(x/h)} \cdot$$

From this,

$$\int_{T_i}^{T} dT = T - T_i = -\frac{Q}{A} \int_0^x \frac{dx}{k_i + (k_o - k_i)(x/h)}$$

$$= -\frac{Q}{A} \frac{h}{k_o - k_i} \ln \frac{k_i + (k_o - k_i)(x/h)}{k_i} \cdot$$

Setting $x = h$ in this, we obtain the following relation between the value of Q and the given data of the problem:

$$T_o - T_i = -\frac{Q}{A} \frac{h}{k_o - k_i} \ln \frac{k_o}{k_i} \cdot \tag{10}$$

With Q taken from (10) we may write the formula for the temperature distribution $T(x)$ in the following form:

$$\frac{T - T_i}{T_o - T_i} = \frac{\ln \{1 + [(k_o/k_i) - 1](x/h)\}}{\ln (k_o/k_i)} \cdot \tag{11}$$

Comparison of (10) with (1) indicates that so far as the rate of heat flow through this nonhomogeneous slab is concerned, we may replace the actual slab by an equivalent homogeneous slab with thermal conductivity k given by

$$k = \frac{k_o - k_i}{\ln k_o/k_i} \cdot$$

If we set $k_o = (1 + \epsilon)k_i$, then

$$k = \frac{\epsilon k_i}{\ln (1 + \epsilon)} \cdot$$

For small values of $|\epsilon|$, we have

$$k = \left(1 + \frac{\epsilon}{2} - \frac{\epsilon^2}{12} \pm \cdots\right) k_i.$$

We may compare this expression for k with the arithmetic mean

$$\frac{k_o + k_i}{2} = \left(1 + \frac{\epsilon}{2}\right) k_i.$$

Evidently less heat is lost through the actual slab than through a homogeneous slab with thermal conductivity equal to the arithmetic mean $\frac{1}{2}(k_o + k_i)$.

EXERCISES

1. A concrete wall is 15 cm thick. If the temperature of the inner surface is 25°C and that of the outer surface is —5°C, find the heat loss during one 8-hr period through one square meter of the wall.

2. A steam pipe with 25 cm outside radius is protected with a 12-cm layer of magnesia. If the temperature of the outer surface of the layer is 20°C and that of the surface of the pipe 150°C, determine the heat loss per day through one meter-length of pipe.

3. Calculate the rate of heat flow Q and the temperature distribution T through a composite slab consisting of two homogeneous layers of thickness h_1 and h_2 with thermal conductivities k_1 and k_2.

4. Show that the thermal conductivity k of a homogeneous slab of thickness $h_1 + h_2$ with the same rate of heat flow as the composite slab of Exercise 3 is given by the relation

$$\frac{h_1 + h_2}{k} = \frac{h_1}{k_1} + \frac{h_2}{k_2}.$$

5. Generalize the result of Exercise 4 to composite slabs consisting of n layers of thickness $h_1, h_2, \ldots, h_n$ with thermal conductivities $k_1, k_2, \ldots, k_n$.

Calculate the rate of heat flow Q and the temperature distribution T through a unit length of circular cylindrical pipe with inner radius r_i and outer radius r_o, and with wall temperatures T_i and T_o, under the assumption that the pipe:

6. is homogeneous;

7. consists of a metal pipe of thickness h_1 surrounded by an insulating jacket of thickness h_2;

8. has a thermal conductivity distribution given by $k_i + (k_o - k_i)(r/h)$.

1–6 Motion along a straight line. In this section we consider the motion of bodies under the influence of forces such that the path of the center of mass of the body is a straight line. Along this straight line, measured from some fixed origin O, let x be the displacement of the center of mass of the body at time t. The velocity v with which the body moves is defined as the rate of change of displacement x:

$$v = \frac{dx}{dt}. \tag{1}$$

Let m be the mass of the body and mv the *momentum* of the body. Newton's law states that the rate of change of momentum equals the acting force F:

$$\frac{d}{dt}(mv) = F. \tag{2}$$

The acting force F may be the sum of several forces, for instance the sum of the force of gravity and a frictional force. It must be given as a function of time t, distance x, and velocity v.

The mass m of the body will here be taken as the standard weight W of the body measured in pounds, divided by the standard acceleration due to gravity, $g = 32.174$ ft/sec^2:

$$m = \frac{W}{g}. \tag{3}$$

For a body with unchanging mass Newton's law assumes the form

$$ma = F, \tag{4}$$

where a is the acceleration of the center of mass of the body:

$$a = \frac{dv}{dt}. \tag{5}$$

Equations (1) and (2) are two simultaneous first-order equations for distance x and velocity v. They may be reduced to one second-order differential equation for x by introducing (1) into (2):

$$\frac{d}{dt}\left(m\,\frac{dx}{dt}\right) = F\left(t,\,x,\,\frac{dx}{dt}\right). \tag{6}$$

To determine the motion of bodies in accordance with the differential equation (6) we must also know, besides the form of the force function F, the position and velocity at the start of the motion. These starting values furnish the *initial conditions* for the solution of the differential equations.

We add one important observation concerning the general differential equation (6). If time t does not occur *explicitly* in it then the second-order equation may be reduced to a first-order equation for v as a function of x, as follows. We write

$$\frac{dx}{dt} = v \quad \text{and} \quad \frac{dmv}{dt} = \frac{dmv}{dx}\frac{dx}{dt} = v\frac{dmv}{dx}. \tag{7}$$

With this, Eq. (6) becomes

$$v\frac{dmv}{dx} = F(x, v). \tag{8}$$

EXAMPLE 1. A body of mass m traveling vertically upward started with velocity v_0. Determine the height H to which it travels, and the time T required to reach this height, assuming that the only force acting is a constant gravitational force.

Let x be the distance from the starting point of the motion, and $-mg$ the force of gravity, which is in the direction of decreasing x (that is, negative). The differential equations (1) and (2) are here

$$\frac{dx}{dt} = v, \quad m\frac{dv}{dt} = -mg.$$

The initial conditions are

$$t = 0: \quad v = v_0, \quad x = 0$$

We see that our problem can be solved directly, by repeated integration. We find

$$v = v_0 - gt \quad \text{and} \quad x = v_0 t - \tfrac{1}{2}gt^2.$$

The time T of travel is found by setting $v = 0$:

$$T = \frac{v_0}{g}.$$

Having T, we find the height of travel H by setting $t = T$ in the expression for x:

$$H = \frac{1}{2}\frac{v_0^2}{g}.$$

These values of both T and H are suitable reference values when it comes to analyzing such effects as air resistance, variable gravitational attraction, and variable particle mass.

EXAMPLE 2. A body of mass m is traveling vertically upward, starting with velocity v_0 at the surface of the earth. Determine the height h to which it travels, neglecting all resistances except the gravitational pull of the earth, which varies inversely as the square of the distance from its center. In particular, show that the mass m will keep on traveling indefinitely provided v_0 is greater than the "escape velocity" $\sqrt{2gR}$, where R is the radius of the earth.

Let x be the distance from the center of the earth and, as before, $v = dx/dt$. The gravitational force is now of the form k/x^2 and the value of the constant k follows from the condition that when $x = R$ this force is of magnitude mg. This means that $k = -mgR^2$ and the differential equation of motion is

$$m \frac{dv}{dt} = -mg \frac{R^2}{x^2}.$$

Initial conditions are now

$$t = 0: \quad v = v_0, \quad x = R.$$

Since t does not occur explicitly in the differential equation, we use the transformation formula (7), in the form

$$\frac{dv}{dt} = v \frac{dv}{dx} = \frac{1}{2} \frac{dv^2}{dx}.$$

This gives a differential equation for v as a function of x:

$$\frac{1}{2} \frac{dv^2}{dx} = -g \frac{R^2}{x^2}.$$

Direct integration gives further

$$\frac{v^2}{2} = g \frac{R^2}{x} + c_0,$$

where c_0 is a constant of integration. In view of the initial condition we have as a relation to determine c_0,

$$\tfrac{1}{2}v_0^2 - gR = c_0,$$

and therewith altogether

$$\frac{v^2}{2} = \frac{v_0^2}{2} - gR\left(1 - \frac{R}{x}\right).$$

The velocity v_0 will be sufficiently great for the mass m to "escape" the earth, provided v^2 is positive, no matter how large the distance x is. This means that for escape $\tfrac{1}{2}v_0^2 > gR$, or

$$v_0 > \sqrt{2gR}.$$

To determine the height h which is reached when v_0 is less than the escape velocity $v_e = \sqrt{2gR}$, we set $v = 0$ for $x = h + R$ in the formula which gives v as a function of x. This leads to the expression

$$h = \frac{v_0^2/v_e^2}{1 - (v_0^2/v_e^2)}\, R.$$

We see, as expected, that a finite value of h requires that $v_0 < v_e$. For small values of v_0/v_e, say less than about $\frac{1}{4}$, we may use the first three terms of a Taylor expansion in the form

$$h \approx \left(\frac{v_0^2}{v_e^2} + \frac{v_0^4}{v_e^4}\right) R,$$

which, in view of the definition of v_e, and with H as in Example 1, is equivalent to

$$\frac{h}{H} \approx 1 + \frac{v_0^2}{v_e^2}.$$

The effect of the decrease in gravitational attraction with height is clearly seen.

EXAMPLE 3. Having considered the effect of variable gravity, we now consider the effect of air resistance. We shall determine the travel height h and the travel time T_a, assuming that the resistance of the air is a constant k times the square of the velocity and also assuming that we may neglect (in the range of distances for which air resistance is of importance) the change of gravitational pull with altitude.

The differential equations (1) and (2) are now

$$\frac{dx}{dt} = v, \qquad m\frac{dv}{dt} = -mg - kv^2,$$

and the initial conditions are again

$$t = 0: \qquad v = v_0, \quad x = 0.$$

The differential equation for v may be written in the form

$$\frac{1}{g + (k/m)v^2}\frac{dv}{dt} = -1$$

or

$$\frac{d}{dt}\left(\int \frac{dv}{g + (k/m)v^2}\right) = \frac{d}{dt}\left(\sqrt{\frac{m}{gk}}\,\tan^{-1}\sqrt{\frac{k}{mg}}\,v\right) = -1.$$

From this,

$$\sqrt{\frac{m}{gk}} \tan^{-1}\left(\sqrt{\frac{k}{mg}}\,v\right) = -t + c_1.$$

Introduction of the initial condition $v(0) = v_0$ determines the constant of integration c_1 in the form

$$c_1 = \sqrt{\frac{m}{gk}} \tan^{-1}\left(\sqrt{\frac{k}{mg}}\,v_0\right).$$

The time T_a it takes the body to reach its highest point is the time for which the velocity v becomes zero. Setting $v(T_a) = 0$, we have

$$T_a = \sqrt{\frac{m}{gk}} \tan^{-1}\left(\sqrt{\frac{k}{mg}}\,v_0\right).$$

In order to have this expression assume a clearer form, let us introduce the corresponding time T in the absence of friction. From Example 1,

$$T = \frac{v_0}{g},$$

and with this

$$\frac{T_a}{T} = \frac{\tan^{-1}\left(\sqrt{k/gm}\,v_0\right)}{\sqrt{k/gm}\,v_0}.$$

Since $\tan^{-1} z = z - \frac{1}{3}z^3 + \frac{1}{5}z^5 - \cdots$, we have for sufficiently small values of the friction coefficient k

$$\frac{T_a}{T} = 1 - \frac{1}{3}\frac{kv_0^2}{mg} + \frac{1}{5}\left(\frac{kv_0^2}{mg}\right)^2 \mp \cdots$$

We see that friction reduces the time it takes to reach the highest point of the path of the body.

It remains to determine the height h to which the body travels. This may be done by integrating the relation $dx/dt = v(t)$. A somewhat simpler procedure is possible by taking advantage of relation (7):

$$\frac{dv}{dt} = \frac{dv}{dx}\frac{dx}{dt} = \frac{dv}{dx}v.$$

Therewith, the differential equation for v becomes

$$\frac{v}{g + (k/m)v^2}\frac{dv}{dx} = -1.$$

This may be written as

$$\frac{d}{dx}\left[\int \frac{v\,dv}{g+(k/m)v^2}\right] = \frac{d}{dx}\left[\frac{m}{2k}\ln\left(g+\frac{k}{m}v^2\right)\right] = -1.$$

From this, by integration,

$$\frac{m}{2k}\ln\left(g+\frac{k}{m}v^2\right) = -x + c_2.$$

The initial conditions for the problem state that $x = 0$ when $v = v_0$. This determines the constant of integration c_2 as

$$c_2 = \frac{m}{2k}\ln\left(g+\frac{k}{m}v_0^2\right).$$

The highest point $x = h$ is reached when $v = 0$, and we have

$$h = \frac{m}{2k}\ln\left(g+\frac{k}{m}v_0^2\right) - \frac{m}{2k}\ln g = \frac{m}{2k}\ln\left(1+\frac{kv_0^2}{mg}\right).$$

Again introducing $H = v_0^2/2g$, we find

$$\frac{h}{H} = \frac{\ln(1+kv_0^2/mg)}{kv_0^2/mg} = 1 - \frac{1}{2}\frac{kv_0^2}{mg} + \frac{1}{3}\left(\frac{kv_0^2}{mg}\right)^2 \mp \cdots$$

As should be expected, friction reduces the height reached by the body.

EXAMPLE 4. A mass m hangs on a spring (Fig. 1–3). The forces acting on the mass are the force of gravity and the spring tension. Let L be the natural length of the spring and let x be the change of length of the spring due to the force F_s acting at its ends. For small changes of length x, F_s may generally be considered as proportional to x,

$$F_s = kx.$$

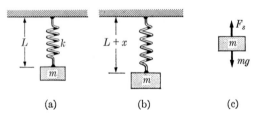

(a)   (b)   (c)

FIGURE 1–3

The equation of motion for the mass m is then

$$m \frac{d^2x}{dt^2} = mg - kx.$$

The minus sign in front of the spring force term indicates that when x is positive the tension in the spring acts as a *restoring force* on the mass.

In addition to the spring force F_s, it is often necessary in actual problems to include a *damping force* F_d. In many instances this damping force may be taken to be proportional to the velocity dx/dt of the moving body. The damping force $F_d = c\,(dx/dt)$ is in the direction of decreasing x when dx/dt is positive and so in the differential equation it occurs with the same sign as the spring force F_s.

The differential equation for the motion of m is now

$$m \frac{d^2x}{dt^2} + c \frac{dx}{dt} + kx = mg.$$

This differential equation for x is a *linear differential equation with constant coefficients*. Its solution is discussed in Chapter 3.

A device which produces damping proportional to velocity is often called a *dashpot*. To indicate the action of a dashpot in the equation of motion with linear damping, part (a) of Fig. 1–3 is modified in one of the two ways shown in Fig. 1–4.

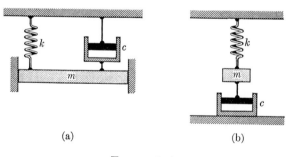

(a)   (b)

Figure 1–4

Example 5. Two masses, m_1 and m_2, resting on a smooth table and connected by a massless spring of natural length L, are set in motion at time $t = 0$ by a force $F(t)$ applied to m_2 in the direction of the line joining the two masses. Determine the positions of m_1 and m_2 as a function of time (Fig. 1–5).

We apply Newton's equation of motion to each of the two masses m_1 and m_2. The action of the spring connecting them is taken into account

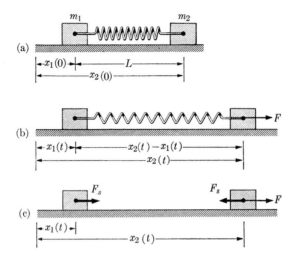

FIGURE 1–5

by two forces F_s acting on m_1 and m_2 in accordance with part (c) of Fig. 1–5. These forces F_s depend on the change of length of the spring:

$$F_s = f(x_2 - x_1 - L).$$

The equations of motion for m_1 and m_2 are than

$$m_1 \frac{d^2 x_1}{dt^2} = f(x_2 - x_1 - L),$$

$$m_2 \frac{d^2 x_2}{dt^2} = -f(x_2 - x_1 - L) + F(t).$$

We see that x_1 and x_2 must be determined by solving two simultaneous second-order differential equations. To carry out this solution we must know the nature of the function f, that is, the characteristics of the spring connecting the two masses.

We remark that the solution of such a system of equations is quite difficult, except when the characteristics of the spring may be taken as linear. For a spring with linear characteristics,

$$f(x_2 - x_1 - L) = k \cdot (x_2 - x_1 - L).$$

The solution of the resulting system of linear differential equations with constant coefficients may be effected by a method described in Chapter 5.

EXAMPLE 6. A mass m subjected to an external force F_e is restrained by two linear springs of the same natural length, with spring constants k_1

and k_2, in such a way that the extensions of the two springs are identical (Fig. 1–6). Writing $\dot{x} \equiv dx/dt$ and $\ddot{x} \equiv d^2x/dt^2$, show that the equation of motion for the mass m is of the form $m\ddot{x} + kx = F_e$ and express the value of the effective spring constant k in terms of k_1 and k_2.

Let x be the extension of the springs and the distance which the mass m has moved at time t. Let F_1 and F_2 be the forces in the springs. The equation of motion for m is

$$m\ddot{x} = F_e - F_1 - F_2,$$

while the force extension relations for the two springs are

$$F_1 = k_1 x, \qquad F_2 = k_2 x.$$

From this

$$m\ddot{x} + (k_1 + k_2)x = F_e,$$

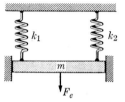

FIGURE 1–6

so that the effective spring constant k is given by $k_1 + k_2$.

EXERCISES

1. A body of mass m is traveling vertically upward, starting with velocity v_0. Assuming a constant gravitational force and air resistance proportional to velocity, determine the height h to which it travels and the time T it takes to reach this height.

2. A body of mass m is traveling vertically upward, starting with velocity v_0 at the surface $x = R$ of the earth. Neglecting all resistances except gravitational pull, and assuming that the gravitational force is of the form $F_g = -mgf(x/R)$, where $f(1) = 1$, show that the value of the escape velocity v_e is given by

$$v_e^2 = 2gR \int_1^\infty f(\xi)\, d\xi.$$

3. Obtain the value of the effective spring constant k in the equation $m\ddot{x} + kx = 0$ for the system given in Fig. 1–7. The natural lengths L_1 and L_2 of the two springs satisfy the relation $L_1 + L_2 = L - a$.

4. Obtain the value of the effective spring constant k in the equation $m\ddot{x} + kx = F_e$ in the system given in Fig. 1–8.

5. Obtain the equation of motion for the mass m in the system sketched in Fig. 1–9.

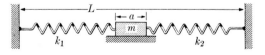

FIGURE 1–7

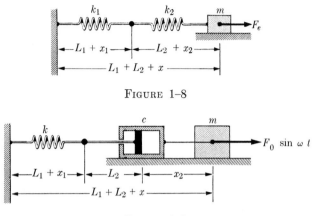

FIGURE 1–8

FIGURE 1–9

1–7 Linear motion with variable mass. Newton's Law, which states that the rate of change of momentum of a body equals the applied force, may be applied to bodies with variable mass (rockets, etc.). We show how this is done for motion along a straight line.

Let mv be the momentum of the body at time t. Let $\Delta m(v + u)$ be the momentum which is added to the body at time t because the body is joined by another body of mass Δm which before joining had the velocity $v + u$ (so that u is the velocity of Δm relative to m). It is assumed that at the instant of joining, the velocity of m changes from v to $v + \Delta v$ and Δm takes on the velocity of m.

We then have for the momentum of the two bodies:

at time t: $mv + \Delta m(u + v)$,

at time $t + \Delta t$: $(m + \Delta m)(v + \Delta v)$.

The change of momentum $\Delta(mv)$ during time Δt is the difference of the two expressions above:

$$\Delta(mv) = m\,\Delta v - u\,\Delta m + \Delta m\,\Delta v. \tag{1}$$

From Newton's Law,

$$\Delta(mv) = \int_{t}^{t+\Delta t} F\,dt. \tag{2}$$

Combination of Eqs. (1) and (2) gives us

$$m\,\Delta v - u\,\Delta m + \Delta v\,\Delta m = \int_{t}^{t+\Delta t} F\,dt. \tag{3}$$

We now divide by Δt and then let Δt tend to zero, assuming that Δm, Δv, and $\int_t^{t+\Delta t} F\, dt$ also tend to zero in such a way that the resulting limits all exist.* In this way we obtain the differential equation

$$m\frac{dv}{dt} - u\frac{dm}{dt} = F \tag{4}$$

for the determination of linear motion with variable mass.

Equation (4) may be written in the alternate form

$$\frac{d\ mv}{dt} = (v + u)\frac{dm}{dt} + F, \tag{4'}$$

which shows the way in which the rate of change of momentum of a body of variable mass is produced, additively, by applying external forces as well as by adding momentum through the device of suitably changing the mass of the body.

EXAMPLE 1. A rocket is traveling vertically upward in such a way that its rate of change of mass, dm/dt, has a constant value $-r$. The lost mass, consisting of burnt fuel, is leaving the rocket at the constant *exhaust speed* c. The rocket is acted upon by a gravitational force mg, where g is assumed constant, and starts with initial velocity v_0 and initial mass m_0. To be determined are velocity v and distance x as functions of time t. In particular we wish to determine the velocity v_1 with which the rocket is traveling at time t_1, when the entire fuel supply is exhausted and the remaining mass m_1 of the rocket is that of its *structure* and *payload*. The velocity v_1 may be designated as *burnout velocity*.

The differential equation of the rocket problem as stated is obtained from (4) by setting in it

$$\frac{dm}{dt} = -r, \quad m = m_0 - rt, \quad u = -c, \quad F = -mg. \tag{5}$$

This gives the simple equation

$$\frac{dv}{dt} = \frac{cr}{m_0 - rt} - g. \tag{6}$$

We integrate and determine the constant of integration such that $v(0) = v_0$. This gives as the expression for v

$$v = v_0 - c\ln\left(1 - \frac{rt}{m_0}\right) - gt. \tag{7}$$

---

* Equation (3) in its original form retains its validity even if $\lim \Delta m$, $\lim \Delta v$, and $\lim \int_t^{t+\Delta t} F\, dt$ are not zero. This is of importance in problems of impact and of collision of two or more finite bodies.

Having v, we obtain x from $dx/dt = v$ and the initial condition $x(0) = 0$ in the form

$$x = v_0 t + \frac{cm_0}{r} \left\{ 1 - \left(1 - \frac{rt}{m_0}\right)\left[1 - \ln\left(1 - \frac{rt}{m_0}\right)\right] \right\} - \frac{1}{2} gt^2. \quad (8)$$

To determine the burnout velocity v_1 we first determine the *burnout time* t_1 in the form

$$t_1 = \frac{m_0 - m_1}{r} \quad (9)$$

and introduce this value of t into the expression for v. In this way we obtain as the expression for the burnout velocity

$$v_1 = v_0 + c \ln \frac{m_0}{m_1} - \frac{(m_0 - m_1)g}{r}. \quad (10)$$

In order to see more clearly the significance of this formula, we write the initial mass m_0 in the form

$$m_0 = m_f + m_p + m_s. \quad (11)$$

The quantity m_f is the mass of the *fuel*, m_p is the mass of the *payload*, and m_s is the mass of the rocket *structure* which is necessary to hold the rocket together and support its payload.

Analogously, the final mass m_1 is given by

$$m_1 = m_p + m_s. \quad (12)$$

Introduction of (11) and (12) into (10) leaves us with the following formula:

$$v_1 = v_0 + c \ln \left(1 + \frac{m_f}{m_s + m_p}\right) - \frac{m_f g}{r}. \quad (13)$$

We shall not attempt a quantitative discussion of this important formula, but add the following remarks. Evidently, other things being equal, the higher the exhaust velocity c of the fuel and the smaller the structural mass m_s, the higher the burnout velocity v_1 of the rocket for given fuel and payload. Since, however, the complexity of the structural design of the rocket depends on the properties of the fuel, and in addition to this the rate of burning r also differs for different fuels, it is not an easy matter to arrive at an optimum rocket design.

Experience also indicates that for no choice of presently available or forseeable fuels and rocket designs is it possible, for a rocket starting from rest, to acquire a burnout velocity v_1 which is as large as the *escape velocity* $v_e = \sqrt{2gR}$. This means that a rocket of this nature cannot be used to initiate a journey of the mass m_1 into space from the surface of the earth.

The solution of this difficulty is found in the use of rockets consisting of *stages*. The elements of the idea of the staged rocket are discussed in the following example.

EXAMPLE 2.   Determine the burnout velocity v_2 of a rocket which sheds part of its structure after a certain fraction of the fuel has been used up.   In other words, determine what gains are possible if only part of the rocket structure needs to be brought up to the same velocity as the payload of the rocket.

To obtain a formula for v_2 we express the structural mass m_s and the fuel mass m_f in the form

$$m_s = m_{s1} + m_{s2}, \qquad m_f = m_{f1} + m_{f2} \tag{14}$$

and we assume that m_{s1} is left behind, i.e., separated from the main body of the rocket, after an amount m_{f1} of fuel has been used up.

If we now designate by v_1 the velocity at this instant, which is the instant of burnout of the first stage of the rocket, we have

$$v_1 = v_0 + c \ln \left(1 + \frac{m_{f1}}{m_{f2} + m_{s1} + m_{s2} + m_p} \right) - \frac{m_{f1}g}{r}. \tag{15}$$

Note that the fuel portion m_{f2} is considered part of the payload of the first-stage rocket.

We now consider v_1 as the initial velocity of the second stage, which proceeds without the structural mass m_{s1}.   Accordingly, we have for its burnout velocity

$$v_2 = v_1 + c \ln \left(1 + \frac{m_{f2}}{m_{s2} + m_p} \right) - \frac{m_{f2}g}{r}. \tag{16}$$

Our final formula is obtained by eliminating v_1 from v_2 by means of (15). This leads to

$$v_2 = v_0 + c \ln \left[\left(1 + \frac{m_{f1}}{m_{f2} + m_{s1} + m_{s2} + m_p} \right) \left(1 + \frac{m_{f2}}{m_{s2} + m_p} \right) \right]$$
$$- \frac{(m_{f1} + m_{f2})g}{r}. \tag{17}$$

We should now be able to show that for given m_f and m_s the smallest value of v_2 is obtained when $m_{s1} = 0$, i.e., when the two-stage rocket degenerates into a one-stage rocket.   We will not undertake to show this, but rather consider the order of magnitude of the possible gain by means of a numerical example.

For the one-stage rocket, setting

$$m_s = 10m_p = \tfrac{1}{10}m_f,$$

we obtain for the logarithmic term in v_1, as given by Eq. (13),

$$\ln\left(1 + \frac{m_f}{m_s + m_p}\right) = \ln\left(1 + \frac{100}{11}\right) = 2.31.$$

For a two-stage rocket of the same initial mass and the same total amount of fuel, for which, further,

$$m_{f1} = m_{f2} = \tfrac{1}{2}m_f,$$

$$m_{s1} = 3m_{s2} = \tfrac{3}{4}m_s,$$

we obtain for the logarithmic term in v_2, as given by Eq. (17),

$$\ln\left[\left(1 + \frac{m_{f1}}{m_{f2} + m_s + m_p}\right)\left(1 + \frac{m_{f2}}{m_{s2} + m_p}\right)\right]$$

$$= \ln\left[\left(1 + \frac{100}{122}\right)\left(1 + \frac{100}{7}\right)\right] = 4.32.$$

Apparently, a burnout velocity increase of the order of one hundred percent has been accomplished.

EXERCISES

1. Determine the burnout velocity for a rocket of initial mass $m_0 = m_{f0} + m_{s0} + m_p$ under the assumptions that $dm_f/dt = -r$ and $dm_s/dt = -q$, where r and q are constants, and that at the instant of burnout both m_f and m_s are zero. Assume further that m_f leaves with an exhaust speed c, while m_s is detached without velocity change, and that the only external force on the rocket is the effect of constant gravity.

2. Determine the velocity of a rocket of initial mass m_0 and initial velocity v_0 with the assumptions of constant rate r of mass loss, constant exhaust speed c, and a resisting force kv.

3. Show that if in addition to the retarding force kv in Exercise 2, we have a retarding force mg, the velocity v of the rocket satisfies the linear first-order differential equation $(m_0 - rt)(dv/dt) + kv = cr - (m_0 - rt)g$.

4. A chain of weight w per unit length is lying on the ground, piled up in one spot. Beginning at time $t = 0$, one end of the chain is hoisted up with constant velocity v_0. Determine the force F, as a function of time t, which is necessary for the hoisting of the chain against the effect of gravity.

5. Show that if Exercise 4 is changed by prescribing a constant hoisting force F_0 instead of a constant hoisting velocity, the problem is governed by the differential equations $dm/dt = wv/g$ and $dmv/dt = F_0 - mg$ for the two functions m and v.

1–8 Plane motion of mass points. We now consider motion in a plane, say the xy-plane, of bodies which are idealized in the sense that they are considered as mathematical points which are endowed with the property of inertia or, equivalently, with the property of mass. It is not an easy matter to discuss the limitations of this concept of the motion of such mass points and of the extent that it can be applied to study the motion of real bodies of finite extent. However, we will here presuppose the existence of an intuitive feeling which allows us to use the notion of mass points in our examples.

We describe plane motion of a point by means of its coordinates as a function of time t. These coordinates will first be taken as the cartesian coordinates $x(t)$ and $y(t)$. We then define a position vector $\mathbf{r}(t)$, which is the radius vector from the origin of the coordinate system to the moving point, by writing

$$\mathbf{r} = x\mathbf{i}_x + y\mathbf{i}_y. \tag{1}$$

The vectors $\mathbf{i}_x$ and $\mathbf{i}_y$ are unit vectors in the direction of the xy-axes, and as such are independent of t.

We next define a velocity vector $\mathbf{v}$ as the rate of change of the position vector $\mathbf{r}$:

$$\mathbf{v} = v_x\mathbf{i}_x + v_y\mathbf{i}_y = \frac{d\mathbf{r}}{dt}, \tag{2}$$

and an acceleration vector $\mathbf{a}$ as the rate of change of the velocity vector $\mathbf{v}$:

$$\mathbf{a} = a_x\mathbf{i}_x + a_y\mathbf{i}_y = \frac{d\mathbf{v}}{dt}. \tag{3}$$

Equations (1) through (3) imply the following relations between the x- and y-components of velocity and acceleration vectors:

$$v_x = \frac{dx}{dt}, \quad v_y = \frac{dy}{dt}, \quad a_x = \frac{dv_x}{dt}, \quad a_y = \frac{dv_y}{dt}. \tag{4}$$

In order to state Newton's Law for plane motion of a mass point, we further define a force vector $\mathbf{F}$ by writing

$$\mathbf{F} = F_x\mathbf{i}_x + F_y\mathbf{i}_y. \tag{5}$$

Newton's Law for the motion of a mass point or particle, with mass independent of time, consists in the statement *mass times acceleration equals force*. In this statement acceleration as well as force are to be interpreted as vectors (which may be vectors in space instead of merely vectors in a plane as in our discussion). The vector equation

$$m\mathbf{a} = \mathbf{F} \tag{6}$$

is equivalent to the two scalar equations $ma_x = F_x$ and $ma_y = F_y$ or, if we make use of (4), to the system of differential equations

$$m \frac{d^2x}{dt^2} = F_x, \qquad m \frac{d^2y}{dt^2} = F_y. \tag{7}$$

Before attempting to solve the system (7) we must have F_x and F_y given as functions of t, x, y, dx/dt, and dy/dt.

A particularly simple example of (7) is the problem of the motion of a projectile with the only force considered a constant gravitational force mg in the direction of decreasing y. Equations (7) are now

$$m \frac{d^2x}{dt^2} = 0, \qquad m \frac{d^2y}{dt^2} = -mg, \tag{8}$$

and this can be solved by direct integrations and by use of initial conditions of the form

$$t = 0: \qquad x = y = 0, \quad \frac{dx}{dt} = v_0 \cos \alpha, \quad \frac{dy}{dt} = v_0 \sin \alpha \tag{9}$$

to furnish the well-known parabolic trajectories.

Plane motion with variable mass. We now consider a particle of variable mass which at time t has mass m and momentum $m\mathbf{v}$. In the interval from t to $t + \Delta t$ it is joined by a particle of mass Δm which before joining had momentum $\Delta m(\mathbf{v} + \mathbf{u})$. The rate of change of momentum of the resultant particle (which is the union of the two particles) incorporates additively the effects of changing momentum by changing mass and of changing momentum through the application of force. The differential equation of motion is then, in generalization of Eq. (6) and of Eq. (4′) of the preceding section,

$$\frac{d\,m\mathbf{v}}{dt} = (\mathbf{v} + \mathbf{u}) \frac{dm}{dt} + \mathbf{F}. \tag{10}$$

To illustrate the use of (10,) consider a projectile, or rocket, which burns fuel at a constant rate r, the products of combustion having an exhaust velocity $\mathbf{c}$ which is assumed tangent to the trajectory of the projectile. The external force $\mathbf{F}$ is again taken in the form $-mg\mathbf{i}_y$ and the initial conditions for the motion are as in (9), with the added stipulation that $m = m_0$ when $t = 0$.

Writing $d(m\mathbf{v})/dt = m\,d\mathbf{v}/dt + \mathbf{v}\,dm/dt$ on the left of (10) and noting that the relative velocity vector $\mathbf{u}$ is now

$$\mathbf{u} = -c \frac{\mathbf{v}}{|\mathbf{v}|}, \tag{11}$$

where $c = |\mathbf{c}|$, we have as the vector differential equation for the motion of the projectile of variable mass

$$\frac{d\mathbf{v}}{dt} = -\frac{\mathbf{v}}{|\mathbf{v}|}\frac{c}{m}\frac{dm}{dt} - g\mathbf{i}_y, \tag{12}$$

where $m = m_0 - rt$. Equation (12) is changed into two scalar equations for v_x and v_y if we write $\mathbf{v} = v_x\mathbf{i}_x + v_y\mathbf{i}_y$ and $|\mathbf{v}| = \sqrt{v_x^2 + v_y^2}$, as follows:

$$\frac{dv_x}{dt} = \frac{cr}{m_0 - rt}\frac{v_x}{\sqrt{v_x^2 + v_y^2}}, \tag{13a}$$

$$\frac{dv_y}{dt} = \frac{cr}{m_0 - rt}\frac{v_y}{\sqrt{v_x^2 + v_y^2}} - g. \tag{13b}$$

Equations (13) must be solved subject to the initial conditions $v_x(0) = v_0 \cos\alpha$, $v_y(0) = v_0 \sin\alpha$. Having determined v_x and v_y as functions of t, we find the coordinates x and y of the projectile by integrating the two relations $dx/dt = v_x$, $dy/dt = v_y$, with the initial conditions $x(0) = 0$, $y(0) = 0$. Since there exists no simple straightforward procedure for solving (13), we shall not proceed further with the discussion of the problem as stated.

EXERCISES

1. Let $\phi = \phi(t)$ be the angle between the x-axis and the tangent to the path curve $x = x(t)$, $y = y(t)$. Introduce tangent unit vectors $\mathbf{i}_T$ and normal unit vectors $\mathbf{i}_N$ (Fig. 1–10) through the equations

$$\mathbf{i}_T = \mathbf{i}_x \cos\phi + \mathbf{i}_y \sin\phi, \qquad \mathbf{i}_N = -\mathbf{i}_x \sin\phi + \mathbf{i}_y \cos\phi.$$

Since the vector $d\mathbf{r}/dt$ is tangent to the curve $\mathbf{r} = \mathbf{r}(t)$, we have that the velocity vector $\mathbf{v}$ is tangent to the path curve and we may write $\mathbf{v} = v\mathbf{i}_T$, where v is the magnitude of the velocity of the point with position $x = x(t)$, $y = y(t)$.

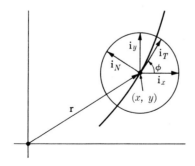

FIGURE 1–10

(i) Writing $\mathbf{a} = a_T \mathbf{i}_T + a_N \mathbf{i}_N$, show that the tangential and normal components of acceleration are given in terms of v and ϕ by means of the formulas

$$a_T = \frac{dv}{dt}, \qquad a_N = v \frac{d\phi}{dt}.$$

(ii) Show that x and y are given in terms of v and ϕ by means of the formulas

$$x = \int v \cos \phi \, dt, \qquad y = \int v \sin \phi \, dt.$$

2. Show that the vector equation (10) for plane motion with variable mass is equivalent to two scalar equations of the form

$$\frac{dv}{dt} = \frac{u_T}{m} \frac{dm}{dt} + \frac{F_T}{m}, \qquad v \frac{d\phi}{dt} = \frac{u_N}{m} \frac{dm}{dt} + \frac{F_N}{m},$$

assuming that $\mathbf{u} = u_T \mathbf{i}_T + u_N \mathbf{i}_N$ and $\mathbf{F} = F_T \mathbf{i}_T + F_N \mathbf{i}_N$.

3. Given a traveling particle of constant mass m subject to a gravitational force $-mg\mathbf{i}_y$ and subject to air resistance of amount kgv^2. Show that the differential equations of this problem may be written in the form

$$m \frac{dv}{dt} = -mg \sin \phi - kgv^2, \qquad v \frac{d\phi}{dt} = -g \cos \phi$$

and that these two equations imply that v can be written as a function of ϕ, which is a solution of the following first-order differential equation:

$$\cos \phi \, \frac{dv}{d\phi} = v \sin \phi + \frac{k}{m} v^3.$$

4. Using the results of Exercises 1 and 3 and taking as initial conditions $x(0) = 0$, $y(0) = 0$, $\phi(0) = \phi_0$, show that it is possible to represent the particle coordinates x and y in terms of t in the form

$$x = -\frac{1}{g} \int_{\phi_0}^{\phi} v^2 \, d\phi, \qquad y = -\frac{1}{g} \int_{\phi_0}^{\phi} v^2 \tan \phi \, d\phi, \qquad t = -\frac{1}{g} \int_{\phi_0}^{\phi} \frac{v \, d\phi}{\cos \phi},$$

where $v = v(\phi)$ satisfies the differential equation

$$\frac{d(v \cos \phi)}{d\phi} = \frac{k}{m} v^3 = \frac{k}{m} \frac{(v \cos \phi)^3}{\cos^3 \phi}.$$

5. Show that the differential equation of Exercise 4 with the initial condition $v(\phi_0) = v_0$ has the solution

$$\frac{1}{(v_0 \cos \phi_0)^2} - \frac{1}{(v \cos \phi)^2} = 2k \int_{\phi_0}^{\phi} \frac{d\phi}{\cos^3 \phi},$$

from which,

$$\frac{1}{kv_0^2 \cos^2 \phi_0} - \frac{1}{kv^2 \cos^2 \phi} = \frac{\sin \phi}{\cos^2 \phi} - \frac{\sin \phi_0}{\cos^2 \phi_0} + \ln \left| \frac{\tan (\frac{1}{4}\pi + \frac{1}{2}\phi)}{\tan (\frac{1}{4}\pi + \frac{1}{2}\phi_0)} \right|.$$

1–9 Plane motion in polar coordinates. For problems of motion in which the external force $\mathbf{F}$ is always in the direction of the line from a fixed point to the moving mass point, it is usually of advantage to define velocity components, acceleration components, and force components in the direction of and perpendicular to this line.

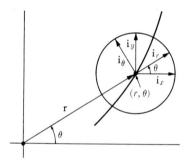

FIGURE 1–11

We let the fixed point be the origin of the coordinate system (Fig. 1–11) and write for the radius vector from the origin to the moving point

$$\mathbf{r} = r\mathbf{i}_r, \tag{1}$$

where $\mathbf{i}_r$ is a unit vector in the direction of r. The unit vector $\mathbf{i}_r$ itself is now dependent on time t, since it depends on the polar angle θ and θ will be a function of t. We have, evidently,

$$\mathbf{i}_r = \mathbf{i}_x \cos \theta + \mathbf{i}_y \sin \theta. \tag{2}$$

A corresponding unit vector $\mathbf{i}_\theta$, perpendicular to $\mathbf{i}_r$ and in the direction of increasing θ, is

$$\mathbf{i}_\theta = -\mathbf{i}_x \sin \theta + \mathbf{i}_y \cos \theta. \tag{3}$$

We note the relations

$$\frac{d\mathbf{i}_r}{d\theta} = \mathbf{i}_\theta, \qquad \frac{d\mathbf{i}_\theta}{d\theta} = -\mathbf{i}_r, \tag{4}$$

which we will make use of in the calculation of velocity and acceleration components.

The velocity vector $\mathbf{v} = d\mathbf{r}/dt$ follows from (1) in the form

$$\mathbf{v} = \frac{d r \mathbf{i}_r}{dt} = \frac{dr}{dt}\mathbf{i}_r + r\frac{d\mathbf{i}_r}{dt} = \frac{dr}{dt}\mathbf{i}_r + r\frac{d\theta}{dt}\mathbf{i}_\theta, \tag{5}$$

and the acceleration vector $\mathbf{a} = d\mathbf{v}/dt$ follows from (5) in the form

$$\mathbf{a} = \frac{d}{dt}\left(\frac{dr}{dt}\mathbf{i}_r + r\frac{d\theta}{dt}\mathbf{i}_\theta\right)$$

$$= \left[\frac{d^2 r}{dt^2} - r\left(\frac{d\theta}{dt}\right)^2\right]\mathbf{i}_r + \left[r\frac{d^2\theta}{dt^2} + 2\frac{dr}{dt}\frac{d\theta}{dt}\right]\mathbf{i}_\theta. \tag{6}$$

If we further set $\mathbf{F} = F_r\mathbf{i}_r + F_\theta\mathbf{i}_\theta$, then the equations of Newton's Law for plane motion of a particle of constant mass m become

$$\frac{d^2 r}{dt^2} - r\left(\frac{d\theta}{dt}\right)^2 = \frac{F_r}{m}, \qquad r\frac{d^2\theta}{dt^2} + 2\frac{dr}{dt}\frac{d\theta}{dt} = \frac{F_\theta}{m}. \tag{7}$$

Equations (7) are two simultaneous second-order differential equations for the two functions $r(t)$ and $\theta(t)$, with F_r and F_θ as given functions of t, r, θ, dr/dt, and $d\theta/dt$.

We consider next several consequences of the system (7).

EXAMPLE 1. A particle is traveling subject to the condition of vanishing force component F_θ. Use this condition to reduce the second of the two differential equations (7) to a first-order equation.

We observe that the second of equations (7) may be written in the form

$$\frac{1}{r}\frac{d}{dt}\left(r^2\frac{d\theta}{dt}\right) = \frac{F_\theta}{m}. \tag{8}$$

Accordingly, when $F_\theta = 0$,

$$r^2\frac{d\theta}{dt} = k, \tag{9}$$

where k is a constant of integration.

We note that $\frac{1}{2}r^2\,d\theta$ is the area swept out by the radius vector r in the time dt. Equation (9) then expresses the well-known fact that the rate of area sweep $\frac{1}{2}r^2\,d\theta/dt$ is constant for motion with purely radial forces $\mathbf{F} = F_r\mathbf{i}_r$.

EXAMPLE 2. Obtain a differential equation for the determination of the path curve $r = f(\theta)$ for motion under the influence of a purely radial force.

To obtain such a differential equation, we combine Eq. (9) with the first of the differential equations (7). This equation contains d^2r/dt^2, in addition to $(d\theta/dt)^2$ which we can take directly from (9).

To eliminate differentiation with respect to t, we utilize the relations

$$\frac{dr}{dt} = \frac{dr}{d\theta}\frac{d\theta}{dt} = \frac{dr}{d\theta}\frac{k}{r^2} \tag{10}$$

and

$$\frac{d^2r}{dt^2} = \frac{d}{dt}\left(\frac{dr}{d\theta}\frac{k}{r^2}\right) = \frac{d}{d\theta}\left(\frac{dr}{d\theta}\frac{k}{r^2}\right)\frac{k}{r^2}. \tag{11}$$

Use of (11) leaves us with a differential equation for r as a function of θ which may be written in the form

$$\frac{d}{d\theta}\left(\frac{1}{r^2}\frac{dr}{d\theta}\right) = \frac{r^2F_r}{k^2m} + \frac{1}{r}. \tag{12}$$

For Eq. (12) to be effectively usable to determine r as a function of θ it is necessary that the force function F_r does not contain t explicitly. The function F_r may, however, depend on r, θ, and $dr/d\theta$.

In the event that F_r depends on r only it is simple to write the second-order equation (12) as a sequence of two first-order equations which may be integrated directly. We set

$$\frac{dr}{d\theta} = p(r) \qquad \text{and} \qquad \frac{d}{d\theta} = p\frac{d}{dr}. \tag{13}$$

This transforms (12) into an equation for p/r^2 of the form

$$\frac{p}{r^2}\frac{d}{dr}\left(\frac{p}{r^2}\right) = \frac{F_r(r)}{k^2m} + \frac{1}{r^3}. \tag{14}$$

Equation (14) has the solution

$$\frac{1}{2}\left(\frac{p}{r^2}\right)^2 = \int\left(\frac{F_r}{k^2m} + \frac{1}{r^3}\right)dr + c_1. \tag{15}$$

Having p, we find the equation of the path curve from the relation

$$\theta = \int\frac{dr}{p} + c_2, \tag{16}$$

which follows from the first of equations (13).

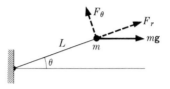

FIGURE 1–12

EXAMPLE 3. We consider briefly the equation of the mathematical pendulum consisting of an inextensible massless string of length L which is fixed at one end and carries a mass m at the other end (Fig. 1–12). The force acting on m is the force due to gravity mg, which for convenience we shall assume to be in the direction of the x-axis, and a tension force F_T in the string which contributes to F_r but not to F_θ. We then have

$$r = L, \qquad F_r = -F_T(\theta) + mg \cos \theta, \qquad F_\theta = -mg \sin \theta, \qquad (17)$$

and the differential equations (7) assume the form

$$-L\left(\frac{d\theta}{dt}\right)^2 = -\frac{F_T(\theta)}{m} + g \cos \theta \qquad (18)$$

and

$$\frac{d^2\theta}{dt^2} + \frac{g}{L} \sin \theta = 0. \qquad (19)$$

The second of these is a differential equation for θ. The first equation serves to determine the string tension F_T once θ has been determined as a function of t.

EXERCISES

1. Show that Eq. (12) for the trajectories of a mass point traveling under the influence of a pure radial force F_r has solutions of the form $r = r_0/(1 + \epsilon \cos \theta)$ provided F_r is of the form $-c/r^2$. Determine the constants k and ϵ in terms of the constants c, m, r_0, and $\omega_0 = (d\theta/dt)_{\theta=0}$.

2. Show that when $F_\theta = 0$ and F_r is independent of θ, then r as a function of t satisfies the differential equation

$$\frac{d^2r}{dt^2} - \frac{k^2}{r^3} = \frac{F_r}{m}.$$

If F_r is also independent of t, this equation evidently possesses solutions of the form $r = r_0 = \text{const}$. By using the relation $r^2 \, d\theta/dt = \epsilon$, determine the time interval T during which the particle m completely traverses its circular orbit. In particular, deduce one of Kepler's Laws for planetary motion which holds when $F_r = -cr^{-2}$ and deduce the value T_s for an earth satellite by choosing $c = mgR^2$ with circular orbit at $R + H$.

3. Obtain a linear differential equation of the second order for the perturbation ρ of the circular orbit $r = r_0$ of Exercise 2 by setting $r = r_0 + \rho(t)$ in the differential equation of the problem and by neglecting higher power terms in ρ.

4. Obtain a linear differential equation for the perturbation η of the circular orbit $r = r_0$ associated with Eq. (12) when $F_r = F_r(r)$ by setting $r = r_0 + \eta(\theta)$ and by neglecting all but first-degree terms in η and its derivatives.

5. Show that when the condition of a vanishing force component F_θ in Eq. (8) is replaced by the condition that this force component is a frictional force of the form $F_\theta = -Cv_\theta = -Cr\, d\theta/dt$, then the equal-area-sweep Eq. (9) is replaced by $r^2\, d\theta/dt = ke^{-(C/m)t}$.

1–10 Electrical networks. The theory of electrical networks deals with the flow of electrical currents through assemblies of certain basic elements under the influence of given impressed voltages. The basic elements are:

1. *Resistances* (–/\\/\\/\\–)

2. *Inductances* (–ʊʊʊ–)

3. *Capacitances* (–|⊢)

The current i, in units of *amperes*, through one of these elements is related to the voltage drop e, in units of *volts*, across it as follows:

1. For a resistance: $e = Ri$.

2. For an inductance: $e = L\dfrac{di}{dt}$.

3. For a capacitance: $i = C\dfrac{de}{dt}$.

The unit for R is the *ohm*, for L the *henry*, and for C the *farad*. We shall assume here that R, L, and C are independent of time t and current i.

The analysis of circuits composed of the above elements is governed by the following two fundamental laws of Kirchhoff.

1. In a closed circuit the sum of the voltage drops across each element of the circuit is equal to the impressed voltage.

2. At a junction of two or more elements of a circuit the amount of current into the junction point equals the amount of current away from the junction point.

EXAMPLE 1. *The simple series, or single-loop, circuit* (Fig. 1–13). Kirchhoff's second law indicates that each of the three elements of the circuit carries the same current i. From Kirchhoff's first law,

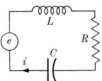

$$e = L \frac{di}{dt} + Ri + \frac{1}{C} \int i\, dt$$

or

$$\frac{de}{dt} = L \frac{d^2 i}{dt^2} + R \frac{di}{dt} + \frac{1}{C} i.$$

FIGURE 1–13

Determination of the current i as a function of time, with the impressed voltage a given function of time, is seen to require the solution of a second-order differential equation. This differential equation for i is called a linear differential equation, since it is linear in i and its derivatives. We speak of *linear* resistances, inductances, and capacitances when we wish to indicate that R, L, and C are independent of i.

EXAMPLE 2. *The simple parallel circuit* (Fig. 1–14). Kirchhoff's first law, applied to the three closed circuits or loops containing the voltage source and (1) the capacitance, (2) the resistance, (3) the inductance, gives the three relations

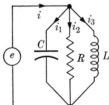

$$e = \frac{1}{C} \int i_1\, dt, \qquad e = Ri_2, \qquad e = L \frac{di_3}{dt}.$$

Kirchhoff's second law gives the further relation

$$i = i_1 + i_2 + i_3.$$

FIGURE 1–14

If the impressed voltage e is given, the first three of these equations give us the currents i_1, i_2, and i_3, and the fourth equation gives us the "impressed current" i. If, on the other hand, the impressed current i is given, then the four equations may be reduced to one differential equation for the determination of the impressed voltage e. We have

$$i = C \frac{de}{dt} + \frac{1}{R} e + \frac{1}{L} \int e\, dt$$

or

$$\frac{di}{dt} = C \frac{d^2 e}{dt^2} + \frac{1}{R} \frac{de}{dt} + \frac{1}{L} e.$$

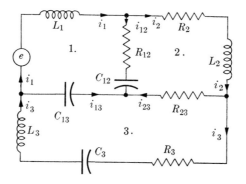

FIGURE 1–15

EXAMPLE 3. *A multiple-loop circuit.* To illustrate the analysis of more complicated circuits we consider the circuit of Fig. 1–15. This circuit has three loops. We designate the elements which belong to only one loop by a single subscript and the elements which belong to two loops by a double subscript, and the same for the currents.

We need six relations to determine the six currents i_1, i_2, i_3, i_{12}, i_{13}, i_{23}. Three of these relations come from Kirchhoff's first law, applied to each of the three loops; namely,

$$e = L_1 \frac{di_1}{dt} + R_{12}i_{12} + \frac{1}{C_{12}} \int i_{12}\, dt - \frac{1}{C_{13}} \int i_{13}\, dt,$$

$$0 = R_2 i_2 + L_2 \frac{di_2}{dt} + R_{23}i_{23} - \frac{1}{C_{12}} \int i_{12}\, dt - R_{12}i_{12},$$

$$0 = \frac{1}{C_{13}} \int i_{13}\, dt - R_{23}i_{23} + R_3 i_3 + \frac{1}{C_3} \int i_3\, dt + L_3 \frac{di_3}{dt},$$

or

$$L \frac{d^2 i_1}{dt^2} + R_{12} \frac{di_{12}}{dt} + \frac{1}{C_{12}} i_{12} - \frac{1}{C_{13}} i_{13} = \frac{de}{dt},$$

$$R_2 \frac{di_2}{dt} + L_2 \frac{d^2 i_2}{dt^2} + R_{23} \frac{di_{23}}{dt} - \frac{1}{C_{12}} i_{12} - R_{12} \frac{di_{12}}{dt} = 0,$$

$$\frac{1}{C_{13}} i_{13} - R_{23} \frac{di_{23}}{dt} + R_3 \frac{di_3}{dt} + \frac{1}{C_3} i_3 + L_3 \frac{d^2 i_3}{dt^2} = 0.$$

The remaining three relations are obtained by applying Kirchhoff's second law to the three exterior junction points. We have

$$i_{12} = i_1 - i_2, \qquad i_{23} = i_2 - i_3, \qquad i_{13} = i_3 - i_1.$$

The corresponding relation for the interior junction point, $i_{12} + i_{13} + i_{23} = 0$, is seen to be a consequence of the relations for the exterior junction points.

Introduction of i_{12}, i_{13}, i_{23} from the three current relations into the three voltage relations leaves us with the following system of three simultaneous differential equations for the currents i_1, i_2, i_3:

$$L_1 \frac{d^2 i_1}{dt^2} + R_{12} \frac{di_1}{dt} + \frac{i_1}{C_{12}} + \frac{i_1}{C_{13}} - R_{12} \frac{di_2}{dt} - \frac{i_2}{C_{12}} - \frac{i_3}{C_{13}} = \frac{de}{dt},$$

$$-R_{12} \frac{di_1}{dt} - \frac{i_1}{C_{12}} + L_2 \frac{d^2 i_2}{dt^2} + (R_2 + R_{23} + R_{12}) \frac{di_2}{dt} + \frac{i_2}{C_{12}}$$
$$-R_{23} \frac{di_3}{dt} = 0,$$

$$-\frac{i_1}{C_{13}} - R_{23} \frac{di_2}{dt} + L_3 \frac{d^2 i_3}{dt^2} + (R_3 + R_{23}) \frac{di_3}{dt} + \frac{i_3}{C_3} + \frac{i_3}{C_{13}} = 0.$$

We add the following two remarks to our brief discussion:

(1) Many of the important practical problems in circuit theory involve nonlinear elements, such as resistances the magnitude of which depends on the current through the element. Also to be considered are vacuum tubes or transistors as power-producing elements or, if one wishes, as nonlinear *negative* resistances.

(2) There are important applications in engineering of the mathematical analogies between mechanical systems and electrical systems. It is possible to identify the differential equations for each electrical system consisting of impressed voltages, inductances, resistances, and capacitances with the differential equations for a certain mechanical system consisting of impressed forces, masses, dashpots, and springs. In order to predict the behavior of a given mechanical system, it is sometimes convenient to build the analogous electrical circuit and to deduce the behavior of the mechanical system from measurements of the current in the analogous circuit.

Obtain the differential equations for the distribution of currents in the four circuits of Fig. 1–16.

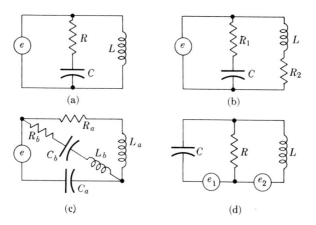

FIGURE 1–16

MISCELLANEOUS EXERCISES. CHAPTER 1

1. Verify that

(a) $y = ce^x$,   (b) $y = c_1 e^{ax} + c_2 e^{bx}$,   (c) $y = c_1 e^{ax} + c_2 x e^{ax}$

are solutions of the differential equations

(a) $y' = y$,   (b) $y'' - (a + b)y' + aby = 0$,
(c) $y'' - 2ay' + a^2 y = 0$,

where a and b are given constants, and c, c_1, and c_2 are arbitrary constants.

2. Solve

(a) $y' = xy^2$,   (b) $y' = x^2 y$,   (c) $yy' = x$
(d) $y'' = y'$,   (e) $y'' = -2x(y')^2$, $y(0) = 0$, $y'(0) = 1$.

3. Determine all plane curves the square of whose slope at any point (x, y) is equal to the ordinate.

4. Determine a plane curve passing through the point $(1, 2)$ and having the property that at any point (x, y) the slope is equal to the quotient of the ordinate divided by the abscissa.

5. Determine a plane curve passing through the point $(2, 3)$ and having the property that at any point (x, y) the slope is equal to the ordinate.

6. Determine the differential equation of the family of all circles with centers on the x-axis.

7. Determine the differential equation of the family of all circles with centers at the origin.

8. Determine the differential equation of all plane curves such that at any point (x, y) the part of the normal from this point to the x-axis is bisected by the y-axis.

9. In Exercise 3(a) of Section 4, if $\frac{3}{4}$ of the volume of water runs out in n sec, find the time required to empty the entire tank.

10. A funnel R_1 ft in radius at the top, R_2 ft in radius at the base, and of height L, is initially full of water. Find the time required to empty.

11. Assuming that a radioactive substance decomposes at a rate proportional to the amount present, and that one-half of a given quantity decomposes in 1200 yr, what percentage of the original amount will be left at the end of 1800 yr?

12. Solve the differential equation $y' + 1 = y + x$ by making the change of variable $z = y + x$.

In Exercises 13, 14, and 15 find functions $y = y(x)$ which do not vanish identically and which satisfy the conditions stated.

13. $\displaystyle\int_0^x [y(s)]^2 \, ds = [y(x)]^4, \quad y(0) = 0.$

14. $\displaystyle\int_0^x [y(s)]^2 \, ds = x[y(x)]^4.$

15. $\displaystyle\int_x^\infty \frac{y(s)}{s} \, ds = y(x), \quad y(\infty) = 0.$

16. Determine the differential equation of the family of straight lines with the y-intercept equal to twice the slope.

17. Determine the differential equation of the family of circles passing through two points $(a, 0)$ and $(-a, 0)$, where a is a given constant different from zero.

CHAPTER 2

THE DIFFERENTIAL EQUATION OF FIRST ORDER

2–1 Introduction. In this chapter we shall consider differential equations of the form

$$F\left(x, y, \frac{dy}{dx}\right) = 0, \tag{1}$$

where F is a given function of the three arguments x, y, and dy/dx. Usually the solution of (1) will be a relation of the form

$$G(x, y, c) = 0, \tag{2}$$

where c is an arbitrary constant. Simple examples of this occurred in Chapter 1.

Given an expression of the form (2) we may obtain a differential equation which is solved by (2) as follows. We differentiate (2) with respect to x,

$$\frac{\partial G}{\partial x} + \frac{\partial G}{\partial y}\frac{dy}{dx} = 0, \tag{3}$$

and eliminate the constant c from (2) and (3). The result of this elimination is a relation of the form (1).

For example, when

$$y - cx + c^2 = 0, \tag{4}$$

we also have

$$\frac{dy}{dx} - c = 0. \tag{5}$$

The differential equation which is obtained by eliminating c reads

$$y - \frac{dy}{dx}x + \left(\frac{dy}{dx}\right)^2 = 0. \tag{6}$$

Equation (6) is equivalent to the two differential equations

$$\frac{dy}{dx} = \frac{1}{2}x + \sqrt{\frac{1}{4}x^2 - y} \tag{7a}$$

and

$$\frac{dy}{dx} = \frac{1}{2}x - \sqrt{\frac{1}{4}x^2 - y}. \tag{7b}$$

45

Both of these differential equations have the solution $y = cx - c^2$ for all values of the constant c.

The question may be asked whether $y = cx - c^2$ represents *all* solutions of either (7a) or (7b). The answer is no. It may be verified that

$$y = \tfrac{1}{4}x^2 \tag{8}$$

also satisfies the differential equations (7a) and (7b), and this expression cannot be obtained from $y = cx - c^2$ through any choice of the constant c.

The example of the differential equation (6) and the two equations (7) derived from it shows that the problem of finding *all* solutions of a given differential equation of the first order will have to be considered with more care than might be expected at first.

A general theorem in regard to the question of all solutions which is concerned with the differential equation

$$\frac{dy}{dx} = f(x, y) \tag{9}$$

and which is proved in Chapter 6 is as follows:

> THEOREM.   Given that the function $f(x, y)$ and its partial derivative $\partial f/\partial y$ are continuous in some region R of the xy-plane. Then for every point (x_0, y_0) in this region there is a unique solution $y = y(x)$ of the differential equation $y' = f(x, y)$ with the initial condition $y(x_0) = y_0$. This solution is defined in some x-interval containing x_0.

The reader who finds it difficult to appreciate the significance of this theorem at this stage is advised to proceed with the study of the following sections and return to the present considerations at a later stage.

When we know the *existence* of a *unique* solution, we are in a position to decide whether a solution $G(x, y, c) = 0$ contains *all* solutions. Clearly, $G(x, y, c) = 0$ will contain all solutions in the region R, given the existence of a unique solution in this region, if it is possible to satisfy the relation $G(x_0, y_0, c) = 0$, by some choice of c, for all (x_0, y_0) in the region.

In what follows we shall call an expression $G(x, y, c) = 0$ which contains *all* solutions of a differential equation $F(x, y, y') = 0$ in a region of the xy-plane the *general solution* of this equation in the region. We note specifically that the theorem which we have quoted is concerned with certain classes of equations $y' = f(x, y)$, and not with the general first-order differential equation $F(x, y, y') = 0$.

A solution obtained from the general solution of a differential equation by assigning a definite value to the constant c will be called a *particular solution*.

It may be instructive to see what the existence and uniqueness theorem which we have quoted implies for the differential equation (7a). The region R in which both f and $\partial f/\partial y$ are continuous is given by $y < \frac{1}{4}x^2$. The function f itself is continuous in $y \le \frac{1}{4}x^2$. The theorem states that there is a unique solution satisfying the condition $y(x_0) = y_0$ provided $y_0 < \frac{1}{4}x_0^2$. The solution $y = cx - c^2$ allows satisfaction of this condition for all admissible values of x_0 and y_0. The appropriate value of c is $c = \frac{1}{2}x_0 + \sqrt{\frac{1}{4}x_0^2 - y_0}$. Consequently $y = cx - c^2$ is the general solution of (7a), *in the region* $y < \frac{1}{4}x^2$. We note further that if $y_0 = \frac{1}{4}x_0^2$ we still have a solution of (7a), but this solution is not unique: both $y = \frac{1}{4}x^2$ and $y = \frac{1}{2}x_0 x - \frac{1}{4}x_0^2$ are solutions of (7a) when $y_0 = \frac{1}{4}x_0^2$.

As another example, consider the problem

$$y' = y^2, \quad y(x_0) = y_0. \tag{10}$$

Since $f = y^2$ and $\partial f/\partial y = 2y$ are continuous everywhere, our theorem states that there is a unique solution for every (x_0, y_0). From the differential equation, we find first that $y = 1/(c - x)$. Determining c by means of the initial condition gives this unique solution in the form

$$y = \frac{y_0}{1 - (x - x_0)y_0}. \tag{11}$$

and this shows that $y = 1/(c - x)$ is the general solution of $y' = y^2$.

The x-interval of definition of the solution (11) which contains x_0 is

$$-\infty < x < x_0 + y_0^{-1} \quad \text{for } y_0 > 0,$$
$$-\infty < x < \infty \quad \text{for } y_0 = 0,$$
$$x_0 + y_0^{-1} < x < \infty \quad \text{for } y_0 < 0.$$

We see that the x-interval in which the solution (11) is defined is not the entire x-axis (except for the case $y_0 = 0$) even though the region R for which f and $\partial f/\partial y$ are continuous contains the entire x-axis.

EXERCISES

In Exercises 1 through 8, find a first-order differential equation with solution as stated.

1. $y = cx$
2. $y = mx + c$ (m constant)
3. $x^2 + y^2 + cy = 0$
4. $y - cx + \frac{1}{3}c^3 = 0$
5. $y - cx + \sin^2 c = 0$
6. $y = \sin(x + c)$
7. $y = 1 + ce^{-\sin x}$
8. $y^2 = 2cx - 4c^2$

9. Show that the differential equation $y - xy' + \frac{1}{3}(y')^3 = 0$ obtained in Exercise 4 has another solution, $y = \frac{2}{3}x^{3/2}$.

10. By analogy with the result for the case $y - xy' + (y')^2 = 0$, obtain a family of solutions of $y - xy' + (y')^n = 0$ $(n \neq 1)$ involving an arbitrary constant c. Verify the existence of another solution of the form $y = Ax^p$, and determine the values of the constants A and p.

11. On one set of axes graph the parabola $y = \frac{1}{4}x^2$ and the straight lines $y - cx + c^2 = 0$ for each of the four values of $c = \pm 1, \pm 2$, and note that each of the straight lines is tangent to the parabola.

12. Show that the differential equation $y' = 3y^{2/3}$ with the initial condition $y(x_0) = 0$ has the family of solutions

$$
y = \begin{cases}
(x - x_2)^3, & x_2 \leq x, \\
0, & x_1 \leq x \leq x_2, \\
(x - x_1)^3, & x \leq x_1
\end{cases}
$$

for any x_1 and x_2 for which $x_1 \leq x_0 \leq x_2$.

State why this result does not contradict the existence and uniqueness theorem.

13. What conditions must be satisfied in order that the linear differential equation

$$
p_0(x)y' + p_1(x)y = q(x)
$$

has a unique solution satisfying the condition $y(x_0) = y_0$ for $a < x_0 < b$ and all finite y_0?

2–2 Geometrical considerations. Isoclines.

The differential equation $F(x, y, dy/dx) = 0$ has a simple geometrical meaning which can give us useful information without our solving it. Let us show this first under the assumption that this differential equation can be written in the form

$$
\frac{dy}{dx} = f(x, y), \tag{1}
$$

where f is a single-valued function. For each pair of values (x, y) we then have just one value of f.

The solutions of (1) can be plotted as curves in an xy-coordinate system. From (1) we know the slope of the solution curve passing through any point (x, y). The curves of constant slope, or *isoclines*, are the curves $f(x, y) = C$. Suppose we plot a number of these isoclines and indicate on them the appropriate slopes by means of short segments of straight lines. On a given isocline $f(x, y) = C$, these straight-line segments will all be parallel to one another, each having the slope C. If the isoclines are sufficiently close together, the solution curves of the differential equation will be nearly straight lines over the distance from halfway between one pair

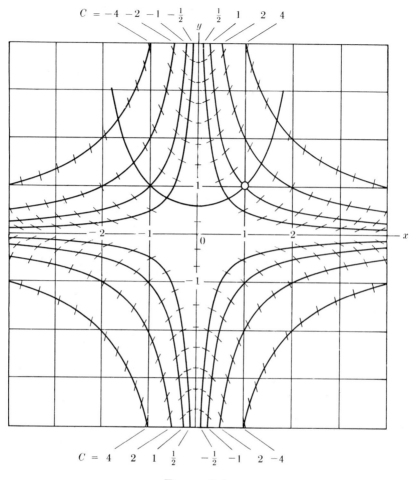

FIGURE 2–1

of adjacent isoclines to halfway between the next pair. Suitable portions of the straight-line segments which we have drawn will give us a qualitatively correct picture of the solution curves of (1).

EXAMPLE. For the differential equation

$$y' = xy \tag{2}$$

the isoclines are the equilateral hyperbolas $xy = C$ together with the two coordinate axes. In Fig. 2–1 we have plotted the isoclines for $C = 0$, $\pm\frac{1}{2}$, ±1, ±2, ±4, together with the appropriate short parallel line segments. With the help of these line segments we can easily draw a number of curves which are approximations to solution curves of (2). Among the family of solution curves we may select a specific curve by prescribing that it pass through a specified point (x_0, y_0), for instance through the point $(1, 1)$.

In general, the relation $F(x, y, dy/dx) = 0$ associates with every point (x, y) not one value, but several values of dy/dx. For example, for the differential equation

$$(y')^2 - (x^2 + y^2) = 0, \tag{3}$$

we have

$$y' = \pm\sqrt{x^2 + y^2}. \tag{4}$$

The isoclines are concentric circles about the origin. We have two systems of parallel line segments associated with each isocline, one of them corresponding to the plus sign in (4) and the other corresponding to the minus sign in (4). The actual approximate construction of solution curves proceeds as in the simpler case of single-valued y' except that now there may be two (or more) solution curves through a given point (x, y). Care must be taken in the construction of a solution curve to remain within the confines of one and the same system of line segments.

While the isocline procedure is useful for a qualitative determination of the solution, it is not in general as practical for quantitative determinations as other approximation methods, such as series solutions or numerical integration procedures.

Exercises

1. Plot the isoclines for $C = 0$, $\frac{1}{2}$, $\frac{3}{4}$, and 1 for the differential equation $y' = \sqrt{1 - y^2}$. On each isocline draw the appropriate short parallel line segments. Using these line segments, draw a curve passing through the origin which is an approximation to the solution curve. Draw one which passes through the point $(0, 1)$. Compare the two approximate solution curves with the curves of Exercise 6, Section 2–1.

2. Plot the isoclines for a few values of C for the differential equation $y' = -x/y$. On each isocline draw the appropriate short parallel line segments. Using these line segments, draw a curve passing through the point $(0, 1)$ which is an approximation to the solution curve through this point.

3. Obtain a qualitative picture of the spiraloid nature of the solutions of the equation $y' = (x + y)/(x - y)$ through the use of a number of lines $y/x = $ const as isoclines.

4. Obtain a qualitative picture of the solution of $y' = y^2 - x$, with $y(1) = 1$, through use of the curves of constant slope 0, ± 1, ± 2, ± 3, in the interval $-3 < x < 3$.

5. Given a family of curves which is determined by the differential equation $y' = -y/x$. What differential equation determines *another* family of curves

which has the property that at any point (x, y) a member of the second family intersects a member of the first family at right angles? Obtain a qualitative picture of portions of the two curves passing through the point $(2, 1)$ by considering the straight lines $y = 0, \frac{1}{4}x, \frac{1}{2}x, x, 2x$ as isoclines.

2–3 Separation of variables. The simplest class of equations $dy/dx = f(x, y)$ which can be readily solved are the equations in which the variables are separable in such a way that

$$N(y) \frac{dy}{dx} + M(x) = 0. \tag{1}$$

We have encountered special cases of Eq. (1) in the preceding chapter and there solved them by simple integration. We can do the same for all equations of the form (1) by *separating variables* as follows:

$$M(x) \, dx + N(y) \, dy = 0. \tag{2}$$

Equation (2) can also be written as

$$d \left(\int M \, dx + \int N \, dy \right) = 0,$$

and this shows that the general solution of (2) is

$$\int M \, dx + \int N \, dy = c. \tag{3}$$

We cannot go further unless we know what M and N stand for.

In particular cases we may be able to carry out the integrations and find y explicitly as a function of x. An example is given by the equation

$$\frac{dy}{dx} + e^y \cos x = 0.$$

The solution (3) becomes

$$\int e^{-y} \, dy + \int \cos x \, dx = c$$

or

$$-e^{-y} + \sin x = c.$$

Solving for y, we have

$$y = \ln \frac{1}{\sin x - c}.$$

The quantity $\sin x - c$ in this solution must be positive in the sense that, given an interval $a < x < b$ in which the solution is to be valid, the constant c is restricted by the condition that $\sin x - c > 0$ for all x in the interval.

In some cases Eq. (1) cannot be solved explicitly for either y or x. For instance, the solution of

$$\frac{dy}{dx} + \frac{x^7 + \alpha x + \beta}{y^5 + \gamma y + \delta} = 0,$$

where α, β, γ, and δ are constants, is obtained in the form

$$\frac{y^6}{6} + \frac{\gamma y^2}{2} + \delta y + \frac{x^8}{8} + \alpha \frac{x^2}{2} + \beta x = c.$$

A class of first-order differential equations which may be made separable by a simple change of variables is

$$\frac{dy}{dx} = g\left(\frac{y}{x}\right), \tag{4}$$

where g is any given function of y/x. The form of this equation suggests that we set

$$\frac{y}{x} = v, \tag{5}$$

so as to have the function g depend only on one variable. Suppose we retain x as the independent variable and consider v as a new dependent variable. If we can find v as a function of x, then, since $y = vx$, we shall have y as a function of x, and thus have the solution of our equation.

To find v, we note that the relation $y = vx$ implies

$$\frac{dy}{dx} = v + x\frac{dv}{dx}. \tag{6}$$

With this (4) becomes

$$v + x\frac{dv}{dx} = g(v). \tag{7}$$

In (7) the variables are separable as follows:

$$\frac{dv}{v - g(v)} + \frac{dx}{x} = 0. \tag{8}$$

Sometimes a given differential equation is not directly given in the form (4) but intelligent inspection reveals that it can be brought into such a form. As a simple example of this sort consider the equation

$$x \frac{dy}{dx} = xe^{-y/x} + y.$$

The substitution $y = vx$ transforms this into

$$v + x \frac{dv}{dx} = e^{-v} + v$$

or

$$e^v \, dv = \frac{dx}{x}.$$

By integration, we have

$$e^v = \ln x + C = \ln cx$$

or

$$v = \ln (\ln cx).$$

The general solution of the given differential equation in an interval $a < x < b$ is then

$$y = x \ln (\ln cx),$$

where the constant c is restricted by the condition that $cx > 1$ in the entire interval $a < x < b$.

EXERCISES

Solve the equations in Exercises 1 through 9.

1. $1 - xy' = 0$

2. $(y')^2 = 1 - y^2$

3. $y' + (y - 1) \cos x = 0$

4. $(1 + x^2) \, dy + (1 + y^2) \, dx = 0$

5. $(1 + x) \, dy + 3y \, dx = 0$

6. $y' - y \tanh x = 0$

7. $y' + y \tan x = 0$

8. $y' - y \tan x = 0$

9. $(y^2 + y) \, dx + x \, dy = 0$

10. $y' = 1 + y/x + (y/x)^2$

11. $y' = 1 + y/x - (y/x)^2$

12. $(3x^2y - y^3) \, dx - (3y^2x - x^3) \, dy = 0$

13. $y' = (y - x)/(y + x)$

14. $(y')^2 - (a + b)yy' + aby^2 = 0$

15. $(y')^2 - (x + 2y)y' + 2xy = 0$

16. Show that the differential equation

$$(a_1x + b_1y + c_1) \, dx + (a_2x + b_2y + c_2) \, dy = 0,$$

with $a_1b_2 - a_2b_1 \neq 0$, can be reduced by the substitution

$$x = X + \alpha, \quad y = Y + \beta,$$

where α and β are suitable constants, to the for n

$$dY/dX = g(Y/X).$$

17. Use the result of Exercise 16 to solve

(a) $(3x + 2y + 1) \, dx + (2x + 3y - 1) \, dy = 0$,

(b) $(x + 2y + 2) \, dx + (2x - y) \, dy = 0$.

By making the substitution $y = vx^n$ and by choosing the value of n appropriately, show that the following differential equations can be reduced to differential equations in which the variables are separated. Obtain their solutions.

18. $\dfrac{dy}{dx} = \dfrac{1 - xy^2}{2x^2y}$.

19. $\dfrac{dy}{dx} = \dfrac{y - xy^2}{x + yx^2}$.

20. Show that the differential equation

$$\frac{1}{x^{n-1}} \frac{dy}{dx} = g\left(\frac{y}{x^n}\right)$$

may be reduced to an equation with variables separated, by the substitution $v = y/x^n$.

21. Solve

$$\frac{dx}{\sqrt{1 - x^2}} + \frac{dy}{\sqrt{1 - y^2}} = 0.$$

22. Show that the expression

$$u \equiv \frac{x\sqrt{1 - y^4} + y\sqrt{1 - x^4}}{1 + x^2y^2} = c$$

is a solution of the differential equation

$$\frac{dx}{\sqrt{1 - x^4}} + \frac{dy}{\sqrt{1 - y^4}} = 0.$$

[*Hint:* Try to write $\partial u/\partial x$ in the form $g(x, y)/\sqrt{1 - x^4}$ and note that $g(x, y) = g(y, x)$.]

23. Determine the interval of existence of the solution $y(x)$ of $xy' = xe^{-y/x} + y$ with the initial condition $y(x_0) = y_0$ when both x_0 and y_0 are positive.

2–4 Exact differential equations. An equation of the form

$$u(x, y) = c \tag{1}$$

evidently satisfies the differential equation

$$du = \frac{\partial u}{\partial x} \, dx + \frac{\partial u}{\partial y} \, dy = 0.$$

For example, the equation $x^2 + xy + y^2 = c$ represents a solution of the differential equation

$$(2x + y)\, dx + (x + 2y)\, dy = 0.$$

Now suppose we have a differential equation

$$M\, dx + N\, dy = 0, \tag{2}$$

where M and N are given functions of the two variables x, y. If M and N are partial derivatives of some function $u(x, y)$ such that

$$M = \frac{\partial u}{\partial x}, \qquad N = \frac{\partial u}{\partial y}, \tag{3}$$

then we can work back and conclude that if (2) and (3) hold, then also

$$u = c. \tag{4}$$

In other words, if the given functions M and N are such that there exists some function $u(x, y)$ for which (3) holds, then the solution of the differential equation (2) is given by (4). In this case, the expression $M\, dx + N\, dy$ is an exact differential, du, and the differential equation $M\, dx + N\, dy = 0$ is called an *exact differential equation*.

A necessary condition on the functions M and N in order that (2) be an exact equation follows from the relation

$$\frac{\partial}{\partial y}\left(\frac{\partial u}{\partial x}\right) = \frac{\partial}{\partial x}\left(\frac{\partial u}{\partial y}\right)$$

in the form

$$\frac{\partial M}{\partial y} = \frac{\partial N}{\partial x}. \tag{5}$$

Let us see whether this condition is also sufficient or, in other words, whether when (5) is true we can always find a function u for which (3) is true. We can certainly find u such that

$$\frac{\partial u}{\partial x} = M \tag{6}$$

is true. The question then is: After determining u so that (6) holds, can we also satisfy the *second* of Eqs. (3)? From (6),

$$u = \int M\, \partial x + K(y), \tag{7}$$

where the symbol ∂x in the integral indicates that we integrate the function M with respect to x, treating y as a constant, and where $K(y)$ is an arbitrary function of y. From (7), we have further

$$\frac{\partial u}{\partial y} = \frac{\partial}{\partial y} \int M \, \partial x + K'(y) = \int \frac{\partial M}{\partial y} \, \partial x + K'(y) \tag{8}$$

We now make use of (5) in order to write (8) in the form

$$\frac{\partial u}{\partial y} = \int \frac{\partial N}{\partial x} \, \partial x + K'(y). \tag{9}$$

We must now see whether setting $\partial u/\partial y = N$ leads to a contradiction. Writing $\partial u/\partial y = N$ in (9), we have

$$K'(y) = N - \int \frac{\partial N}{\partial x} \, \partial x. \tag{10}$$

Since the partial derivative of the right side with respect to x vanishes, this right side is, in fact, independent of x and consequently depends only upon y, and we have no contradiction.

To find the function K we must return to Eq. (8) and in it set $\partial u/\partial y = N$; that is, we find $K(y)$ from the equation

$$K'(y) = N - \frac{\partial}{\partial y} \int M \, \partial x, \tag{11}$$

where $\int M \, \partial x$ has the same form as in Eq. (7).

Summarizing, we can say that *the differential equation* (2) *is an exact equation when* $\partial M/\partial y = \partial N/\partial x$ *and that then its solution is of the form* $u = c$, *where* u *is given by* (7) *and* (11).

As an example, consider the differential equation

$$(3x^2 + 2xy) \, dx + (ax^2 + by^2) \, dy = 0.$$

We have

$$\frac{\partial M}{\partial y} = 2x, \qquad \frac{\partial N}{\partial x} = 2ax.$$

Thus the equation will be exact if $a = 1$. We then have

$$\frac{\partial u}{\partial x} = M = 3x^2 + 2xy,$$

$$u = \int (3x^2 + 2xy) \, \partial x + K(y)$$

$$= x^3 + x^2 y + K(y),$$

and from this

$$\frac{\partial u}{\partial y} = x^2 + K'(y).$$

Since also

$$\frac{\partial u}{\partial y} = N = x^2 + by^2,$$

we see that

$$K'(y) = by^2$$

or

$$K(y) = \tfrac{1}{3}by^3 + c_0.$$

The solution of the given differential equation, with $a = 1$, is then

$$u \equiv x^3 + x^2y + \tfrac{1}{3}by^3 = c,$$

where the constant c_0 has been incorporated in the constant c.

It is worth stressing that it is not the function u but rather the relation $u = c$ which represents the solution of our differential equation.

EXERCISES

Show that the following differential equations are exact, and integrate:

1. $\sin y \, dx + (x \cos y + 3y^2) \, dy = 0$
2. $(x^2 + y) \, dx + (x + e^y) \, dy = 0$
3. $y \, dx + (x - y^3) \, dy = 0$
4. $\sin x \cos y \, dx + \cos x \sin y \, dy = 0$
5. $(3x^2e^y - 2x) \, dx + (x^3e^y - \sin y) \, dy = 0$
6. $3x^2 \ln |y| \, dx + (x^3/y) \, dy = 0.$

Determine for what, if any, of the values of the constants a and b the following differential equations are exact and solve the exact equations.

7. $(y + x^3) \, dx + (ax + by^3) \, dy = 0$
8. $(x + my) \, dx + (ax + by) \, dy = 0$
9. $\ln y \, dx + [(x/y) + ax] \, dy = 0$
10. $y^2 \, dx + (yx + a \sin x + b \cos x) \, dy = 0$
11. $[y^2 \cos (xy^2) + a] \, dx + [bx \cos (xy^2) + 3y]y \, dy = 0$

2–5 Integrating factor. Consider the differential equation

$$y \, dx - (x + y^3) \, dy = 0. \tag{1}$$

We have

$$M = y, \qquad N = -(x + y^3).$$

Since

$$\frac{\partial M}{\partial y} = 1, \qquad \frac{\partial N}{\partial x} = -1,$$

the equation is not exact. However, if we write Eq. (1) in the form

$$y\, dx - x\, dy = y^3\, dy,$$

and if we recall the formula for $d(x/y)$, we are led to multiply the above equation by $1/y^2$ (which we can do so long as $y \neq 0$) so as to have

$$\frac{y\, dx - x\, dy}{y^2} = y\, dy. \qquad (2)$$

This, however, is equivalent to $d(x/y) = \frac{1}{2} d(y^2)$ or

$$du = 0,$$

where

$$u = \frac{x}{y} - \frac{y^2}{2}.$$

Consequently,

$$\frac{x}{y} - \frac{y^2}{2} = c \qquad (3)$$

is the solution of (2) and also of (1). What we have done is to change the nonexact Eq. (1) into the exact Eq. (2) by multiplication by a suitable factor.

This raises the question: To what extent may we reduce other nonexact equations to exact equations by multiplying the nonexact equation by a suitable function? In other words, we wish to see in what circumstances the equation

$$M\, dx + N\, dy = 0, \qquad (4)$$

with

$$\frac{\partial M}{\partial y} \neq \frac{\partial N}{\partial x},$$

can be made an exact equation of the form

$$\mu M\, dx + \mu N\, dy = 0, \qquad (5)$$

where μ is a suitable function of x and y. When this is possible we call μ an *integrating factor* of Eq. (4).

The condition for exactness of Eq. (5) is

$$\frac{\partial(\mu M)}{\partial y} = \frac{\partial(\mu N)}{\partial x}$$

or

$$\frac{\partial \mu}{\partial y} M - \frac{\partial \mu}{\partial x} N = \left(\frac{\partial N}{\partial x} - \frac{\partial M}{\partial y}\right)\mu. \tag{6}$$

We see that the systematic determination of an integrating factor of a nonexact equation requires the solution of a partial differential equation and so we have merely replaced one differential equation problem by another.

Without going into the question of how to solve the partial differential equation (6) for μ, we may turn the question around and ask for conditions on M and N such that the integrating factor μ is of special given form. Perhaps the most useful result of this nature is obtained when the equation for μ has a solution which depends on x alone. In this case we have $\partial \mu/\partial y = 0$, and Eq. (6) may be written as

$$\frac{1}{\mu}\frac{d\mu}{dx} = \frac{\partial M/\partial y - \partial N/\partial x}{N}. \tag{7}$$

Since the left side of this equation depends only on x, the right side must do the same, and we have the result that we can find an integrating factor $\mu = \mu(x)$ provided the right side of (7) is a function of x alone. In this case, we set as an abbreviation

$$\frac{\partial M/\partial y - \partial N/\partial x}{N} = p(x), \tag{8}$$

and we obtain from (7),

$$\mu = e^{\int p(x)\,dx}. \tag{9}$$

After multiplication by this factor, the solution of the resultant differential equation is obtained by the method of the preceding section.

EXERCISES

1. Show that the existence of an integrating factor of the form $\mu = e^{ay}p(x)$ requires that the expression

$$\frac{-aM + \partial N/\partial x - \partial M/\partial y}{N}$$

be independent of y.

Solve the following:

2. $(1/x)\,dx - (1 + xy^2)\,dy = 0$

3. $(3xe^y + 2y)\,dx + (xe^y + 1)x\,dy = 0$

4. $(y^2 - 2x^2e^y)\,dx + (2xy \ln x - x^3e^y)\,dy = 0$

5. Show that

$$1/(x^2 + y^2)$$

is an integrating factor of the differential equation

$$(x + y)\,dx + (y - x)\,dy = 0,$$

and solve.

In Exercises 6, 7, and 8 show that the differential equation has an integrating factor of the form indicated, determine the integrating factor in each case, and solve the differential equation.

6. $y\,(\ln y - 2x)\,dx + (x + y)\,dy = 0, \quad \phi(y)$

7. $x\,dy + y\,dx - 2x^2y^3\,dy = 0, \quad (xy)^n$

8. $(3x/y^2 + 14 + 5x^3y^3)\,dx + (14x/y + 5x^4y^2 + 4y/x)\,dy = 0, \quad x^my^n$

2–6 The linear differential equation of the first order. An important equation for which we have an integrating factor μ depending only on x is the differential equation

$$\frac{dy}{dx} + P(x)y = Q(x). \tag{1}$$

Since both the dependent variable y and its derivative dy/dx occur in (1) in linear form, Eq. (1) is called a *linear differential equation*.

We may write (1) in the form

$$[P(x)y - Q(x)]\,dx + dy = 0. \tag{2}$$

Setting

$$Py - Q = M, \qquad 1 = N,$$

we see that

$$\frac{\partial M/\partial y - \partial N/\partial x}{N} = P(x).$$

By comparison with Eqs. (8) and (9) of the preceding section, we see that there is an integrating factor of the form

$$\mu = e^{\int P\,dx}.$$

If we multiply both sides of (1) by this integrating factor, our differential equation reads

$$e^{\int P dx}\left[\frac{dy}{dx} + Py\right] = e^{\int P dx}Q.$$

This is equivalent to

$$\frac{d}{dx}[e^{\int P dx}y] = e^{\int P dx}Q,$$

and from this we find the solution of Eq. (1) of the form

$$e^{\int P dx}y = \int e^{\int P dx}Q\,dx + c. \tag{3}$$

As an example, consider the equation

$$y' + ay = bx, \tag{4}$$

where a and b are constants. An integrating factor is

$$e^{\int a dx} = e^{ax}$$

and by (3) the solution is

$$e^{ax}y = b\int xe^{ax}\,dx + c.$$

Integrating by parts and dividing both sides by e^{ax}, we have

$$y = \frac{b}{a}x - \frac{b}{a^2} + ce^{-ax}. \tag{5}$$

As another example, take the following:

$$y' + 3x^2y = 1. \tag{6}$$

An integrating factor is

$$e^{\int 3x^2 dx} = e^{x^3}$$

and the solution is

$$ye^{x^3} = \int e^{x^3}\,dx + c. \tag{7}$$

The integral on the right cannot be expressed in terms of a finite number of known elementary functions. We may, if we wish, evaluate this integral by numerical methods or by means of term-by-term integration of the known Taylor series for e^{x^3}. This series is

$$e^{x^3} = 1 + x^3 + \frac{x^6}{2!} + \frac{x^9}{3!} + \cdots$$

If we insert the series into (7) we obtain the following formula for the solution y:

$$y = e^{-x^3}\left[\int e^{x^3}\,dx + c\right]$$

$$= e^{-x^3}\left[\int\left(1 + x^3 + \frac{x^6}{2!} + \cdots\right)dx + c\right]$$

$$= e^{-x^3}\left[c + x + \frac{x^4}{4} + \frac{x^7}{7\cdot 2!} + \frac{x^{10}}{10\cdot 3!} + \cdots\right]. \tag{8}$$

2–7 Method of variation of parameter for solving linear first-order differential equations. To solve the differential equation

$$\frac{dy}{dx} + P(x)y = Q(x) \tag{1}$$

the following alternate method may be used. We first solve the *reduced* or *homogeneous* equation

$$\frac{dy_h}{dx} + P(x)y_h = 0 \tag{2}$$

by separation of variables, obtaining

$$y_h = c_0\,u, \tag{3}$$

where

$$u = e^{-\int P(x)\,dx}. \tag{4}$$

We now *choose* to write the solution of the complete Eq. (1) in the form

$$y = v(x)u(x). \tag{5}$$

It should be realized that this choice of writing y is nothing but an inspired guess. The importance of its success lies in the fact that the same approach will later be found just as useful in the study of higher-order linear differential equations. Let us realize also that what we have done is to replace the constant c_0, the *parameter* in the solution of the homogeneous equation, by a factor varying with x. This is the reason for calling this the method of *variation of parameter*.

Substitution of (5) in (1) gives a differential equation for the factor function $v(x)$:

$$\frac{dv}{dx}u + v\frac{du}{dx} + P(x)vu = Q(x). \tag{6}$$

The second and third terms on the left of (6) cancel each other if account is taken of Eqs. (2) and (3), and we are left with

$$\frac{dv}{dx} u = Q(x). \tag{7}$$

From this, by simple integration,

$$v = \int \frac{Q(x)}{u} \, dx + c. \tag{8}$$

Combination of (4), (8), and (5) gives

$$y = e^{-\int P dx} \left(\int Q(x) e^{\int P dx} \, dx + c \right). \tag{9}$$

Equation (9) is, as it should be, the same as Eq. (3) of the preceding section.

EXERCISES

Solve the differential equations in Exercises 1 through 8.

1. $y' - y = e^{2x}$　　　　　　　　2. $y' - y = e^x$
3. $y' - (a/x)y = x^m$　　　　　　4. $y' + e^x y = e^x$
5. $y' + y = 1/(1 + e^x)$　　　　6. $dx/dy + x \cot y = \sec y$
7. $(x + x^3)y' + 4x^2 y = 2$　　8. $y \, dx - (3x + y^4) \, dy = 0$

9. Show that the differential equation

$$y' + P(x)y = Q(x)y^n$$

(which is known as Bernoulli's equation) can be reduced to a linear differential equation for u by the substitution $1/y^{n-1} = u$.

10. Solve　$y' - y = xy^2$　　　　11. Solve　$x^2 y' - y^2 = 2xy$
12. Solve　$xy' + y = y^2 \ln x$

13. The differential equation

$$\frac{df(y)}{dy} \frac{dy}{dx} + P(x)f(y) = Q(x)$$

is a linear differential equation for $f(y)$. Use this fact to solve the equation

$$y' + \tan y = x \sec y.$$

14. Solve

$$y' \sin y + \sin x \cos y = \sin x$$

2–8 Clairaut's differential equation. Clairaut's differential equation is a differential equation of the form

$$y = y'x + f(y'),$$ (1)

where $f(y')$ is any function of y'. If $f(y')$ is linear, that is, if $f(y') = \alpha y' + \beta$, then Eq. (1) is linear; otherwise it is nonlinear.

An example of Clairaut's equation is the differential equation

$$y = y'x - y'^2.$$ (2)

In Section 2–1 we saw that the differential equation (2) has the family of solutions

$$y = cx - c^2,$$ (3)

and we also observed that it has another solution

$$y = \tfrac{1}{4}x^2.$$ (4)

If we sketch the function (3) for various values of c, we see that the graphs give a family of straight lines with x-intercepts c and y-intercepts $-c^2$. The solution (4) is a parabola with vertex at the origin and with the y-axis as axis. We now show that each member of the family of straight lines given by (3) is tangent to the parabola, and indeed that at each point of the parabola there is one such line.

In order to see this we first note that the straight line (3) intersects the parabola (4) whenever

$$\tfrac{1}{4}x^2 = cx - c^2,$$

that is, whenever $x^2 - 4cx + 4c^2 = 0$ or $x = 2c$ and therewith $y = c^2$. At the point $(2c, c^2)$ the parabola (4) has the slope $y'(2c) = \tfrac{1}{2}x]_{x=2c} = c$, which is the same as the slope of the straight line (3). Thus the straight line (3) is tangent to the parabola (4) at the point $(2c, c^2)$. As c ranges over all real numbers, the points $(2c, c^2)$ cover the whole parabola. Hence at each point of the parabola one of the straight lines is tangent to it.

As a general definition, if we have a family H of curves,

$$y = h(x, c),$$ (5)

and a curve C,

$$y = g(x),$$ (6)

which touches every member of the family H and which, at each of its points, is tangent to at least one of the curves of the family H, then C is called the *envelope* of H. In the example just considered, the solution (4) is then the envelope of the straight lines (3).

We now return to the general form (1) of Clairaut's equation. In order to solve this equation we first assume that the function f possesses a continuous first derivative and that the desired solution y has a second derivative. We may then differentiate both sides of (1) with respect to x. We obtain

$$y'(x) = y'(x) + xy''(x) + f'[y'(x)]y''(x) \tag{7}$$

or

$$y''(x)\{x + f'[y'(x)]\} = 0. \tag{8}$$

This latter equation can be satisfied whenever either factor is zero, that is, whenever

$$y'' = 0 \tag{9}$$

or

$$x + f'(y') = 0. \tag{10}$$

The first of these equations gives $y' = c$, and if we insert this into the original differential equation (1), we obtain the family of solutions

$$y = cx + f(c). \tag{11}$$

While in the derivation we required that the given function f on the right of Eq. (1) possess a first derivative, the function (11) represents a solution of (1) regardless of whether or not f has a derivative.

We now turn to the vanishing second factor in the differentiated Clairaut equation. Equation (10), together with (1), may be considered as a parametric representation of this solution if we write

$$x = -f'(y'), \qquad y = -y'f'(y') + f(y'), \tag{12}$$

y' being the parameter.

To illustrate, we consider once more Eq. (2). The family (3) follows from (11). The additional solution (4), which we previously obtained more or less by guessing, now follows from (12), which assumes the form

$$x = 2y', \qquad y = -y'(-2y') - (y')^2 = (y')^2.$$

This parametric representation is readily changed to $y = \frac{1}{4}x^2$, by elimination of the parameter.

As a second example, consider the differential equation

$$y = y'x - \frac{1}{4}(y')^4.$$

On differentiating, we obtain

$$y' = y' + xy'' - (y')^3y'' \qquad \text{or} \qquad y''[x - (y')^3] = 0.$$

From $y'' = 0$ we obtain $y' = c$, and thus a family of solutions is

$$y = cx - \tfrac{1}{4}c^4.$$

From $x - (y')^3 = 0$ we obtain $y' = x^{1/3}$. On putting this into the given differential equation, we obtain $y = x^{4/3} - \tfrac{1}{4}x^{4/3}$ or

$$y = \tfrac{3}{4}x^{4/3}.$$

This is another solution, and we may again show that this is the envelope of the family.

Exercises

For each of the following three examples of Clairaut's equation find a family of solutions involving an arbitrary constant, and also find a further solution not obtainable from the family by specialization of the constant. In each example show that the second solution is the envelope of the family of solutions.

1. $y = y'x - e^{y'}$ 2. $y = y'x - \tfrac{1}{2}(y' - 4)^2$ 3. $y = y'x + y'^2$

4. Obtain all plane curves with the property that the portions of each tangent between the coordinate axes are of unit length.

2–9 Power-series solutions of linear first-order differential equations. A special case. In Section 2–6 we encountered a differential equation for which the solution appeared in the form of an integral which could not be evaluated in closed form. On that occasion we evaluated the integral in question by means of term-by-term integration of the known Taylor series of the integrand. The series which we obtained for the solution depended upon our knowing the integral form [Eq. (7), Section 2–6] of the solution of our differential equation.

We shall choose the same equation as a first example for obtaining a solution in the form of a power series without using the integral expression for the solution. In so doing we shall become aware of the possibility of treating in this fashion much more general problems than the particular example in question. Many of these more general problems will be such that application of the series method will be the most convenient procedure and, in fact, it may sometimes be the only practical one.

In the equation

$$y' + 3x^2y = 1 \tag{1}$$

we try to write the solution in the form

$$y = c_0 + c_1x + c_2x^2 + \cdots, \tag{2}$$

that is, we try to determine the coefficients c_0, c_1, c_2, ... in such a manner that (2) satisfies (1).

When we write the series (2) we understand it to mean that the solution of (1) may be so represented in some definite interval around the point $x = 0$. The actual size of this interval is of no concern for the moment.

From (2) follows

$$y' = c_1 + 2c_2x + 3c_3x^2 + \cdots, \tag{3}$$

and consequently (1) becomes

$$(c_1 + 2c_2x + 3c_3x^2 + \cdots) + (3c_0x^2 + 3c_1x^3 + 3c_2x^4 + \cdots) = 1 \tag{4}$$

or

$$(c_1 - 1) + 2c_2x + (3c_3 + 3c_0)x^2 + (4c_4 + 3c_1)x^3 + \cdots = 0. \tag{5}$$

Now (5) can vanish for all values of x in an interval about the origin only if the coefficients of every power of x are zero. This gives the following equations for the determination of the coefficients of the series (2):

$$c_1 - 1 = 0, \quad 2c_2 = 0, \quad 3c_3 + 3c_0 = 0,$$

$$4c_4 + 3c_1 = 0, \quad 5c_5 + 3c_2 = 0, \quad 6c_6 + 3c_3 = 0, \quad \ldots \tag{6}$$

or

$$c_1 = 1, \quad c_2 = 0, \quad c_3 = -c_0, \quad c_4 = -\tfrac{3}{4}, \quad c_5 = 0, \quad c_6 = \tfrac{1}{2}c_0, \quad \ldots \tag{7}$$

We note that no condition is imposed on c_0, and that the first few terms of the series (2) for y appear in the form

$$y = (x - \tfrac{3}{4}x^4 + \cdots) + c_0(1 - x^3 + \tfrac{1}{2}x^6 + \cdots). \tag{8}$$

To show agreement between this result and Eq. (8) of Section 2–6 it is necessary to insert the Taylor series development of e^{-x^3} in the last line of that equation and to multiply the two series term by term.

EXERCISES

Solve the differential equations in Exercises 1 through 3 by series in powers of x.

1. $y' = x^2 - y$ 2. $y' - x^3y = 1$ 3. $(1 - x^2)y' = 4y$

For each of the following three differential equations obtain a series solution in powers of x, and in each case check your result by solving the differential equation explicitly.

4. $(1 + x)y' = 3y$ 5. $(1 + x)y' = 3y + 1$

6. $(1 + x)y' = 3y + 3 - 2x$

7. The differential equation

$$dz/dt - at^2z = b,$$

where a and b are constants, may be reduced by the substitutions $z = \alpha y$, $t = \beta x$, where α and β are constants, to the differential equation (1). Determine α and β in terms of a and b and use this result to write the series solution of the given equation.

Obtain the first three nonvanishing terms in the power-series development of each of the equations in Exercises 8, 9, and 10 in powers of $x - 1$.

8. $y' = x^2 - y$ 9. $y' + 3x^2y = 1$ 10. $y' + 2xy = x^2$

2–10 Further examples of power-series solutions. While we can always solve a linear first-order differential equation by the method of Sections 2–6 and 2–7 (integrating factor or variation of parameter), it will be helpful to us in the later consideration of higher-order equations to consider at this time power-series solutions of certain classes of linear equations of the first order.

An obvious generalization of the differential equation (1) of the preceding section is the differential equation

$$y' + (a_0 + a_1x + a_2x^2 + \cdots)y = b_0 + b_1x + b_2x^2 + \cdots, \quad (1)$$

where the coefficients $a_0, a_1, \ldots, b_0, b_1, \ldots$ are *given* constants, and where we assume that the two series converge in some interval $-R < x < R$.

We again assume the solution in the form (2) of Section 2–9 and insert (2) and (3) of that section into (1) above, giving

$$(c_1 + 2c_2x + 3c_3x^2 + \cdots)$$
$$+ (a_0 + a_1x + a_2x^2 + \cdots)(c_0 + c_1x + c_2x^2 + \cdots) \quad (2)$$
$$= b_0 + b_1x + b_2x^2 + \cdots$$

Equation (2) can be rearranged to read as follows:

$$(c_1 + a_0c_0 - b_0) + (2c_2 + a_0c_1 + a_1c_0 - b_1)x$$
$$+ (3c_3 + a_0c_2 + a_1c_1 + a_2c_0 - b_2)x^2 + \cdots = 0. \quad (3)$$

We satisfy (3) by setting in it the coefficient of each power of x equal to zero. If we write the resulting equations in the form

$$c_1 = b_0 - a_0 c_0,$$
$$2c_2 = b_1 - a_0 c_1 - a_1 c_0, \qquad (4)$$
$$3c_3 = b_2 - a_0 c_2 - a_1 c_1 - a_2 c_0,$$

we see that the coefficient c_0 remains arbitrary and the remaining coefficients may be expressed successively in terms of c_0 and the given series coefficients $a_0, a_1, \ldots, b_0, b_1, \ldots$.

We may note the symmetrical structure of the system (4) as far as it has been written out and expect from this that the equation determining the general coefficient c_n will be

$$nc_n = b_{n-1} - a_0 c_{n-1} - a_1 c_{n-2} - \cdots - a_{n-1} c_0. \qquad (5)$$

That this is indeed correct may readily be shown.

It may be recalled that we have assumed that the coefficient series occurring in the differential equation (1) converge in the interval $-R < x < R$. We do not as yet know the interval of convergence of the solution series. We shall find later (Example 1, Section 2–14) that for this linear differential equation (1) the interval of convergence of the solution series is at least as large as the interval of convergence of the coefficient series occurring in (1).

We have seen that the linear differential equation (1) can always be solved by means of a power series of the form (2) of Section 2–9. If, however, the term y' is also multiplied by a function of x, then this may no longer be possible. A simple example of this is the following equation:

$$xy' + (a_0 + a_1 x)y = 0, \qquad (6)$$

where we will assume that x is positive.

To see what kind of *series* solution we may expect for (6), let us note that the solution of (6) may be obtained in the form

$$y = cx^{-a_0} e^{-a_1 x}. \qquad (7)$$

We may expand the term $e^{-a_1 x}$ in powers of x. This gives the solution of (6) in the form

$$y = x^{-a_0}(c_0 + c_1 x + c_2 x^2 + \cdots), \qquad (8)$$

where

$$c_n n! = (-a_1)^n.$$

We see that the solution (8) is a power series of the form (2) of Section 2–9 only if a_0 is a negative integer or zero. In all other cases a new type of series has arisen.

The foregoing suggests that if we wish to *start* with a power series solution of (6) we should modify the series (2) of Section 2–9 as follows:

$$y = c_0x^s + c_1x^{s+1} + c_2x^{s+2} + \cdots, \tag{9}$$

where s as well as the coefficients c_0, c_1, c_2, ... now must be determined by substitution in Eq. (6). In (9) we shall assume $c_0 \neq 0$. (If c_0 were zero and $c_1 \neq 0$ we would have the same series with s replaced by $s + 1$.) We should expect the determination of s and of the coefficients c_n to lead to the value $s = -a_0$. Let us illustrate this for a special case of (6) with $a_0 = \frac{3}{2}$ and $a_1 = 2$:

$$xy' + (\tfrac{3}{2} + 2x)y = 0. \tag{10}$$

We insert (9) into (10) and obtain

$$x[c_0sx^{s-1} + (s + 1)c_1x^s + (s + 2)c_2x^{s+1} + \cdots]$$
$$+ (\tfrac{3}{2} + 2x)[c_0x^s + c_1x^{s+1} + c_2x^{s+2} + \cdots] = 0$$

or, rearranging terms,

$$(s + \tfrac{3}{2})c_0x^s + [(s + \tfrac{5}{2})c_1 + 2c_0]x^{s+1} + [(s + \tfrac{7}{2})c_2 + 2c_1]x^{s+2} + \cdots = 0.$$

The coefficient of each power of x must again vanish, and so we have

$$(s + \tfrac{3}{2})c_0 = 0, \quad (s + \tfrac{5}{2})c_1 + 2c_0 = 0, \quad (s + \tfrac{7}{2})c_2 + 2c_1 = 0, \quad \ldots \tag{11}$$

Since $c_0 \neq 0$, we must have $s = -\frac{3}{2}$ in order to satisfy the first of these conditions. With this value of s we can then express c_1 in terms of c_0, c_2 in terms of c_1, etc. as follows:

$$c_1 = -2c_0, \quad c_2 = -\frac{2c_1}{2} = 2c_0, \quad \ldots \tag{12}$$

Still more general series than (9) may sometimes have to be used, as is explained in advanced treatises on the subject.

EXERCISES

By means of series in powers of x, solve the equations of Exercises 1 and 2.

1. $y' + (1 + x + x^2 + \cdots)y = x$

2. $y' + \left(x - \dfrac{x^3}{3!} + \dfrac{x^5}{5!} - \cdots\right)y = 1 + x + x^2 + \cdots$

3. Solve the differential equation

$$\frac{dy}{dx} - \frac{y}{1 - x^2} = 1$$

by power series. Carry out the calculations by writing the given differential equation both in the form

$$(1 - x^2)y' - y = 1 - x^2$$

and in the form

$$y' - (1 + x^2 + x^4 + \cdots)y = 1.$$

(What can you say about the number of terms in the recurrence relations for the determination of the series coefficients obtained from either form of the differential equation?)

4. Solve the differential equation

$$x\frac{dy}{dx} + \frac{y}{1 - x^2} = 0$$

by means of a series of the form

$$y = c_0 x^s + c_1 x^{s+1} + \cdots \qquad (c_0 \neq 0).$$

5. Solve each of the differential equations

(a) $xy' + y/(1 - x) = 0$ (b) $xy' - y/(1 - x^2) = 0$

by means of a series of the form

$$y = c_0 x^s + c_1 x^{s+1} + \cdots \qquad (c_0 \neq 0).$$

In each case check your result by solving the differential equation explicitly.

6. Obtain a *particular* solution y_p of the equation

$$x\frac{dy}{dx} + \frac{y}{1 - x^2} = 1$$

in the form

$$y_p = C_0 + C_1 x + C_2 x^2 + \cdots$$

7. Show that

$$y = \frac{c}{x}\left(1 - \frac{x^2}{2} - \frac{x^4}{8} - \frac{x^6}{16} - \cdots\right)$$

$$+ \left(1 - \frac{1}{3}x^2 - \frac{2 \cdot 1}{5 \cdot 3}x^4 + \frac{4 \cdot 2 \cdot 1}{7 \cdot 5 \cdot 3}x^6 + \cdots\right)$$

satisfies the differential equation of Exercise 6 and accordingly is the general solution of this equation for those values of x for which both series converge.

8. Show that the differential equation $x^2 \, (dy/dx) + y = 0$ does *not* admit solutions of the form $y = c_0 x^s + c_1 x^{s+1} + \cdots$.

9. Show, by considering the exact solution of $x^m y' - (a_0 + a_1 x + \cdots)y = 0$, where m is not zero and is not a positive integer, that this equation possesses a power-series solution of the form

$$y = c\{1 + x^{-m}[A_{10} + A_{11}x + \cdots] + x^{-2m}[A_{20} + A_{21}x + \cdots] + \cdots\}$$

$$= c\sum_{j=0}^{\infty}\sum_{k=0}^{\infty} A_{jk}x^{-jm+k},$$

where c is an arbitrary constant and the A_{jk} are constants which depend upon m and the given constants a_s. Obtain the value of A_{00}, A_{01}, A_{02}, A_{10}, A_{11}, A_{12}, A_{20}, A_{21}, A_{22}.

2–11 Power-series solutions of nonlinear first-order differential equations.

We have seen how to use series of powers of x for the solution y of linear differential equations. Let us now consider the problem of applying this procedure to the solution of the nonlinear equation

$$y' = f(x, y). \tag{1}$$

We try again to obtain a solution of the form

$$y = c_0 + c_1 x + c_2 x^2 + \cdots \tag{2}$$

Direct substitution of (2) in (1) leaves us with the relation

$$c_1 + 2c_2 x + 3c_3 x^2 + \cdots = f(x, c_0 + c_1 x + c_2 x^2 + \cdots). \tag{3}$$

Instead of attempting to evaluate this relation, let us proceed as follows. We know that the series (2) can be written in the equivalent form

$$y = y(0) + \frac{y'(0)}{1!}x + \frac{y''(0)}{2!}x^2 + \cdots + \frac{y^{(n)}(0)}{n!}x^n + \cdots \tag{4}$$

If we designate the starting value $y(0)$ by y_0, then the differential equation (1) gives us $y'(0)$ in the form

$$y'(0) = f(0, y_0). \tag{5}$$

To obtain the higher derivatives $y''(0), \ldots, y^{(n)}(0)$, we differentiate Eq. (1) successively and in the result set $x = 0$.

It is clear that a necessary condition for the success of this procedure is the existence of all the derivatives which are involved. This in turn requires that all partial derivatives of the function $f(x, y)$ exist.

The second and third derivatives of the solution function y are given by the following expressions:

$$\frac{d^2y}{dx^2} = \frac{\partial f}{\partial x} + \frac{\partial f}{\partial y}\frac{dy}{dx} = \frac{\partial f}{\partial x} + \frac{\partial f}{\partial y}f, \tag{6}$$

$$\frac{d^3y}{dx^3} = \frac{\partial}{\partial x}\left(\frac{\partial f}{\partial x} + \frac{\partial f}{\partial y}f\right) + \frac{\partial}{\partial y}\left(\frac{\partial f}{\partial x} + \frac{\partial f}{\partial y}f\right)\frac{dy}{dx}$$

$$= \frac{\partial^2 f}{\partial x^2} + 2\frac{\partial^2 f}{\partial x\,\partial y}f + \frac{\partial^2 f}{\partial y^2}f^2 + \frac{\partial f}{\partial y}\frac{\partial f}{\partial x} + \left(\frac{\partial f}{\partial y}\right)^2 f. \tag{7}$$

By continuing this process we may obtain derivatives of any order.

EXAMPLE. As an illustration, consider the equation

$$\frac{dy}{dx} = 1 + xy^2, \tag{8}$$

with the initial condition

$$y(0) = 0. \tag{9}$$

From (8) follows

$$y'(0) = 1. \tag{10}$$

To determine the subsequent coefficients in the solution (4), we calculate

$$\frac{d^2y}{dx^2} = y^2 + 2xy\frac{dy}{dx}, \tag{11}$$

$$\frac{d^3y}{dx^3} = 2y\frac{dy}{dx} + 2\left[y\frac{dy}{dx} + x\left(\frac{dy}{dx}\right)^2 + xy\frac{d^2y}{dx^2}\right], \tag{12}$$

$$\frac{d^4y}{dx^4} = 6\left(\frac{dy}{dx}\right)^2 + 6y\frac{d^2y}{dx^2} + 6x\frac{dy}{dx}\frac{d^2y}{dx^2} + 2xy\frac{d^3y}{dx^3}. \tag{13}$$

In Eqs. (11) through (13) we set $x = 0$, $y = 0$, and $y'(0) = 1$. This gives us successively

$$y''(0) = 0, \qquad y'''(0) = 0, \qquad y^{iv}(0) = 6. \tag{14}$$

We see that the power-series solution (2) for Eq. (8) with the initial condition (9) begins as follows:

$$y = x + \tfrac{1}{4}x^4 + \cdots \tag{15}$$

Suppose that instead of the initial condition (9) we prescribe the initial condition

$$y(0) = 1. \tag{16}$$

Equation (8) then gives

$$y'(0) = 1 \tag{17}$$

and Eqs. (11) through (13) give

$$y''(0) = 1, \quad y'''(0) = 4, \quad y^{iv}(0) = 12. \tag{18}$$

The solution series y is now of the form

$$y = 1 + x + \tfrac{1}{2}x^2 + \tfrac{2}{3}x^3 + \tfrac{1}{2}x^4 + \cdots \tag{19}$$

We may make the following observations.

(i) The nth derivative of the solution y of the differential equation (1) can be expressed as a combination of partial derivatives of the function $f(x, y)$ which occurs on the right of (1). These expressions evidently become more and more complicated as higher-order derivatives of y are calculated. Consequently it would be desirable to have a somewhat simpler procedure for the determination of the coefficients c_n in the solution series (2). Such a simpler procedure will be discussed in the following section.

(ii) We do not at this stage have any information concerning the interval of convergence of the series solution (4). From a comparison of the solutions (19) and (15) of Eq. (8) it appears possible that the interval of convergence may be different for different initial conditions for one and the same differential equation.

EXERCISES

1. Given the differential equation

$$y' = \cos (x + y).$$

Obtain the first few nonvanishing terms of the power-series solution of this equation with the initial conditions (a) $y(0) = 0$, (b) $y(0) = \pi/4$, (c) $y(0) = \pi/2$.

2. By making the substitution $x + y = u$ the differential equation of Exercise 1 is reduced to an equation in which the variables are separated. Use this fact to obtain the explicit solution of the differential equation of Exercise 1.

3. Given the differential equation

$$y' = \cos (x^2 + y),$$

with the initial conditions (a) $y(0) = 0$, (b) $y(0) = \pi/2$. Obtain the first few nonvanishing terms of the power-series solutions for these conditions.

Use series in powers of x to solve the following differential equations with the initial conditions stated

4. $y' = x^2 + y^2$ (a) $y(0) = 0$,   (b) $y(0) = 1$
5. $y' = 1 + \sin xy$ (a) $y(0) = 0$,   (b) $y(0) = \frac{1}{2}$
6. $y' = 1 + x + y^2$ (a) $y(0) = 0$,   (b) $y(0) = 1$
7. $y' = 1 + x^2 + y^2$ (a) $y(0) = 0$,   (b) $y(0) = 1$

2–12 Method of undetermined coefficients. An alternate, and often more convenient, way of solving the differential equation $dy/dx = f(x, y)$ depends on first developing the function f in powers of x and y. Let us assume that we are able to write

$$f(x, y) = A_{00} + A_{10}x + A_{01}y + A_{20}x^2 + A_{11}xy + A_{02}y^2 + \cdots$$
$$= \sum_m \sum_n A_{mn}x^m y^n. \tag{1}$$

According to Taylor's theorem for functions of two variables, the coefficients A_{mn} are given by the relation

$$A_{mn} = \frac{1}{m!n!} \left[\frac{\partial^{m+n} f(x, y)}{\partial x^m \partial y^n} \right]_{\substack{x=0 \\ y=0}}, \tag{2}$$

but often it will not be necessary to use this general formula.

We take first the case that the initial condition for the solution of the given differential equation has the special form

$$y(0) = 0. \tag{3}$$

With this initial condition the solution series is

$$y = c_1 x + c_2 x^2 + \cdots \tag{4}$$

Upon substitution of (1) and (4) in the differential equation $dy/dx = f$, we have to satisfy the relation

$$c_1 + 2c_2 x + 3c_3 x^2 + \cdots$$
$$= A_{00} + A_{10}x + A_{01}(c_1 x + c_2 x^2 + \cdots)$$
$$+ A_{20}x^2 + A_{11}x(c_1 x + c_2 x^2 + \cdots)$$
$$+ A_{02}(c_1 x + c_2 x^2 + \cdots)^2 + \cdots \tag{5}$$

To satisfy (5) we carry out the multiplications on the right of (5), and equate the coefficients of corresponding powers of x on the left and on the right. The first three equations obtained in this way are seen to be

$$c_1 = A_{00}, \quad 2c_2 = A_{10} + A_{01}c_1,$$

$$3c_3 = A_{20} + A_{11}c_1 + A_{02}c_1^2 + A_{01}c_2.$$

(6)

We shall not write down the general equation for the coefficients of x^n. It is sufficient to see that this equation will give us c_{n+1} in terms of certain of the coefficients A_{mn} and in terms of the previously determined solution coefficients $c_1, c_2, \ldots, c_n$.

EXAMPLE. We again take the differential equation

$$y' = 1 + xy^2$$

with the initial condition (3). Introduction of the series (4) into the differential equation gives

$$c_1 + 2c_2x + 3c_3x^2 + \cdots = 1 + x(c_1x + c_2x^2 + \cdots)^2$$
$$= 1 + c_1^2x^3 + 2c_1c_2x^4 + (c_2^2 + 2c_1c_3)x^5$$
$$+ (2c_1c_4 + 2c_2c_3)x^6 + \cdots$$

Equating the coefficients of corresponding powers of x, we have

$$c_1 = 1, \quad c_2 = 0, \quad c_3 = 0, \quad 4c_4 = c_1^2 = 1, \quad 5c_5 = 2c_1c_2 = 0,$$
$$6c_6 = c_2^2 + 2c_1c_3 = 0, \quad 7c_7 = 2c_1c_4 + 2c_2c_3 = \tfrac{1}{2}, \quad \cdots$$

The first few terms of the solution series are seen to be

$$y = x + \tfrac{1}{4}x^4 + \tfrac{1}{14}x^7 + \cdots$$

A comparison with the corresponding work done on this example in Section 2–11, where we obtained the first two of the foregoing three terms, shows the advantages of the method of undetermined coefficients.

For the general initial condition

$$y(x_0) = y_0,$$

(7)

we modify the form of our series solution for y to

$$y = y_0 + c_1(x - x_0) + c_2(x - x_0)^2 + \cdots$$

(8)

In the differential equation $dy/dx = f(x, y)$ the function $f(x, y)$ must now be expansible, as follows, instead of in the form (1):

$$f(x, y) = \sum_m \sum_n B_{mn}(x - x_0)^m(y - y_0)^n.$$

(9)

The use of (9) rather than of the expansion (1) in conjunction with the initial condition (7) avoids certain difficulties which become apparent if an attempt is made to use (7) and (1) simultaneously.

If we introduce new variables ξ and η, defined as

$$\xi = x - x_0, \qquad \eta = y - y_0, \tag{10}$$

then we have $dy/dx = d\eta/d\xi$, and we may write

$$f(x, y) = f(\xi + x_0, \eta + y_0) = \phi(\xi, \eta). \tag{11}$$

This shows that the transformation (10) reduces the general case of the initial condition (7) to the special case of the initial condition (1), that is, our differential equation in the new variables is $d\eta/d\xi = \phi(\xi, \eta)$ and the initial condition is $\eta(0) = 0$. The series expansion $\phi(\xi, \eta) = \sum\sum B_{mn}\xi^m\eta^n$ corresponds to the expansion (9) in terms of the original variables.

EXAMPLE. We take again the equation

$$y' = 1 + xy^2,$$

but now with the initial condition

$$y(1) = 1.$$

We write

$$x - 1 = \xi, \qquad y - 1 = \eta,$$

and this transforms the given differential equation into

$$\frac{d\eta}{d\xi} = 1 + (1 + \xi)(1 + \eta)^2 = 2 + \xi + 2\eta + 2\xi\eta + \eta^2 + \xi\eta^2$$

with the initial condition $\eta(0) = 0$. The solution series is taken in the form

$$\eta = c_1\xi + c_2\xi^2 + \cdots$$

and the differential equation becomes

$$c_1 + 2c_2\xi + 3c_3\xi^2 + \cdots = 2 + \xi + 2(c_1\xi + c_2\xi^2 + \cdots)$$
$$+ 2\xi(c_1\xi + c_2\xi^2 + \cdots) + (c_1\xi + c_2\xi^2 + \cdots)^2 + \xi(c_1\xi + c_2\xi^2 + \cdots)^2.$$

Equating corresponding powers of ξ, we have

$$c_1 = 2, \qquad 2c_2 = 1 + 2c_1, \qquad 3c_3 = 2c_2 + 2c_1 + c_1^2,$$
$$4c_4 = 2c_3 + 2c_2 + 2c_1c_2 + c_1^2, \ldots,$$

and from this

$$\eta = 2\xi + \tfrac{5}{2}\xi^2 + \tfrac{13}{3}\xi^3 + \tfrac{83}{12}\xi^4 + \cdots$$

or

$$y = 1 + 2(x - 1) + \tfrac{5}{2}(x - 1)^2 + \tfrac{13}{3}(x - 1)^3 + \tfrac{83}{12}(x - 1)^4 + \cdots$$

EXERCISES

Obtain the first four nonvanishing terms of the power-series solution in each of Exercises 1 through 6.

1. $y' = x + y^2$, $y(0) = 0$ 2. $y' = 1 + x \cos y$, $y(0) = 0$

3. $y' = \cos(x^2 + y)$, $y(0) = 0$ 4. $y' = e^{xy}$; (a) $y(0) = 0$, (b) $y(0) = 1$

5. $y' = 1 + x + \cos y$, $y(0) = 0$ 6. $y' = 1 + x + \sin y$, $y(0) = 0$

7. Obtain the coefficients of all zeroth, first, and second degree terms in the development

$$\cos(x^2 + y) = \sum\sum A_{mn}(x - 1)^m(y - 1)^n.$$

8. Use the results of Exercise 7 to obtain the power-series solution for

$$y' = \cos(x^2 + y), \qquad y(1) = 1$$

up to terms in $(x - 1)^3$.

9. Solve $y' = x + \sin y$, $y(1) = \pi/2$ by means of a power series $y = c_0 + c_1(x - 1) + c_2(x - 1)^2 + \cdots$. [*Hint.* Reduce the problem to one of the form $d\eta/d\xi = 1 + \xi + \cos \eta$, $\eta(0) = 0$, and use the result of Exercise 5.]

By introduction of new variables η and ξ reduce the initial value problems 10 and 11 to the form $d\eta/d\xi = \phi(\xi, \eta)$ with $\eta(0) = 0$.

10. $y' = x + y^2$; (a) $y(1) = 2$, (b) $y(2) = 1$

11. $y' = 1 + x \cos y$; (a) $y(1) = \pi/2$, (b) $y(-1) = \pi$

12. Solve $y' = x + \sin y$, $y(-1) = \pi$ by means of a power series $y = c_0 + c_1(x + 1) + c_2(x - 1)^2 + \cdots$

2–13 Convergence of series solutions. In using power series for the solution of differential equations one is always confronted by the question to what extent these series represent the actual solution of the problem under consideration. It is clear that if the series do not converge, they cannot be the solution.* One would like to say that the converse is also

---

* However, even if the formal solution series does not converge, it is possible that certain of its partial sums represent adequate approximations to the solution. In such cases, one generally speaks of an *asymptotic* development of the solution. Questions of this sort are considered in more advanced treatments of the subject.

true, that is, that a convergent solution series is a solution everywhere in its interval of convergence. Very often this will be true. There are, however, some difficulties with a statement of this sort which may be illustrated as follows. The differential equation

$$\frac{dy}{dx} = \begin{cases} x \text{ for } |x| \leq 1, \\ 1 \text{ for } |x| > 1 \end{cases}$$

has as a solution for $|x| \leq 1$ the expression $y = \frac{1}{2}x^2$. This "solution series" converges for all values of x but evidently is not a solution of the given differential equation in the interval $|x| > 1$.

In spite of a situation of this kind, questions about intervals of convergence of solution series are of basic importance and will be discussed in what follows. In some instances it is easy to determine exactly the range of convergence of the series. In other instances it is difficult to do more than to say that the series will definitely converge in some interval $x_1 < x < x_2$, but that it may converge in a larger interval.

In those cases where the solution of a given differential equation can be obtained without the use of series, the question of convergence need not, of course, be considered. However, if such a solution has a power-series development, we may study its convergence. This will be useful from two points of view. It will give us some indication of what to expect in general from a series solution with regard to range of convergence. Secondly, as we shall see, we may obtain information concerning the range of convergence of direct series solutions by suitable *comparison tests* with the solution of differential equations which can be solved without the use of infinite series.

EXAMPLE 1. The linear differential equation

$$y' = 1 + y,$$

with the initial condition $y(0) = y_0$, has the solution

$$y = (1 + y_0)e^x - 1.$$

Since the power series for e^x converges for all values of x, we know that the power-series solution of the given differential equation converges for all values of x.

EXAMPLE 2. The linear differential equation

$$\frac{dy}{dx} = \frac{y}{1 + x^2},$$

with the initial condition $y(0) = y_0$, has the solution

$$y = y_0 e^{\tan^{-1} x}.$$

The series

$$e^{\tan^{-1} x} = 1 + x + \frac{x^2}{2!} - \frac{x^3}{3!} - \frac{7x^4}{4!} + \frac{5x^5}{5!} + \cdots$$

is known to converge in the interval $-1 < x < 1$. We see that the range of convergence of the series solution coincides with the range of convergence of the series for the coefficient function

$$\frac{1}{1 + x^2} = 1 - x^2 + x^4 - x^6 + \cdots$$

EXAMPLE 3. The nonlinear differential equation

$$y' = y^2,$$

with the initial condition $y(0) = y_0$, has the solution

$$y = \frac{y_0}{1 - y_0 x}.$$

The series

$$\frac{1}{1 - y_0 x} = 1 + y_0 x + y_0^2 x^2 + \cdots$$

converges for

$$|x| < \frac{1}{|y_0|}.$$

We note that while for the linear differential equations of Examples 1 and 2 the convergence properties were independent of the initial conditions imposed on the solution, this is no longer the case for the present nonlinear equation.

The following example requires some knowledge of the convergence properties of series representing functions of a complex variable.

EXAMPLE 4. The nonlinear differential equation

$$y' = 1 + y^2,$$

with the initial condition $y(0) = y_0$, has the solution

$$y = \tan(x + \tan^{-1} y_0).$$

To obtain the interval of convergence for the series in powers of x representing $\tan (x + \tan^{-1} y_0)$, we may look at the behavior of the function $\tan (z + \tan^{-1} y_0)$ of the complex variable $z = x + iv$. The series

$$\tan (z + \tan^{-1} y_0) = A_0 + A_1 z + A_2 z^2 + \cdots$$

converges in the circle $|z| < |z_0|$, where z_0 is the singularity nearest to $z = 0$, that is, the point nearest to the origin at which the function ceases to be analytic. In the present case, the only singular points are given by $z + \tan^{-1} y_0 = \pm \pi/2, \pm 3\pi/2, \ldots$. Consequently, when $y_0 > 0$, we have $z_0 = \pi/2 - \tan^{-1} y_0$, and when $y_0 < 0$, we have $z_0 = -\pi/2 - \tan^{-1} y_0$. We conclude from this that the power-series solution of the given differential equation converges in the interval

$$-(\pi/2 - \tan^{-1} y_0) < x < \pi/2 - \tan^{-1} y_0 \quad \text{when } y_0 > 0,$$

and in the interval

$$-(\pi/2 + \tan^{-1} y_0) < x < \pi/2 + \tan^{-1} y_0 \quad \text{when } y_0 < 0.$$

The interval of convergence is again dependent on the initial condition.

EXERCISES

Determine the interval of convergence of the series in powers of x for the solution of the differential equations in Exercises 1 through 9, all with the initial condition $y(0) = y_0$.

1. $y' = x + y$ 　　　　2. $y' = (1 + x)y + a$ 　　　3. $y' = \dfrac{y}{1 + x}$

4. $y' = \dfrac{y}{1 + x} + a$ 　　5. $y' = \dfrac{y}{1 + x^2}$ 　　　6. $y' = \dfrac{1}{y}$

7. $y' = xy^2$ 　　　　8. $y' = \dfrac{1}{y^3}$ 　　　　9. $y' = e^y$

2–14 Comparison tests. A possible way of obtaining information about convergence of the series solution

$$y = y(0) + \frac{y'(0)}{1!} x + \frac{y''(0)}{2!} x^2 + \cdots + \frac{y^{(n)}(0)}{n!} x^n + \cdots \tag{1}$$

of the differential equation

$$y' = f(x, y) \tag{2}$$

is the following. We construct a function $Y(x)$ with the property that its derivatives for $x = 0$, $Y^{(n)}(0)$, are all positive and, moreover,

$$|y^{(n)}(0)| \leq Y^{(n)}(0). \tag{3}$$

If this is done, the series (1) will certainly converge for all values of x for which the series

$$Y(x) = Y(0) + \frac{Y'(0)}{1!} x + \frac{Y''(0)}{2!} x^2 + \cdots + \frac{Y^{(n)}(0)}{n!} x^n + \cdots \tag{4}$$

converges. Let the interval of convergence of the series for Y be $-a < x < a$. The series for y will converge at least in the same interval. The actual interval of convergence of the y-series may be larger than the interval of convergence of the Y-series, but we will not be able to say how much larger.

We have seen in Section 2–11 that the derivatives $y^{(n)}(x)$ of the solution y of Eq. (2) are all expressible in terms of the function f and its partial derivatives with respect to x and y. Correspondingly, the derivatives $Y^{(n)}(x)$ of the function Y will all be expressible in terms of a function $F(x, Y)$ and its partial derivatives with respect to x and Y, provided Y is the solution of the differential equation

$$Y' = F(x, Y). \tag{5}$$

This observation permits us to conclude that the relations (3) are satisfied provided all partial derivatives of the function F are positive and the following relations are satisfied:

$$\left| \frac{\partial^{m+n} f(x, y)}{\partial x^m \, \partial y^n} \right|_{\substack{x=0 \\ y=0}} \leq \left. \frac{\partial^{m+n} F(x, Y)}{\partial x^m \, \partial Y^n} \right]_{\substack{x=0 \\ Y=0}}. \tag{6}$$

What we need to do in any given problem is to find a function F for which (6) is true and for which the differential equation (5) can be solved explicitly. The interval of convergence of the Taylor series development of this explicit solution Y gives us the desired lower limits for the interval of convergence of the series solution y with which we are concerned.

EXAMPLE 1.   As a first example, let us take the linear differential equation

$$y' + (a_0 + a_1 x + \cdots)y = b_0 + b_1 x + \cdots, \tag{7}$$

under the assumption that the two infinite series occurring in this equation converge in the interval $-r < x < r$. What we intend to prove is that the solution series

$$y = c_0 + c_1 x + c_2 x^2 + \cdots \qquad (8)$$

possesses the same interval of convergence independent of the value of $y(0)$. In this proof we make use of the fact known from the theory of infinite series that since $a_0 + a_1 x + \cdots$ and $b_0 + b_1 x + \cdots$ converge in the interval $-r < x < r$ the magnitude of the coefficients is limited by the relation

$$|a_n|, \ |b_n| < \frac{M}{r_1^n}, \qquad (9)$$

where r_1 may be any positive number less than r and where M is a suitably chosen positive number. We make use of this fact by choosing as comparison function Y the solution of the following differential equation:

$$\frac{dY}{dx} = M \left(1 + \frac{x}{r_1} + \frac{x^2}{r_1^2} + \cdots \right) Y + M \left(1 + \frac{x}{r_1} + \frac{x^2}{r_1^2} + \cdots \right)$$

$$= \frac{M(1 + Y)}{1 - (x/r_1)}. \qquad (10)$$

The solution of this differential equation can be written in the form

$$1 + Y = C \left(1 - \frac{x}{r_1} \right)^{-M r_1}. \qquad (11)$$

Since the function of x on the right can be expanded in a series in powers of x which converges for $-r_1 < x < r_1$, it follows that the series solution (8) of the given differential equation (7) also converges in the interval $-r_1 < x < r_1$. Since this is true for every $r_1 < r$, we have thus proved that the interval of convergence of the series solution is as large as the smaller of the intervals of convergence of the coefficient series in the given linear differential equation.

EXAMPLE 2. We consider the differential equation

$$y' = f(x, y) = \sum_m \sum_n A_{mn} x^m y^n, \quad y(0) = 0, \qquad (12)$$

where we assume that we have the following bounds for the coefficients A_{mn}:

$$|A_{mn}| \leq \frac{M}{a^m b^n}. \qquad (13)$$

The relation (13) implies that the series in (12) converges for $|x| < a$ and $|y| < b$.

We may choose for comparison the differential equation

$$\frac{dY}{dx} = F(x, Y) = M \sum_{m} \sum_{n} \left(\frac{x}{a}\right)^m \left(\frac{Y}{b}\right)^n, \quad Y(0) = 0, \qquad (14)$$

which ensures that the fundamental relations (6) and (3) are satisfied.
Equation (14) can be solved explicitly by writing it in the form

$$\frac{dY}{dx} = \frac{M}{(1 - x/a)(1 - Y/b)}, \quad Y(0) = 0. \qquad (15)$$

We have

$$\frac{b}{2} \left(1 - \frac{Y}{b}\right)^2 = aM \ln\left(1 - \frac{x}{a}\right) + \frac{b}{2}$$

or

$$\frac{Y}{b} = 1 - \sqrt{1 + \frac{2aM}{b} \ln\left(1 - \frac{x}{a}\right)}. \qquad (16)$$

To develop the right side of (16) in powers of x, we must be able
to develop it first in a convergent series in powers of the quantity
$(aM/b) \ln[1 - (x/a)]$. For this to be possible we must have

$$\frac{2aM}{b} \left|\ln\left(1 - \frac{x}{a}\right)\right| \le 1. \qquad 17)$$

Since

$$\left|\ln\left(1 - \frac{x}{a}\right)\right| \le \left|\ln\left(1 - \frac{|x|}{a}\right)\right| = -\ln\left(1 - \frac{|x|}{a}\right),$$

for $|x| < a$, we may guarantee (17) by requiring

$$-\ln\left(1 - \frac{|x|}{a}\right) \le \frac{b}{2aM}$$

or

$$\frac{|x|}{a} \le 1 - e^{-b/2aM}. \qquad (18)$$

Since we have $|x|/a < 1$ for all x satisfying (18), we will have no
trouble from the remaining expansions of $\{\ln[1 - (x/a)]\}^n$ in powers of x.

We have then shown that a series solution in powers of x of the dif-
ferential equation (12) possesses an interval of convergence $|x| < \rho$,
where ρ is at least as large as ρ_0, and where

$$\rho_0 = a[1 - e^{-b/2aM}]. \qquad (19)$$

The actual value of ρ may often be much larger than the lower bound which we have here obtained.

EXAMPLE 3. The differential equation

$$y' = 1 + xy^2, \tag{20}$$

with the initial condition $y(0) = 0$, has the Taylor series solution

$$y = x + \tfrac{1}{4}x^4 + \tfrac{1}{14}x^7 + \cdots \tag{21}$$

We may choose as comparison function Y the solution of the differential equation

$$Y' = (1 + x)(1 + Y^2), \tag{22}$$

with the initial condition $Y(0) = 0$. The function

$$F(x, Y) = (1 + x)(1 + Y^2) = 1 + xY^2 + x + Y^2$$

has been chosen in such a way that Eqs. (6) are satisfied and the resulting differential equation can be solved by separation of variables. The solution is

$$Y = \tan(x + \tfrac{1}{2}x^2). \tag{23}$$

The interval of convergence of the series solution of the given differential equation is at least as large as the interval of convergence of the Taylor expansion of the function $\tan(x + \tfrac{1}{2}x^2)$ about $x = 0$. To obtain this interval of convergence, we determine the radius of convergence in the complex z-plane of the function $\tan(z + \tfrac{1}{2}z^2)$. The singularities nearest to the origin of this function are given by $z + \tfrac{1}{2}z^2 = \pm\tfrac{1}{2}\pi$. The plus sign of the right side gives the smaller radius of convergence. Its magnitude is $\sqrt{1 + \pi} - 1 = 1.0351$.

We conclude from this that the series solution (21) of the differential equation (20) converges at least in the interval

$$-1.0351 < x < 1.0351. \tag{24}$$

EXERCISES

1. Given the differential equation

$$\frac{dy}{dx} = \frac{1}{1 - xy} \qquad \text{with} \qquad y(0) = 0,$$

show that the inequality (13) for the coefficients A_{mn} is satisfied by choosing $M = 1, b = 1/a$, regardless of the value of $a > 0$. What is the expression for ρ_0 and for what value of a (approximately) is ρ_0 largest?

2. Show that for

$$\frac{dy}{dx} = \frac{k^2}{1 - x^p y^q} \qquad \text{with} \qquad y(0) = 0,$$

where p and q are positive integers, we may choose in (13) $M = k^2$, $b^{-q} = a^p$, with $a > 0$ arbitrary. Determine ρ_0 and obtain an approximate value for $\rho_{0,\text{max}}$ when

  (a) $k = 1$, $p = 1$, $q = 2$,
  (b) $k = 2$, $p = 1$, $q = 1$,
  (c) $k = 1$, $p = 2$, $q = 2$.

3. Show that when

$$y' = 1 + xy^2, \qquad y(0) = 0,$$

Eq. (13) is satisfied for arbitrary positive a and b and $M = 1 + ab^2$. Show that ρ_0 is largest when $a = 1/b^2$ and $b^3 = 3$ (approximately) and $\rho_{0,\text{max}} = .26$ (approximately). [Compare this result with Eq. (24).]

2–15 Further consideration of series methods. In the preceding section we have discussed the power-series method of solution for the equation $y' = f(x, y)$ in the neighborhood of a point $x = x_0$, $y = y_0$ under the assumption that all partial derivatives of the function f at this point are finite. It is often possible, however, to obtain series solutions even when these partial derivatives are not all finite. Special considerations leading to a change of variables will often result in a suitable series development.

As an example of such a problem, consider the equation

$$y' = 1 + \sqrt[3]{xy}, \tag{1}$$

with the initial condition*

$$y(0) = 0. \tag{2}$$

To obtain an idea of the nature of the solution, we notice that for sufficiently small values of $|x|$ we will have $y' \approx 1$, and so $y \approx x$. If we make use of this fact to account roughly for the second term, we then have $y' \approx 1 + x^{2/3}$ and $y \approx x + \frac{3}{5}x^{5/3}$. Putting this approximate value into (1), we now have

$$y' \approx 1 + \sqrt[3]{x(x + \frac{3}{5}x^{5/3})} = 1 + x^{2/3}\sqrt[3]{1 + \frac{3}{5}x^{2/3}}.$$

---

* If instead of (2) we have $y(a) = b$, where both a and b are different from zero, then evidently no special considerations are necessary. If, however, either $a = 0$ or $b = 0$, then we would again need special considerations.

Using the binomial theorem, this becomes

$$y' \approx 1 + x^{2/3}\left\{1 + \frac{\frac{1}{3}}{1!}\left(\frac{3}{5}x^{2/3}\right) + \frac{\frac{1}{3}(-\frac{2}{3})}{2!}\left(\frac{3}{5}x^{2/3}\right)^2 + \cdots\right\}$$

$$= 1 + x^{2/3} + \tfrac{1}{5}x^{4/3} - \tfrac{1}{15}x^{6/3} + \cdots,$$

and from this, by integration,

$$y \approx x + \tfrac{3}{5}x^{5/3} + \tfrac{3}{35}x^{7/3} - \tfrac{1}{45}x^{9/3} + \cdots \tag{3}$$

We observe that Eq. (3) is of the form

$$y \approx x\{a_0 + a_1 x^{2/3} + a_2 x^{2 \cdot 2/3} + a_3 x^{3 \cdot 2/3} + \cdots\},$$

where the a_n have suitable numerical values. We should then expect that if we try at the outset a series expansion of the form

$$y = x^s[c_0 + c_1 x^k + c_2 x^{2k} + c_3 x^{3k} + \cdots] \tag{4}$$

for the solution of the problem given by (1) and (2), we shall be led directly to the appropriate values for the exponents s and k and for the coefficients c_n.

Introducing the series (4) into (1), we have the relation

$$x^{s-1}[sc_0 + (s+k)c_1 x^k + (s+2k)c_2 x^{2k} + \cdots]$$

$$= 1 + \sqrt[3]{x^{s+1}(c_0 + c_1 x^k + c_2 x^{2k} + \cdots)}$$

$$= 1 + x^{(s+1)/3}\sqrt[3]{c_0 + c_1 x^k + c_2 x^{2k} + \cdots}. \tag{5}$$

We have a constant term on the right, namely unity, and we should then have the same constant term on the left. This may be accomplished by setting

$$s = 1, \qquad c_0 = 1. \tag{6}$$

Equation (5) now reads

$$(1 + k)c_1 x^k + (1 + 2k)c_2 x^{2k} + \cdots = x^{2/3}\sqrt[3]{1 + c_1 x^k + c_2 x^{2k} + \cdots}.$$

To go on from here we apply the binomial theorem to the cube root term and obtain

$$(1 + k)c_1 x^k + (1 + 2k)c_2 x^{2k} + \cdots$$

$$= x^{2/3}[1 + \tfrac{1}{3}(c_1 x^k + c_2 x^{2k} + \cdots)$$

$$- \tfrac{1}{9}(c_1 x^k + c_2 x^{2k} + \cdots)^2 + \cdots]. \tag{7}$$

In order to be able to match corresponding powers of x on the left and on the right we must choose

$$k = \tfrac{2}{3}. \tag{8}$$

With this value of k we now equate coefficients of like powers of x on the two sides of Eq. (7) to obtain

$$(1 + \tfrac{2}{3})c_1 = 1,$$

$$(1 + \tfrac{4}{3})c_2 = \tfrac{1}{3}c_1, \tag{9}$$

$$(1 + \tfrac{6}{3})c_3 = \tfrac{1}{3}c_2 - \tfrac{1}{9}c_1^2, \quad \cdots$$

Equations (9) give

$$c_1 = \tfrac{3}{5}, \qquad c_2 = \tfrac{3}{35}, \qquad c_3 = -\tfrac{2}{525}, \ldots \tag{10}$$

and the series development of our solution is seen to be

$$y = x[1 + \tfrac{3}{5}x^{2/3} + \tfrac{3}{35}x^{4/3} - \tfrac{2}{525}x^{6/3} + \cdots]. \tag{11}$$

It is interesting to observe that the approximate solution (3) agrees with the series solution (11) so far as the first three terms are concerned, but the coefficients of the fourth term are different.

The series (11) is, of course, not a Taylor series in x but rather a power series for the function y/x in integral powers of the quantity $x^{2/3}$. This suggests that we should be able to reduce the differential equation (1) to one where the Taylor's series method would work directly, by making the following substitutions:

$$x^{2/3} = t, \qquad \frac{y}{x} = z(t). \tag{12}$$

We now expect to be able to develop $z(t)$ as a Taylor series in t. To see this, we introduce (12) into the original differential equation (1). We have

$$\frac{dy}{dx} = \frac{dy}{dt}\frac{dt}{dx} = \frac{d(t^{3/2}z)/dt}{dx/dt}$$

$$= \frac{t^{3/2}\,(dz/dt) + \tfrac{3}{2}t^{1/2}z}{\tfrac{3}{2}t^{1/2}} = \frac{2}{3}\,t\,\frac{dz}{dt} + z. \tag{13}$$

Our differential equation now is of the form

$$\frac{2}{3} t \frac{dz}{dt} + z = 1 + t\sqrt[3]{z}$$

or

$$\frac{dz}{dt} = \frac{3}{2}\left[\frac{1-z}{t} + z^{1/3}\right].$$ (14)

The initial condition (2), when formulated in terms of z and t, appears at first as an indeterminate form, namely,

$$z(0) = \lim_{x \to 0} \frac{y(x)}{x}.$$

The limit on the right represents $y'(0)$, since $y(0) = 0$, and in view of the differential equation (1) this is equal to unity. Thus the initial condition on z is

$$z(0) = 1.$$ (15)

We are now ready to attempt a Taylor series solution

$$z(t) = 1 + c_1 t + c_2 t^2 + c_3 t^3 + \cdots$$ (16)

for (14). Substitution of (16) in (14) gives us

$$c_1 + 2c_2 t + 3c_3 t^2 + \cdots$$
$$= \tfrac{3}{2}\{-(c_1 + c_2 t + c_3 t^2 + \cdots) + [1 + (c_1 t + c_2 t^2 + \cdots)]^{1/3}\}. \quad (17)$$

If we now develop the cube root in (17) by means of the binomial theorem and then equate the coefficients of corresponding powers of t on the right and on the left, we arrive at a system of recurrence relations for the coefficients which, while appearing in a different form, agrees with the system (9).

There is one other kind of information concerning the solution of (1) which we can obtain without difficulty. Our series (11) tells us what the behavior of the solution is for sufficiently small values of $|x|$. But what about y for large values of $|x|$? Suppose we suspect that for large $|x|$ the function y behaves like some power of x, in the sense that sufficiently nearly

$$y \approx kx^n.$$ (18)

Then also

$$y' \approx knx^{n-1}.$$ (19)

If (18) and (19) hold and if $n > 0$, then certainly for sufficiently large x

the term 1 is small compared with $\sqrt[3]{xy}$ and we might think of neglecting it. If this is done, we shall have from (1), (18), and (19),

$$knx^{n-1} = k^{1/3}x^{(n+1)/3}. \tag{20}$$

Equation (20) can be satisfied by setting

$$n - 1 = \tfrac{1}{3}(n + 1), \quad kn = k^{1/3} \tag{21}$$

or

$$n = 2, \quad k = \frac{\pm 1}{2\sqrt{2}}, \tag{22}$$

and consequently

$$y \approx \frac{\pm 1}{2\sqrt{2}} x^2. \tag{23}$$

From the form of the differential equation and also the series solution (11), we conclude that the positive value of k must be taken for large positive values of x and the negative value of k for large negative values of x. This indicates that the solution of (1) satisfies the limiting relations

$$\lim_{x \to +\infty} \frac{y(x)}{x^2} = \frac{1}{2\sqrt{2}}, \quad \lim_{x \to -\infty} \frac{y(x)}{x^2} = -\frac{1}{2\sqrt{2}}. \tag{24}$$

These limiting relations may be proved directly. One way to do this is to transfer "the point at infinity" to the origin by means of the substitution

$$x = t^{-1}, \quad y(x) = u(t). \tag{25}$$

When we do this, the differential equation (1) becomes

$$\frac{du}{dt} = -\frac{1}{t^2} - \frac{u^{1/3}}{t^{7/3}}. \tag{26}$$

If we now proceed as we did at the beginning of this section, we are led to try a series solution of the form

$$u = at^{-2} + bt^{-1} + c_0 + c_1 t + c_2 t^2 + \cdots \tag{27}$$

Putting this into the differential equation (26) and equating to zero the coefficients of like powers of t, we find in particular

$$a = \frac{\pm 1}{2\sqrt{2}}, \quad b = 3. \tag{28}$$

The problem of calculating the values of a few of the coefficients c_n is left to the reader.

It must not be left unmentioned that for a complete solution of this problem consideration must be given to the continuous transition from the solution valid for sufficiently small x to the solution for sufficiently large x. This may be the most difficult part of the problem.

EXERCISES

1. Determine the nature of a suitable power-series solution of the form (4) for

$$y' = m + x^p y^q, \qquad y(0) = 0,$$

where m, $p > 0$, $q > 0$ are given real constants.

2. Determine the first three nonvanishing terms of the power series about $x = 0$ for

(a) $y' = 1 + \sqrt{xy}$, $y(0) = 0$ (b) $y' = 2 + xy^{1/2}$, $y(0) = 0$

3. Show that the differential equation $x^{1/2}y' = 1 + xy^2$ with the initial condition $y(0) = 0$ has a solution of the form $y = x^{1/2}(c_0 + c_1 x^2 + c_2 x^4 + \cdots)$ and determine the values of the first three coefficients c_0, c_1, c_2.

4. Show that the problem

$$x^m y' = 1 + xy^2: \ 0 \le m < 1; \ y(0) = 0$$

has a solution of the form

$$y = x^a(c_0 + c_1 x^b + c_2 x^{2b} + c_3 x^{3b} + \cdots) \qquad \text{for} \qquad x \ge 0$$

and determine a, b, c_0, c_1.

MISCELLANEOUS EXERCISES. CHAPTER 2

Solve the following differential equations.

1. $(1 + x^2)y' + 2xy = x^3(1 + x^2)$ 2. $2x\,dy + 3y\,dx = 0$
3. $dy + y \sin x\, dx = \sin x\, dx$ 4. $e^{3x}\, dx - 2\,dy = 0$
5. $y^2\, dx + (3xy - x^2)\, dy = 0$ 6. $y^3\, dx + (2x^2y + x^3)\, dy = 0$
7. $(e^{x/y} + x^2/y^2)\, dx + \sin(x/y)\, dy = 0$
8. $y' + y = e^x$
9. $(e^x \cos y + 3x^2)\, dx - e^x \sin y\, dy = 0$
10. $2xy^3\, dx + (3x^2y^2 + \cos y)\, dy = 0$
11. $(2y^3 + 3xy)\, dx + (3xy^2 + x^2)\, dy = 0$

12. $(y')^2 - 3yy' + 2y^2 = 0$ 13. $dy + (2x + 3y)\, dx = 0$

14. $xy' - 3 + 2y = 0$ 15. $y = xy' + \frac{1}{4}(y')^4$

16. $xy' - y^2 = 1$ 17. $xy' + y^2 = 1$

18. $y' \cot x + 1 - y^2 = 0$ 19. $(x + y)^2 y' = (x + y + 2)^2$

20. $4y \ln |y|\, dx + x\, dy = 0$

21. $[x^2 \cos (x^2 y) + 3y^2]\, dy + 2xy \cos (x^2 y)\, dx = 0$

22. $y' - y = 2x + \cos x$ 23. $(x^2 - y^2)\, dx + 2xy\, dy = 0$

24. $y' + y \tan x = \cos^2 x$ 25. $y' - y \tan x = \sin 2x$

26. $x(e^{-y/x} + 1)y' + x - y = 0$

27. $\sin (y^2 + 1)\, dx + 2xy \cos (y^2 + 1)\, dy = 0$

28. $(1 + x)y' - y = 3x^2(1 + x)^2$

29. $xy' + y = x^2$ 30. $(y^4 + y)\, dx + x\, dy = 0$

31. $[2x + (y^2 - x^2)^{-1/2}]\, dx + [y^2 - xy^{-1}(y^2 - x^2)^{-1/2}]\, dy = 0$

32. $(1 + xy)\, dx + x^2\, dy = 0$ 33. $xy' + 2y = x^2$

34. $2xyy' + 2x^3 - y^2 = 0$ 35. $x\, dx + y\, dy = (x^2 + y^2 + 1)\, dx$

36. $3x^2 y\, dx + (x^3 + y^3)\, dy = 0$ 37. $y\, dx - x \ln (y/x)\, dy = 0$

38. $(2ye^{y/x} - 3x)y' + 6x + 3y = 0$

39. $x(y^2 + 2) \ln (y^2 + 2)\, dx + (x^2 + 3)y\, dy = 0$

40. $xy' - (x + 1)y = x^2 - x^3$

41. $y' = 3 + 2x + y$

42. $xy' = 3 + 2x + y$

43. $x + yy' = 3(1 + \ln |x|)(x^2 + y^2)^{1/2}$

44. $x^3 y' = (x^2 + y^2)y$

45. $(y')^2 - x(y + 2)y' + x^2(y + 1) = 0$

46. $x\, dy = 3(x^3 + y)\, dx$ 47. $y' = 2 \sec x - y \cot x$

48. $y' = (2 + 4x - y)^2$

49. $(x^3 + 2xy + y^3)\, dx + (x^2 + 3xy^2 + y^4)\, dy = 0$

50. $y' + 3y = x/y$ 51. $(y^2 - xy)\, dx + x^2\, dy = 0$

52. $(3x^2 y^2 + y)\, dx - x\, dy = 0$ 53. $xy' = (1 - xy)y$

54. $(2 + x)y' = 3x + 2y$ 55. $(x^3 + 3y^2 + y^3)y' + 3x^2 = 0$

56. $y' \cos y - \sin x \sin y = \sin x$ 57. $y = (x - 1)(y')^2$

58. $(y')^3 - (y')^2 - 4y' + 4 = 0$

In Exercises 59, 60, and 61 a is a constant different from zero, and in Exercise 62, a is a constant different from zero and one. Solve.

59. $dy + (ay - e^{ax})\, dx = 0$

60. $(x + y)^2 y' = a^2$ [*Hint.* Let $z = x + y$]

61. $y' - y \cos ax - \sin 2ax = 0$ 62. $xy' = 1 + x + ay$ $(x > 0)$

63. Given that $y = f(x)$ satisfies the differential equation $y' + P(x)y = 0$, show that $z = f[g(x)]$ satisfies a differential equation $z' + Q(x)z = 0$, and express Q in terms of P and g.

64. Find a differential equation with solution

(a) $y = cx^3$ (b) $x^2 - y^2 = c$ (c) $xy = c$

In Exercises 65 and 66 determine the constants a and b so that the resulting differential equation is exact. Solve the resulting differential equation.

65. $(axy + \cos x + 3e^y) \, dx + (x^2 + bxe^y) \, dy = 0$

66. $(3x^2 - y^2 + 2e^{xy})y \, dx + (x^2 + ay^2 + be^{xy})x \, dy = 0$

In Exercises 67, 68, and 69 determine the family of all plane curves with the property indicated.

67. The ordinate at any point (x, y) is equal to the perpendicular from the origin to the normal at that point.

68. At each point (x, y) the x-intercept of the tangent is the square of the abscissa of the point of tangency.

69. At each point (x, y) the slope is (a) twice the reciprocal of the abscissa, (b) the square of the abscissa, (c) the ordinate.

In Exercises 70 and 71 show that the differential equation has an integrating factor of the form indicated, and solve.

70. $[3 + 2y^3/x] \, dx + [2x/y + 5y^2] \, dy = 0$, $(xy)^n$

71. $(4xy^2 + 3y) \, dx + (3x^2y + 2x) \, dy = 0$, $x^m y^n$

72. Solve the differential equation $y' = y/(x + y)$ with the initial condition (a) $y(0) = 1$, (b) $y(0) = 2$, (c) $y(1) = 1$.

In Exercises 73 through 78 solve by means of series in powers of x. In Exercises 73 through 76 check your solution by obtaining an exact solution.

73. $y' = 2xy$ 74. $y' = 3x^2y$

75. $y' + y = 2x + 1$ 76. $y' + (1 - x + x^2 - x^3 + \cdots)y = x^2$

77. $y' + \left(1 - \dfrac{x^2}{2!} + \dfrac{x^4}{4!} - \dfrac{x^6}{6!} + \cdots\right)y = 1 - x + x^2 - x^3 + \cdots$

78. $y' = 2x + y^2$, $y(0) = 2$

In Exercises 79 and 80 determine the first three nonvanishing coefficients in the series solution of the form

$$y = c_0 + c_1(x - 1) + c_2(x - 1)^2 + \cdots .$$

79. $y' + (x - 1)y = x + 2$ 80. $y' + 3(x - 1)^2y = x - 1$

81. Solve the differential equation

$$(4x^2 - 2x)y' + (2x + 1)y = 0$$

by means of a series of the form $y = c_0 x^s + c_1 x^{s+1} + \cdots$ ($c_0 \neq 0$). Check your answer by obtaining an exact solution.

In Exercises 82 and 83 determine the interval of convergence of the series solution in powers of x.

82. $y^2 y' = 1$, $y(0) = y_0$ 83. $y' = 2xy$, $y(0) = y_0$

CHAPTER 3

SECOND-ORDER DIFFERENTIAL EQUATIONS

3-1 Introduction. We now turn to differential equations which, besides a first derivative term, include a second derivative term, and which we may write in completely general form as

$$F(x, y, y', y'') = 0. \tag{1}$$

In our discussion of first-order differential equations we found that some problems were difficult and that a variety of approaches toward a solution existed. We should expect that the addition of a second derivative term will often result in even greater difficulties. While this is indeed so, we shall find that there are types of second-order differential equations which can be discussed and solved rather completely. In this chapter we shall restrict ourselves to the class of second-order differential equations of the form

$$y'' = f(x, y, y') \tag{2}$$

(or to equations readily reducible to this form). Very many problems in physics and engineering lead to just such second-order differential equations.

To see what degree of generality to expect from the solution of a second-order differential equation, let us first consider the simple example

$$y'' - x = 0. \tag{3}$$

By repeated integration, we find that this equation has solutions of the form

$$y - \tfrac{1}{6}x^3 + c_1 x + c_2 = 0, \tag{4}$$

where c_1 and c_2 are arbitrary constants. To determine one specific solution from such a family we need two conditions. We shall take as these two conditions the following *initial conditions:*

$$y(x_0) = y_0, \qquad y'(x_0) = y_0', \tag{5}$$

where x_0, y_0, and y_0' are given. Geometrically speaking, this means that we intend to single out from the family of solution curves given by (4) one specific solution curve which passes through a given point (x_0, y_0) with given slope y_0'. The determination of the constants c_1 and c_2 in the solution (4) by means of (5) evidently requires the satisfaction of the following two relations:

$$x_0 c_1 + c_2 = \tfrac{1}{6} x_0^3 - y_0, \quad c_1 = \tfrac{1}{2} x_0^2 - y_0'. \tag{6}$$

These two conditions may be satisfied regardless of the values specified for x_0, y_0 and y_0'. We find

$$c_1 = \tfrac{1}{2} x_0^2 - y_0', \quad c_2 = x_0 y_0' - y_0 - \tfrac{1}{3} x_0^3. \tag{7}$$

Just as in the case of first-order differential equations of the form $y' = f(x, y)$, there is a general *existence and uniqueness theorem* for second-order differential equations of the form $y'' = f(x, y, y')$, where $f(x, y, z)$ is a function of three real variables x, y, z which is defined and continuous in a region R of xyz-space, and which is such that the two partial derivatives $\partial f/\partial y$ and $\partial f/\partial z$ are also continuous in R. Under these conditions the theorem guarantees, for every point (x_0, y_0, y_0') in R, the existence of a unique solution $y = y(x)$ of the differential equation $y'' = f(x, y, y')$ which satisfies the initial conditions $y(x_0) = y_0$, $y'(x_0) = y_0'$. This solution is defined in some x-interval containing x_0.

With this in mind we may now define the concept of a general solution of a differential equation $F(x, y, y', y'') = 0$. We shall call a solution $G(x, y, c_1, c_2) = 0$ the *general solution* of this equation in some x-interval if it contains *all* solutions in this interval.

If we assign definite values to one or both of the arbitrary constants in the general solution, the special solution so obtained is called a *particular solution*. For example, the relation $y - \tfrac{1}{6} x^3 = 0$ is a particular solution of $y'' - x = 0$.

Given an expression

$$G(x, y, c_1, c_2) = 0, \tag{8}$$

we may obtain a second-order differential equation of which this is a solution by differentiating (8) twice with respect to x:

$$\frac{dG}{dx} = \frac{\partial G}{\partial x} + \frac{\partial G}{\partial y} \frac{dy}{dx} = 0, \tag{9}$$

$$\frac{d^2 G}{dx^2} = \frac{\partial^2 G}{\partial x^2} + 2 \frac{\partial^2 G}{\partial x\, \partial y} \frac{dy}{dx} + \frac{\partial^2 G}{\partial y^2} \left(\frac{dy}{dx}\right)^2 + \frac{\partial G}{\partial y} \frac{d^2 y}{dx^2} = 0, \tag{10}$$

and by eliminating c_1 and c_2 from the three equations (8), (9), and (10). For example, when

$$y - c_1 x - \tfrac{1}{2} c_2 x^2 - c_2^2 = 0, \tag{11}$$

we also have

$$y' - c_1 - c_2 x = 0, \quad y'' - c_2 = 0. \tag{12}$$

From (12) follows $c_2 = y''$, $c_1 = y' - xy''$, and a differential equation which has the solution (11) is seen to be

$$(y'')^2 - \tfrac{1}{2}x^2y'' + xy' - y = 0. \tag{13}$$

If we solve for y'' we obtain two differential equations,

$$y'' = \tfrac{1}{4}x^2 + \sqrt{\tfrac{1}{16}x^4 - xy' + y}, \tag{14a}$$

and

$$y'' = \tfrac{1}{4}x^2 - \sqrt{\tfrac{1}{16}x^4 - xy' + y}, \tag{14b}$$

each of which is of the form (2). The region R where f, $\partial f/\partial y$, and $\partial f/\partial z$ are continuous may be any region of xyz-space in which $\tfrac{1}{16}x^4 - xz + y$ is positive. To show that the solution (11) is the general solution of both (14a) and (14b) in R, we consider the initial conditions

$$y_0 - c_1x_0 - \tfrac{1}{2}c_2x_0^2 - c_2^2 = 0, \quad y_0' - c_1 - c_2x_0 = 0. \tag{15}$$

Equations (15) can be satisfied with real c_1 and c_2 so long as the following relation holds:

$$0 \le \tfrac{1}{16}x_0^4 - x_0y_0' + y_0. \tag{16}$$

Recalling that the region R for this example is any region in which $\tfrac{1}{16}x^4 - xz + y$ is positive, we see that the conditions (16) can certainly always be satisfied for any point (x_0, y_0, y_0') in R. Thus (11) is the general solution of both Eqs. (14a) and (14b) in R.

Inspection of the differential equation (13) suggests that it might also have a solution of the form $y = kx^4$, where k is a constant. Substitution in (13) shows that the only admissible value of k, besides the trivial $k = 0$, is $k = \tfrac{1}{48}$. Clearly,

$$y = \tfrac{1}{48}x^4 \tag{17}$$

is a solution of Eq. (13), as well as of Eqs. (14a) and (14b), and it is not obtainable from the family of solutions (11) by specialization of the constant c. But we observe that *it does not lie in the region R*, since for it $y' = \tfrac{1}{12}x^3$ and hence $\tfrac{1}{16}x^4 - x \cdot y' + y = 0$, while the region R was defined by $\tfrac{1}{16}x^4 - xy' + y > 0$. Hence the occurrence of the solution $y = \tfrac{1}{48}x^4$, in addition to the solution (11), is not inconsistent with the statement of the general existence and uniqueness theorem.

EXERCISES

In each of the Exercises 1 through 12, find a second-order differential equation with solution as stated.

1. $y = 6x + c_1x^2 + c_2$ 2. $y = c_1 \cos 2x + c_2 \sin 2x$

3. $y = c_1e^{2x} + c_2e^{-2x}$ 4. $y = (c_1 + c_2x)e^{2x}$

5. $y = c_1 e^x + c_2 \sin x$ 6. $y = (c_1 + c_2 x)^{1/2}$

7. $y = x + c_1 \ln x + c_2$ 8. $x = c_1 \int e^{-y^2/2} \, dy + c_2$

9. $x^2 + c_1 xy + c_2 = 0$ 10. $y^2 = c_1 + c_2 x^2$

11. $y - c_1 x - \frac{1}{2} c_2 x^2 + c_2^n = 0$ 12. $y^2 = (x + c_1)^2 + c_2$

In Exercises 1, 2, 3, and 6 above determine c_1 and c_2 so as to satisfy each of the following sets of conditions:

13. $y(0) = 0, \quad y'(0) = 1$ 14. $y(1) = 1, \quad y'(1) = 0$

15. $y(a) = 0, \quad y'(a) = 0$ 16. $y(0) = 1, \quad y(1) = 0$

17. Discuss the problem of satisfying the conditions $y(0) = a$, $y'(0) = b$ for each of the Exercises 1 and 7 above.

18. By assuming $y = Ax^m$, find an additional solution of the differential equation of Exercise 11.

3–2 Second-order equations which are reducible to first-order equations. Some types of second-order differential equations can be reduced by simple substitutions to first-order differential equations.

If in the equation $y'' = f(x, y, y')$ the letter y does not occur by itself, so that we have an equation of the form

$$y'' = f(x, y'), \tag{1}$$

then one may consider y' as a basic new variable and write

$$y' = p. \tag{2}$$

Equation (1) now reads

$$p' = f(x, p) \tag{3}$$

and this is a first-order equation for p.

Note that what we have accomplished is, in fact, a reduction of the second-order equation (1) to two *successive* first-order equations. We must first solve Eq. (3) for p and then, having p, in order to get y as a function of x we must solve (2), which is another (particularly simple) differential equation of the first order.

As an example, take the equation

$$y'' + xy' = 0. \tag{4}$$

From

$$p' + xp = 0 \tag{4a}$$

follows, by separation of variables,

$$p = c_1 e^{-x^2/2} \tag{5}$$

and then

$$y = \int p \, dx = c_1 \int e^{-x^2/2} \, dx + c_2. \tag{6}$$

If in the equation $y'' = f(x, y, y')$ the letter x does not occur, so that we have

$$y'' = f(y, y'), \tag{7}$$

then we may proceed as follows. We write again

$$y' = p, \tag{2}$$

and since now the letter y has a preferred status in the differential equation it is natural to see whether one cannot introduce a derivative with respect to y into the differential equation. This can be done by writing

$$y'' = \frac{dp}{dx} = \frac{dp}{dy}\frac{dy}{dx} = \frac{dp}{dy}p. \tag{8}$$

Equation (7) is now

$$p\frac{dp}{dy} = f(y, p), \tag{9}$$

which is a first-order equation for p as a function of y. After determination of p we obtain y as a function of x from the first-order equation

$$\frac{dy}{dx} = p(y). \tag{10}$$

The following example may serve as an illustration:

$$y'' - 2yy' = 0. \tag{11}$$

The substitution (8) changes (11) to

$$p\frac{dp}{dy} - 2yp = 0. \tag{12}$$

This is satisfied either by setting $p = 0$, which gives us the solution

$$y = c, \tag{13}$$

or by setting

$$\frac{dp}{dy} - 2y = 0. \tag{14}$$

From this,

$$p = y^2 + c_1, \tag{15}$$

and then, according to (10),

$$x = \int \frac{dy}{y^2 + c_1} + c_2 \tag{16}$$

or

$$x = \begin{cases} \dfrac{1}{\sqrt{c_1}} \tan^{-1} \dfrac{y}{\sqrt{c_1}} + c_2, & \text{when } c_1 > 0, \\[2ex] -\dfrac{1}{y} + c_2, & \text{when } c_1 = 0, \\[2ex] \dfrac{1}{2\sqrt{-c_1}} \ln \left| \dfrac{y - \sqrt{-c_1}}{y + \sqrt{-c_1}} \right| + c_2, & \text{when } c_1 < 0. \end{cases} \tag{17}$$

In all three cases we may, if we wish, solve Eq. (17) so as to have y as a function of x. The solution $y = c$ obtained in (13) is a particular case of (17) obtainable by setting $c_1 = -c^2$ and then letting c_2 tend to $+\infty$.

Besides the two types of equations (1) and (7) discussed above, there are some other types of second-order equations which can be reduced directly to first-order equations. These, however, are of a more special nature and will be encountered only rarely.

EXERCISES

Solve the equations in Exercises 1 through 16.

1. $xy'' + y' = 0$

2. $xy'' + y' = 1$

3. $x^2 y'' + 2xy' = 1$

4. $y'' + y'^2 = 0$

5. $y'' + y'^2 = 1$

6. $y'' - k^2 y = 0, \quad k \neq 0$

7. $y'' + k^2 y = 0, \quad k \neq 0$

8. $y'' - k^2 y^2 = 0$

9. $y'' + k^2 y^2 = 0$

10. $y'' - k^2 y^3 = 0$

11. $y'' + k^2 y^3 = 0$

12. $y'' + y'^2 = yy'$

13. $y'' = yy'^2$

14. $yy'' + y'^2 = 0$

15. $yy'' - (y')^2 = 0$

16. $y'' + 2(1 - y^2)y = 0, \quad y(0) = 0, \quad y'(0) = 1$

17. Given that the second-order differential equation

$$\frac{dR(x, y, y')}{dx} \equiv \frac{\partial R}{\partial x} + \frac{\partial R}{\partial y} \frac{dy}{dx} + \frac{\partial R}{\partial y'} \frac{d^2 y}{dx^2} = 0$$

is reducible to the first-order differential equation $R(x, y, y') = c_1$, what condition must the function f in the second-order differential equation $y'' = f(x, y, y')$ fulfill in order that this equation may be reduced to the first-order equation $R(x, y, y') = c_1$?

18. Using the result of the preceding problem, show that the differential equation

$$y'' + \frac{xy' + y}{xy} y' = 0$$

may be reduced to the first-order equation $xyy' = c_1$.

3-3 The linear differential equation of the second order.

A class of second-order equations which is important both because of its many applications and also because of the extent to which the theory has been developed is of the form

$$P(x)y'' + Q(x)y' + R(x)y = S(x). \tag{1}$$

This equation is called *linear*, since it is of the first degree in the unknown function y and its derivatives.

We assume that P, Q, R, and S are continuous in some interval $a < x < b$ and that P is different from zero in this interval. We will find that once we have solved Eq. (1) with the right member zero, then there is a simple general procedure for finding the solution of the corresponding equation with the right member not equal to zero. Therefore, most of what we will have to say will concern the equation

$$P(x)y'' + Q(x)y' + R(x)y = 0, \tag{2}$$

which we shall call the *homogeneous* equation or, alternatively, the *reduced* equation associated with (1).

Because Eq. (2) is both linear and homogeneous, its solutions obey what we call the *superposition principle*. By this we mean that *if we have two solutions u_1 and u_2 both satisfying (2), then the linear combination*

$$c_1 u_1 + c_2 u_2, \tag{3}$$

where c_1 and c_2 are arbitrary constants, also satisfies the equation. The proof is simple. We substitute (3) for y in the left side of (2) and have

$$P(c_1 u_1 + c_2 u_2)'' + Q(c_1 u_1 + c_2 u_2)' + R(c_1 u_1 + c_2 u_2)$$
$$= c_1[Pu_1'' + Qu_1' + Ru_1] + c_2[Pu_2'' + Qu_2' + Ru_2]. \tag{4}$$

The right side of (4) vanishes because both u_1 and u_2 were assumed to be solutions of (2), and therefore the left side vanishes also. This proves that (3) is a solution of (2), whatever the values of c_1 and c_2.

We note as a particular consequence of this result that any constant multiple of a solution of the differential equation (2) is also a solution of this differential equation.

If u_1 and u_2 are such that neither is a constant multiple of the other, then it can be shown that the expression $c_1u_1 + c_2u_2$ involves two constants of integration in such a manner that we can satisfy with it the conditions of arbitrarily prescribed values of $y(x_0)$ and $y'(x_0)$ for $a < x_0 < b$. To see this, we must show that we can determine c_1 and c_2 from the two equations

$$c_1u_1(x_0) + c_2u_2(x_0) = y_0,$$

$$c_1u_1'(x_0) + c_2u_2'(x_0) = y_0'.$$
(5)

This will be possible whenever the determinant

$$\begin{vmatrix} u_1(x_0) & u_2(x_0) \\ u_1'(x_0) & u_2'(x_0) \end{vmatrix} \neq 0.$$
(6)

The proof of the fact that this determinant does not vanish can be carried out in two steps. First, it can be shown (Exercise 7 below) that the determinant

$$W(x) = \begin{vmatrix} u_1(x) & u_2(x) \\ u_1'(x) & u_2'(x) \end{vmatrix}$$
(7)

can vanish for $x = x_0$ only if it vanishes identically in the entire interval, $a < x < b$. Secondly, one can show (Exercise 8) that if $W(x) = 0$, then one of the solutions u_1, u_2 must be a constant multiple of the other.

Two functions u_1 and u_2 having the property that neither is a constant multiple of the other over an interval are often said to be *linearly independent* over that interval. The concept of linear independence is of importance in a much more general way than appears here.

The function $W(x)$ is called the *Wronskian* of the two functions u_1 and u_2, in honor of the mathematician Wronski (1778–1853).

The general theorem stated in Section 3–1 assures the existence of a *unique* solution of the problem consisting of the differential equation (2) and of the initial condition $y(x_0) = y_0$, $y'(x_0) = y_0'$ for $a < x_0 < b$. We have shown that $c_1u_1 + c_2u_2$ is a solution of the problem as stated, so long as $W(x) \neq 0$ in $a < x < b$. The uniqueness property assures us that there are no other solutions. Consequently

$$y = c_1u_1 + c_2u_2$$
(8)

is the general solution of (2) *in the interval* $a < x < b$ *provided* $W(x) \neq 0$ *in this interval.*

We now return to the nonhomogeneous equation (1). The general existence and uniqueness theorem also applies to this equation. Let y_p be any solution of (1). It is readily shown that the expression $y_p + c_1u_1 + c_2u_2$

also satisfies (1). Since the conditions

$$y_p(x_0) + c_1u_1(x_0) + c_2u_2(x_0) = y_0,$$
$$y_p'(x_0) + c_1u_1'(x_0) + c_2u_2'(x_0) = y_0' \tag{9}$$

can be satisfied whenever the corresponding conditions (5) for the homogeneous differential equation (2) can be satisfied, it follows that if $c_1u_1 + c_2u_2$ is the general solution of the homogeneous equation, then

$$y = y_p + c_1u_1 + c_2u_2 \tag{10}$$

is the general solution of the nonhomogeneous differential equation (1).

We finally state a superposition principle for the determination of particular solutions of the differential equation (1). Let $y_{p,1}$ be a particular solution of (1) with $S(x) = S_1(x)$. Let $y_{p,2}$ be a particular solution of (1) for $S(x) = S_2(x)$. A particular solution of (1) for $S(x) = k_1S_1(x) + k_2S_2(x)$, where k_1 and k_2 are constants, is then given by $y_p = k_1y_{p,1} + k_2y_{p,2}$. To prove this statement, multiply the differential equation for $y_{p,1}$ by k_1 and the differential equation for $y_{p,2}$ by k_2, add the two equations, and rearrange the left side of the resulting equation.

EXERCISES

1. Show that $u_1 = 1$ and $u_2 = \ln x$ are solutions of the differential equation (a) $xy'' + y' = 0$. Apply the superposition principle to obtain the general solution of Eq. (a). (Compare Exercise 1 of the preceding section.)

2. Show that $u_1 = 1$ and $u_2 = \ln x$ are solutions of the differential equation (b) $y'' + y'^2 = 0$. Does the superposition principle yield the general solution of Eq. (b)? (Compare Exercise 4 of the preceding section.)

3. Determine the value of A for which $y_p = Ax^2$ is a particular solution of the differential equation (c) $xy'' + y' = 3x$. Use this solution and the result of Exercise 1 to obtain the general solution of Eq. (c).

4. Determine the value of A for which $y_p = Ax^3$ is a particular solution of the differential equation $x^2y'' + 2xy' = x^3$. Use this result and the result of Exercise 3 of the preceding section to obtain the general solution of the differential equation $x^2y'' + 2xy' = 4x^3 - 7$.

5. Show that $u_1 = e^x$ and $u_2 = e^{2x}$ are solutions of the differential equation $y'' - 3y' + 2y = 0$. What is the general solution?

6. Determine A and B so that $y_p = Ax + B$ is a solution of the differential equation (d) $y'' - 3y' + 2y = 4x$. Use this result and the result of Exercise 5 to obtain the general solution of Eq. (d).

7. Show that the function $W(x)$ defined by Eq. (7) satisfies the differential equation

$$PW' + QW = 0,$$

so that $W = e^{-\int(Q/P)dx}$.

8. If u_1 and u_2 are solutions of the homogeneous equation (2) and if $u_1(x) \not\equiv 0$, then

$$\frac{d(u_2/u_1)}{dx} = \frac{W(x)}{u_1^2}.$$

Use this fact to show that if $W(x) \equiv 0$ in an interval, then u_1 and u_2 are linearly dependent in the interval.

9. Given the differential equation $Py'' + Qy' + Ry = S$ in an interval in which $P \neq 0$. Show that by the substitution $y = vu$ it is possible to obtain a second-order differential equation for u with no u'-term present, and determine v and the coefficients in the equation for u in terms of the coefficients of the original differential equation.

10. Calculate the Wronskian for the differential equation in u of Exercise 9.

11. Show that if y satisfies the second-order linear differential equation $y'' + f(x)y' + g(x)y = 0$, then the expression $z = y'/y$ satisfies the first-order nonlinear equation $z' + z^2 + fz + g = 0$.

12. Given that y satisfies the equation $y'' + f(x)y' + g(x)y = 0$, what first-order equation is satisfied by the expression $z = y'(x)/[h(x)y(x)]$?

3–4 Solution of the linear homogeneous equation with constant co-efficients. For the linear homogeneous second-order differential equation we first consider the case when the functions P, Q, and R reduce to constants. We assume that the first coefficient is different from zero (otherwise we would have a first-order equation). We may then divide through by it and write Eq. (2) of the preceding section in the form

$$y'' + 2ay' + by = 0. \tag{1}$$

We shall assume that a and b are real. Since the variable x does not occur directly in (1), we could reduce this to a first-order equation by setting $p = y'$ and $y'' = p\,(dp/dy)$. It is preferable, however, to use a more direct method which also carries over to higher-order equations with constant coefficients.

We start by observing that the function e^{rx} has the property that its derivatives are constant multiples of the function itself. So if we introduce e^{rx} for y into Eq. (1) we will be able to factor it out. We tentatively set

$$y = e^{rx}. \tag{2}$$

Equation (1) now becomes

$$e^{rx}(r^2 + 2ar + b) = 0. \tag{3}$$

Since the factor e^{rx} cannot be zero, the equation is satisfied only when the second factor is zero, that is, when r satisfies the quadratic equation

$$r^2 + 2ar + b = 0. \tag{4}$$

This equation will be designated as the *auxiliary equation*. We denote by r_1 and r_2 the two roots of the auxiliary equation:

$$r_1 = -a + \sqrt{a^2 - b}, \quad r_2 = -a - \sqrt{a^2 - b}. \tag{5}$$

If we assume that r_1 and r_2 are different from each other, then we have, on using the superposition principle proved in the preceding section, solutions of the form

$$y = c_1 e^{r_1 x} + c_2 e^{r_2 x}. \tag{6}$$

Since $r_1 \neq r_2$, the two functions $e^{r_1 x}$ and $e^{r_2 x}$ are linearly independent and (6) is accordingly the general solution of the differential equation (1).

When r_1 and r_2 are real, the constants c_1 and c_2 must also be real if y is to be real.

Suppose now that r_1 is complex. Then, since the coefficients of the quadratic (4) are real, r_2 is its conjugate, $\bar{r}_1$. Write

$$r_1 = \alpha + i\beta, \quad r_2 = \bar{r}_1 = \alpha - i\beta, \tag{7}$$

where α and β are real. In order now to have a real solution y, it will turn out that the constants c_1 and c_2 will have to be conjugate complex. This we may show as follows:

$$\begin{aligned} y &= c_1 e^{\alpha x + i\beta x} + c_2 e^{\alpha x - i\beta x} = e^{\alpha x}[c_1 e^{i\beta x} + c_2 e^{-i\beta x}] \\ &= e^{\alpha x}[c_1 (\cos \beta x + i \sin \beta x) + c_2 (\cos \beta x - i \sin \beta x)] \\ &= e^{\alpha x}[(c_1 + c_2) \cos \beta x + i(c_1 - c_2) \sin \beta x]. \end{aligned} \tag{8}$$

In (8) the coefficients $(c_1 + c_2)$ and $i(c_1 - c_2)$ must be real, and we write, with two real constants C_1 and C_2,

$$c_1 + c_2 = C_1, \quad i(c_1 - c_2) = C_2. \tag{9}$$

In terms of C_1 and C_2 the original coefficients c_1 and c_2 are of the form

$$c_1 = \tfrac{1}{2}(C_1 - iC_2), \quad c_2 = \tfrac{1}{2}(C_1 + iC_2) = \bar{c}_1. \tag{10}$$

We have thus found that when r_1 and r_2 are given in the form (7) the real solution of our differential equation may be written in the form

$$y = e^{\alpha x}[C_1 \cos \beta x + C_2 \sin \beta x], \tag{11}$$

where C_1 and C_2 are arbitrary real constants.

In view of (7) and (10), the real solution (11) may also be written in the compact form

$$y = c_1 e^{r_1 x} + \bar{c}_1 e^{\bar{r}_1 x}, \tag{12}$$

where c_1 is an arbitrary complex constant related to the real constants C_1 and C_2 in (11) by means of the first of equations (10).

We may then also say that the real solutions of (1) can always be taken in the form (6) with the understanding that when r_1 is a complex number the corresponding coefficient c_1 is also complex, and we have $r_2 = \bar{r}_1$ and $c_2 = \bar{c}_1$.

EXAMPLE 1.

$$y'' - 4y' + 3y = 0;$$

$$r^2 - 4r + 3 = 0, \quad r_1 = 1, \quad r_2 = 3;$$

$$y = c_1 e^x + c_2 e^{3x}.$$

EXAMPLE 2.

$$y'' - 2y' + 2y = 0.$$

$$r^2 - 2r + 2 = 0, \quad r_1 = 1 + i, \quad r_2 = 1 - i;$$

$$y = e^x(C_1 \cos x + C_2 \sin x),$$

or

$$y = c_1 e^{(1+i)x} + \bar{c}_1 e^{(1-i)x}.$$

EXERCISES

Solve the differential equations of Exercises 1 through 8.

1. $y'' - 3y' + 2y = 0$ 2. $y'' + y' + 2y = 0$
3. $y'' - 5y' + 6y = 0$ 4. $y'' + 4y = 0$
5. $y'' - 4y = 0$ 6. $y'' + 5y' + 6y = 0$
7. $y'' + 3y' = 0$ 8. $y'' + 2y' + 3y = 0$

3–5 The case of equal roots of the auxiliary equation. There is one case that still needs to be considered, and that is the case of equal roots of the auxiliary equation (4) in the preceding section. This arises when

$$a^2 = b$$

and we then have

$$r_1 = r_2 = -a.$$

There is then effectively only one constant of integration in the solution (6) above, namely, $c_1 + c_2$. Since we need two constants of integration for the general solution, it becomes necessary to obtain an expression of a form different from the e^{rx} which we used in (2). The following result holds. In the case of two equal roots $r_1 = r_2$, for which the differential equation (1) in the preceding section may be written in the form

$$y'' - 2r_1 y' + r_1^2 y = 0, \tag{1}$$

not only is $e^{r_1 x}$ a solution but so is $xe^{r_1 x}$. These two are linearly independent, and consequently the general solution of (1) is

$$y = (c_1 + c_2 x)e^{r_1 x}. \tag{2}$$

A direct derivation of this result may be carried out by means of a general method which we consider in Section 3–9.

So long as we do not have the general method, we may obtain the result as follows. We write Eq. (1) in the form

$$y'' - r_1 y' - r_1(y' - r_1 y) = 0. \tag{1'}$$

If we now set

$$y' - r_1 y = z, \tag{3}$$

then we have further

$$z' - r_1 z = 0, \tag{4}$$

and we see that the second-order equation (1) for y has been reduced to a succession of two first-order equations for z and y. Their solution, by the methods of Chapter 2, leads directly to the solution (2).

EXERCISES

Solve the differential equations of Exercises 1 through 4.

1. $y'' - 2y' + y = 0$ 2. $y'' + 5y' + \frac{25}{4}y = 0$
3. $y'' + 2y' + y = 0$ 4. $y'' - 2\sqrt{3}\, y' + 3y = 0$

3–6 Further consideration of the second-order equation with constant coefficients. We summarize the results of the preceding two sections in the following form. The general solution of the differential equation

$$y'' + 2ay' + by = 0, \tag{1}$$

with a and b real constants, is

$$y = \begin{cases} c_1 e^{r_1 x} + c_2 e^{r_2 x}, & \text{if } a^2 > b, \\ (c_1 + c_2 x)e^{r_1 x}, & \text{if } a^2 = b, \\ e^{\alpha x}(c_1 \cos \beta x + c_2 \sin \beta x), & \text{if } a^2 < b, \end{cases} \tag{2}$$

where c_1 and c_2 are arbitrary real constants and

$$r_1 = -a + \sqrt{a^2 - b}, \qquad r_2 = -a - \sqrt{a^2 - b};$$

$$\alpha = -a, \qquad \beta = \sqrt{b - a^2}. \tag{3}$$

It will have been noticed that the procedure which was used to obtain the solution, except for the case of equal roots of the auxiliary equation, could have been applied to an nth-order linear homogeneous differential equation with constant coefficients, rather than merely to a second-order one. We shall take up this general problem in Section 4–2.

Evidently the qualitative behavior of the graphs of the solution (2) can be greatly changed by a change in the numerical values of the coefficients a and b. This fact is of great importance for the physical and engineering problems which lead to the differential equation (1). The following may be read from Eq. (2) and is discussed in great detail in texts dealing with physical applications. When $b < a^2$ and when $a < 0$, then at least one of the terms in the solution increases exponentially with x. When $0 < b < a^2$ and when $a > 0$, then both the terms in the solution decrease exponentially as x approaches infinity. When $a^2 < b$, the qualitative behavior again depends upon the sign of a. When $a > 0$, the solution curves are waves with exponentially decreasing amplitude. When $a < 0$, the solution curves are waves with exponentially increasing amplitude. When $a = 0$ (and $b > 0$), the solution curves are waves with constant amplitude.

We have so far assumed that the coefficients a and b in (1) are real. This, however, is not a necessary restriction. Even if a and b are complex, Eq. (1) still has solutions of the form

$$\begin{aligned} c_1 e^{r_1 x} + c_2 e^{r_2 x}, &\qquad a^2 \neq b, \\ (c_1 + c_2 x)e^{r_1 x}, &\qquad a^2 = b, \end{aligned} \tag{4}$$

where, as before, r_1 and r_2 are given by (3). Now, however, the solution y need not be real, and c_1 and c_2 are two arbitrary complex constants of integration.

EXERCISES

1. Show that the general solution of

$$y'' + \lambda^2 y = 0,$$

where λ is real, may be written in the form $y = A \cos(\lambda x - \theta)$, where A and θ are constants of integration.

2. Show that the general solution of

$$y'' + 2ay' + by = 0, \qquad a^2 < b,$$

may be written in the form

$$y = Ae^{-ax} \cos (\sqrt{b - a^2}\, x - \theta).$$

3. Show that the general solution of

$$y'' - \lambda^2 y = 0,$$

where λ is real, may be written in terms of hyperbolic functions as

$$y = c_1 \cosh \lambda x + c_2 \sinh \lambda x.$$

Solve the differential equations of Exercises 4 through 6.

4. $y'' + (1 - i)y' - iy = 0$ 5. $y'' - 2iy' - y = 0$ 6. $y'' + iy = 0$

7. Given the two simultaneous differential equations

$$y'' - z = 0, \qquad z'' + y = 0.$$

Show that the function $w = y + iz$ satisfies

$$w'' + iw = 0$$

and use the solution of Exercise 6 to obtain real solutions y and z of the given simultaneous differential equations.

8. Given the differential equation $y'' + 2ay' + by = 0$, where $a = a_1 + ia_2$, $b = b_1 + ib_2$, and a_1, a_2, b_1, b_2 are real. Derive the two simultaneous second-order equations satisfied by the two real functions y_1 and y_2 in $y = y_1 + iy_2$.

9. Using the result of Exercise 12 of Section 3–3, solve the differential equation $z' = x^{-1}z^2 + x^{-1}z - x$.

10. Show that the differential equation

$$\frac{1}{g'(\xi)} \frac{d}{d\xi} \left[\frac{1}{g'(\xi)} \frac{dy}{d\xi} \right] + y = 0,$$

where $g(\xi)$ is any given function, has the solution $y = c_1 \cos g(\xi) + c_2 \sin g(\xi)$.

11. Show that the equation

$$\frac{d^2 y}{d\xi^2} - \frac{g''(\xi)}{g'(\xi)} \frac{dy}{d\xi} - [g'(\xi)]^2 y = 0,$$

where $g(\xi)$ is any given function, has the solution $y = c_1 \cosh g(\xi) + c_2 \sinh g(\xi)$.

Using Exercises 10 and 11, solve the following:

12. $y'' - (n - 1)x^{-1}y' - n^2\lambda^2 x^{2n-2}y = 0$

13. $y'' - ky' - k^2\lambda^2 e^{2kx}y = 0$ 14. $y'' - ky' + k^2\lambda^2 e^{2kx}y = 0$

15. $y'' - \dfrac{n - 1 + knx^n}{x} y' - (kn\lambda)^2 \dfrac{x^{2n}}{x^2} e^{2kx^n} y = 0$

3–7 The equidimensional equation. The differential equation

$$\frac{d^2y}{dx^2} + \frac{\gamma}{x}\frac{dy}{dx} + \frac{\delta}{x^2}y = 0, \tag{1}$$

where γ and δ are constants and where we will assume that x is positive, can be readily reduced to a second-order equation with constant coefficients by means of the substitution

$$x = e^t \qquad \text{or} \qquad t = \ln x.$$

We have

$$\frac{dy}{dx} = \frac{dy}{dt}\frac{dt}{dx} = \frac{dy}{dt}\frac{1}{x},$$

$$\frac{d^2y}{dx^2} = \frac{d^2y}{dt^2}\left(\frac{dt}{dx}\right)^2 + \frac{dy}{dt}\frac{d^2t}{dx^2} = \frac{d^2y}{dt^2}\frac{1}{x^2} - \frac{dy}{dt}\frac{1}{x^2}.$$

Introducing these expressions for dy/dx and d^2y/dx^2 into Eq. (1) and factoring out the term $1/x^2$, Eq. (1) becomes

$$\frac{d^2y}{dt^2} + (\gamma - 1)\frac{dy}{dt} + \delta y = 0.$$

The solution is then obtained from (1) and (2) of the preceding section, with

$$\gamma - 1 = 2a, \qquad \delta = b, \qquad \text{and} \qquad t = \ln x.$$

This shows that when γ and δ are real the solution of Eq. (1) will have one of the following forms:

$$y = \begin{cases} c_1 x^{r_1} + c_2 x^{r_2}, & \text{if } (\gamma - 1)^2 > 4\delta, \\ (c_1 + c_2 \ln x)x^{r_1}, & \text{if } (\gamma - 1)^2 = 4\delta, \\ x^\alpha[c_1 \cos (\beta \ln x) + c_2 \sin (\beta \ln x)], & \text{if } (\gamma - 1)^2 < 4\delta, \end{cases} \tag{2}$$

where

$$r_1, r_2 = \tfrac{1}{2}[1 - \gamma \pm \sqrt{(\gamma - 1)^2 - 4\delta}] \tag{3}$$

and

$$\alpha = \tfrac{1}{2}(1 - \gamma), \qquad \beta = \tfrac{1}{2}\sqrt{4\delta - (\gamma - 1)^2}. \tag{4}$$

Another way of arriving at the foregoing results is as follows. We know that the derivatives of terms of the form x^r are rx^{r-1}, $r(r - 1)x^{r-2}$, etc. Consequently, if we introduce into (1) an expression of the form

$$y = x^r$$

we will have a common factor x^{r-2} and be left with the algebraic equation

$$r(r - 1) + \gamma r + \delta = 0. \tag{5}$$

If we have two distinct real roots r_1 and r_2 of this equation we shall also have, because of the superposition principle, the solution

$$y = c_1 x^{r_1} + c_2 x^{r_2}. \tag{6}$$

The case of equal roots, or of conjugate complex roots, may be discussed separately, and the results, of course, must coincide with those listed in (2). For the result in the case of conjugate complex roots we make use of the formula

$$x^{i\beta} = e^{i\beta \ln x} = \cos (\beta \ln x) + i \sin (\beta \ln x), \tag{7}$$

which holds for $x > 0$.

When x is negative we may obtain results corresponding to Eqs. (2) by making the substitution $x = -\xi$ in the differential equation (1) and then proceeding as before. The resultant formulas may be written in the form

$$y = \begin{cases} C_1 |x|^{r_1} + C_2 |x|^{r_2}, & (\gamma - 1)^2 > 4\delta, \\ (C_1 + C_2 \ln |x|)|x|^{r_1}, & (\gamma - 1)^2 = 4\delta, \\ |x|^{\alpha}[C_1 \cos (\beta \ln |x|) + C_2 \sin (\beta \ln |x|)], & (\gamma - 1)^2 < 4\delta. \end{cases} \tag{8}$$

In general, the solution (8) for negative x and the solution (2) for positive x do not merge into each other in any simple way for $x = 0$. A complete understanding of what happens in this regard requires that the differential equation be considered with x replaced by a complex variable z.

EXERCISES

Solve the differential equations of Exercises 1 through 4.

1. $y'' + 2x^{-1}y' + 3x^{-2}y = 0$ 2. $y'' + x^{-1}y' - n^2 x^{-2}y = 0$
3. $2x^2 y'' + 3xy' - y = 0$ 4. $x^2 y'' + y = 0$

In Exercises 5 through 12 determine γ and δ in the differential equation (1) in such a way that the solution for positive x is of the form given.

5. $y = c_1 x + c_2 x^2$ 6. $y = c_1 x^{-1} + c_2 x^{-2}$
7. $y = c_1 x^{1/2} + c_2 x^{-1/2}$ 8. $y = c_1 x^2 + c_2 x^{-2}$
9. $y = (c_1 + c_2 \ln x)x$ 10. $y = (c_1 + c_2 \ln x)x^{-1}$
11. $y = c_1 \cos (2 \ln x) + c_2 \sin (2 \ln x)$
12. $y = c_1 x^{-1} \cos (\ln x) + c_2 x^{-1} \sin (\ln x)$

13. Show that the differential equation

$$\frac{d^2y}{dx^2} + \frac{\gamma}{x}\frac{dy}{dx} + \frac{\delta}{x^2}y = f(x)$$

can be written in the form

$$x^{-(p+q)}\frac{d}{dx}\left[x^p\frac{d}{dx}(x^qy)\right] = f$$

and determine the values of p and q in terms of γ and δ.

14. Use the result of Exercise 13 to find the general solution of the equation

$$y'' + x^{-1}y' - n^2x^{-2}y = x^m, \qquad n^2 \neq (m+2)^2, \qquad n \neq 0.$$

15. By making the substitution $x = e^t$, $y(x) = z(t)$, reduce the differential equation $x^2y'' = f(xy', y)$ to a differential equation for z in which the independent variable t does not occur explicitly.

3–8 The method of undetermined coefficients. The method of undetermined coefficients is a simple method for finding a particular solution of some linear differential equations with the right side not equal to zero. This method is applicable only for certain forms of the right side. In comparison with another method, which is applicable no matter what the form of the right side of the differential equation, it is found to be sufficiently simpler in applications to justify its study.

As an example, consider the equation

$$y'' + 2ay' + by = e^{kx}, \tag{1}$$

where a, b, and k are constants. In view of the property of the exponential function of reproducing itself when differentiated, one thinks naturally that a particular solution of (1) may have the form

$$y_p = Ae^{kx}. \tag{2}$$

The constant A is the *undetermined* coefficient which we have at our disposal in order to satisfy (1). Substitution of (2) in (1) gives

$$Ae^{kx}[k^2 + 2ak + b] = e^{kx}, \tag{3}$$

and consequently we find for the value of the undetermined coefficient

$$A = \frac{1}{k^2 + 2ak + b}. \tag{4}$$

There is one case, and only one case, in which we have not obtained a particular integral of (1) in the form (2). Equation (4) is valid only if the denominator in the term on the right does not vanish or, in other words, only if k is not a root of the auxiliary equation (4) of Section 3–4. This restriction is quite natural if we consider the fact that when k is a root of the auxiliary equation, then Ae^{kx} satisfies the corresponding reduced differential equation, Eq. (1) of Section 3–4, no matter what value A has, and so it cannot possibly take care of a right side different from zero.

Since a constant A in (2) will not give our particular solution in the exceptional case, perhaps multiplication of e^{kx} by some simple function of x will enable us to carry through the procedure. Once this possibility is thought of, it is seen that it may be possible to get a particular integral in the form

$$y_p = Axe^{kx}. \tag{5}$$

Substitution of (5) in (1) gives

$$Axe^{kx}[k^2 + 2ak + b] + Ae^{kx}[2k + 2a] = e^{kx}. \tag{6}$$

The expression in the first set of brackets vanishes because k was taken to be equal to a root of the auxiliary equation. We are left with an equation in which e^{kx} again factors out on both sides, and we have

$$A = \frac{1}{2(k + a)}. \tag{7}$$

Equation (7) will hold so long as $k \neq -a$ or, in other words, unless k is a double root of the auxiliary equation (4) of Section 3–4. When k is a double root, $k = -a$, we cannot possibly have a particular integral of the form (5), since in this case the function Axe^{kx} is a solution of the associated reduced equation, regardless of the value of A.

Having first gone from e^{kx} to xe^{kx}, one will expect that now the particular integral may be of the form

$$y_p = Ax^2e^{kx}. \tag{8}$$

Substitution of (8) in (1) and use of the fact that k is a double root of the auxiliary equation give now

$$A = \tfrac{1}{2}. \tag{9}$$

In summary, we see that if k is not a root of the auxiliary equation, then there is a particular solution of the form Ae^{kx}. If k is a simple root of the auxiliary equation, then there cannot be a particular solution of the form Ae^{kx}, but there is one of the form Axe^{kx}. If k is a double root, there can be no particular solution of the form Ae^{kx} or of the form Axe^{kx}, but there is one of the form Ax^2e^{kx}. The procedure for determining the coefficient A in the various cases is simple enough so that there is no need to use the general formulas for A.

Another important special case in which the method of undetermined coefficients is applicable concerns the differential equation (1) with e^{mx} on the right side replaced by a linear combination of $\cos mx$ and $\sin mx$. While we can, of course, replace $\cos mx$ and $\sin mx$ by $\frac{1}{2}(e^{imx} + e^{-imx})$ and $-\frac{1}{2}i(e^{imx} - e^{-imx})$ and thereby reduce the problem to the case already discussed, we may also directly set

$$y_p = A \sin mx + B \cos mx \tag{10}$$

and obtain the undetermined coefficients A and B by matching corresponding terms on the right and left. There is again an exceptional case, namely, when the expression (10) is a solution of the reduced equation or, in other words, when the roots of the auxiliary equation are of the form $r = \pm im$. In this exceptional case the trial solution (10) must be replaced by

$$y_p = x(A \sin mx + B \cos mx). \tag{11}$$

EXAMPLE. Consider

$$y'' + k^2 y = \cos mx, \qquad m \neq 0. \tag{12}$$

Substitution of (10) into (12) gives

$$-Am^2 \sin mx - Bm^2 \cos mx + Ak^2 \sin mx + Bk^2 \cos mx = \cos mx. \tag{13}$$

Equation (13) is satisfied if we set

$$(k^2 - m^2)A = 0, \qquad (k^2 - m^2)B = 1, \tag{14}$$

and thus when $k^2 \neq m^2$ a particular solution of (12) is

$$y_p = \frac{\cos mx}{k^2 - m^2}. \tag{15}$$

When $k^2 = m^2$ Eq. (15) ceases to be valid and we must take y_p as in (11). Substitution of (11) in $y'' + m^2 y = \cos mx$ gives

$$x[-Am^2 \sin mx - Bm^2 \cos mx + Am^2 \sin mx + Bm^2 \cos mx]$$
$$+ 2Am \cos mx - 2Bm \sin mx = \cos mx. \tag{16}$$

Equation (16) is satisfied by setting

$$2Am = 1, \qquad 2Bm = 0, \tag{17}$$

and therewith

$$y_p = \frac{1}{2m} x \sin mx. \tag{18}$$

Our last important special case concerns the differential equation with the right side given by a positive integral power of x, namely,

$$y'' + 2ay' + by = x^n. \tag{19}$$

Since differentiation of positive integral powers of x gives us again positive integral powers of x, we are led to particular integrals of the form

$$y = A_0 x^n + A_1 x^{n-1} + \cdots + A_n. \tag{20}$$

If we substitute (20) into the left side of (19), the coefficients $A_0, A_1, \ldots, A_n$ must be determined so that the resulting polynomial on the left reduces to the single term x^n which occurs on the right. This will always be possible if the coefficient b in (19) is different from zero. In the exceptional case when $b = 0$ we see that the highest possible power on the left side would be x^{n-1}, and thus we are led to multiply (20) on the right by x before insertion into (19). There is one further exceptional case, namely, the one in which a and b are both zero, but the solution of the resulting equation $y'' = x^n$ is obvious.

EXAMPLE.

$$y'' + k^2 y = x^3, \qquad k \neq 0;$$
$$y_p = Ax^3 + Bx^2 + Cx + D;$$
$$y_p'' + k^2 y_p = k^2 A x^3 + k^2 B x^2 + (6A + k^2 C)x + (2B + k^2 D) = x^3;$$
$$k^2 A = 1, \qquad k^2 B = 0, \qquad k^2 C + 6A = 0, \qquad k^2 D + 2B = 0;$$

$$y_p = \frac{x^3}{k^2} - \frac{6x}{k^4}.$$

When $k = 0$, we find $y_p = \frac{1}{20} x^5$.

EXERCISES

Solve the differential equations of Exercises 1 through 10.

1. $y'' - 2y' - 3y = 2e^{2x} + 3 \sin x$
2. $y'' + 5y' + 2y = \sqrt{2}\, e^{\sqrt{2}x} + \sqrt{3} \cos \sqrt{3}\, x$
3. $y'' + 2y' + y = 3e^x$ 4. $y'' + 2y' + y = 4e^{-x}$
5. $y'' - 2y' + y = 2 \cos 2x + \sin 2x + 2e^{-x}$
6. $y'' + 4y = 2 \cos 2x + \sin x + 2e^{-x}$
7. $y'' + y' + y = x^3 + 2x^2$ 8. $y'' + y' = x^3 + 2x^2$
9. $y'' + y = \sin x$ 10. $y'' + y = 4x \sin x$

3–9 Method of variation of parameters. We propose now to show that there exists a general method of obtaining the general solution of any linear second-order differential equation provided we already know, one way or another, a certain portion of what we wish to know. We recall that the general solution of the differential equation

$$Py'' + Qy' + Ry = S \tag{1}$$

will be of the form

$$y = y_h + y_p, \tag{2}$$

where y_h is the general solution of the associated homogeneous or reduced equation, and where y_p is some particular solution of the complete equation (1). The function y_h is of the form

$$y_h = c_1 u_1 + c_2 u_2, \tag{3}$$

where c_1 and c_2 are the two constants of integration and u_1 and u_2 are any two solutions of the associated homogeneous equation neither of which is a constant multiple of the other.

What we shall assume is that we know one of the two functions u_1 and u_2, say u_1. We shall then show how to determine u_2 as well as y_p.

It is sometimes much easier to find part of the solution than the complete solution, as the following example may illustrate. For the equation

$$y'' + xy' - y = 0 \tag{4}$$

inspection shows that *one* solution is kx. In this, the parameter k may have any constant value we wish. So for this equation we may take $u_1 = x$.

A second solution of the reduced equation. Assuming that a solution u_1 of the homogeneous or reduced equation

$$Py'' + Qy' + Ry = 0 \tag{5}$$

is known, we may obtain a second solution u_2 by the following procedure, valid in any interval in which $P \neq 0$. If k is any constant, we know that the function $ku_1(x)$ is also a solution of (5). To determine a second solution $u_2(x)$ which is not a constant multiple of u_1, we tentatively set

$$u_2(x) = k(x)u_1(x), \tag{6}$$

where now the factor k is a function of x rather than a constant. In other words, we consider *variations* of the parameter k. It is not at all obvious that writing u_2 in this form will simplify the problem of obtaining it. This, however, turns out to be the case, as we shall see.

We introduce (6) and the derived formulas

$$u_2' = k'u_1 + ku_1',$$

$$u_2'' = k''u_1 + 2k'u_1' + ku_1'' \tag{7}$$

into (5). The resultant equation can be arranged in the form

$$k[Pu_1'' + Qu_1' + Ru_1] + k'[2Pu_1' + Qu_1] + k''[Pu_1] = 0. \tag{8}$$

The expression in the first bracket vanishes because u_1 is a solution of (5). The remainder of (8) is then a first-order differential equation in k'. Its solution is

$$k' = e^{-\int[2(u_1'/u_1)+Q/P]dx} = \frac{1}{u_1^2} e^{-\int(Q/P)dx}. \tag{9}$$

The function k follows from this by integration and we have

$$y_h = c_1u_1 + c_2\left(\int \frac{e^{-\int(Q/P)dx}}{u_1^2} dx\right) u_1. \tag{10}$$

In the example (4), we had $P = 1$, $Q = x$, and $u_1 = x$. Equation (10) shows that the reduced equation associated with (4) has the general solution

$$y_h = c_1x + c_2\left(\int \frac{e^{-x^2/2}}{x^2} dx\right) x. \tag{11}$$

As a second example, consider Eq. (1) of Section 3–5:

$$y'' - 2r_1y' + r_1^2 y = 0. \tag{12}$$

We have $u_1 = e^{r_1x}$, $Q/P = -2r_1$ and therewith, from (10),

$$y = c_1e^{r_1x} + c_2xe^{r_1x}. \tag{13}$$

This is the same result which was obtained earlier by a special procedure.

EXERCISES

1. Show that $y = x$ is a solution of the differential equation

$$y'' + x^{-2}y' - x^{-3}y = 0,$$

and use this fact to obtain the general solution.

2. Show that $y = x^2$ is a solution of

$$y'' + (\tfrac{1}{2}x - x^{-1})y' - y = 0$$

and obtain the general solution.

3. Solve $(1 - x^2)y'' + xy' - y = 0$.

4. Solve $(1 - x^2)y'' + y' - (2 - x^2)y = 0$.

5. Solve $xy'' - (x + 2)y' + y = 0$.

6. Show that $y = x$ is a solution of

$$y'' + f(x)[xy' - y] \equiv y'' + xf(x)y' - f(x)y = 0$$

and obtain the general solution.

7. Show that $y = e^x$ is a solution of

$$(y'' - y') + f(x)(y' - y) \equiv y'' + [f(x) - 1]y' - f(x)y = 0$$

and find the general solution.

8. Find the general solution of the equation

$$(y'' - 4y') + x^2(y' - 4y) = 0.$$

9. Find the general solution of the equation

$$\left(\frac{d^2y}{dx^2} - \frac{n-1}{x}\frac{dy}{dx}\right) + f(x)\left(\frac{dy}{dx} - \frac{n}{x}y\right)$$

$$\equiv \frac{d^2y}{dx^2} + \left[f(x) - \frac{n-1}{x}\right]\frac{dy}{dx} - f(x)\frac{n}{x}y = 0.$$

3–10 A particular solution of the complete equation. Having seen how to obtain a second solution u_2 of the reduced equation (5) of the preceding section when one solution u_1 was known, our next step in the solution of the complete differential equation is to find a particular solution y_p in terms of u_1 and u_2.

We set

$$y_p = C_1(x)u_1(x) + C_2(x)u_2(x) \tag{1}$$

and plan to introduce this and its derivatives,

$$y_p' = C_1'u_1 + C_2'u_2 + C_1u_1' + C_2u_2',$$

$$y_p'' = C_1''u_1 + C_2''u_2 + 2(C_1'u_1' + C_2'u_2') + C_1u_1'' + C_2u_2'', \tag{2}$$

into the differential equation (1) of Section 3–9. If we do this we find *one* differential equation for the *two* unknown functions C_1 and C_2. Since we need only to determine *some one* particular solution y_p, we are satisfied with *any* pair of functions C_1 and C_2 which makes (1) satisfy $Py'' + Qy' + Ry = S$. Consequently, we may arbitrarily introduce an additional condition relating C_1 and C_2. It would be perfectly possible, for instance, to set $C_2 = 0$.

A more symmetrical procedure, which also has the advantage of carrying over to the nth-order differential equations, is as follows. We choose as our arbitrary condition

$$C_1'u_1 + C_2'u_2 = 0. \tag{3}$$

This makes (2) have the simpler form

$$y_p' = C_1u_1' + C_2u_2', \tag{4}$$

$$y_p'' = C_1'u_1' + C_2'u_2' + C_1u_1'' + C_2u_2''.$$

If we now introduce (1) and (4) into $Py'' + Qy' + Ry = S$, we have

$$C_1[Pu_1'' + Qu_1' + Ru_1] + C_2[Pu_2'' + Qu_2' + Ru_2]$$

$$+ C_1'Pu_1' + C_2'Pu_2' = S. \tag{5}$$

The contents of the first two sets of brackets vanish, since u_1 and u_2 are solutions of the associated homogeneous equation. Consequently, (5) reduces to

$$C_1'u_1' + C_2'u_2' = \frac{S}{P} \tag{6}$$

in any interval in which $P \neq 0$. In (3) and (6) we have two simultaneous equations for C_1' and C_2'. Their solution may be written in the form

$$C_1' = \frac{-(S/P)u_2}{W}, \qquad C_2' = \frac{(S/P)u_1}{W}, \tag{7}$$

where W is the Wronskian:

$$W = \begin{vmatrix} u_1 & u_2 \\ u_1' & u_2' \end{vmatrix}, \tag{8}$$

which does not vanish (see Section 3–3). From (7) we obtain C_1 and C_2 by integration.

Altogether we obtain by combination of (1) and (7) the following general solution of the nonhomogeneous equation $Py'' + Qy' + Ry = S$ in terms of the general solution $c_1u_1 + c_2u_2$ of the associated homogeneous equation:

$$y = \left[-\int \frac{Su_2}{PW} \, dx + c_1\right]u_1 + \left[\int \frac{Su_1}{PW} \, dx + c_2\right]u_2. \tag{9}$$

In (9) the function W is given by (8) and is different from zero, and Eq. (9) holds in any interval in which $P \neq 0$.

EXAMPLE. Consider the equation

$$y'' + y = \tan x. \tag{10}$$

For this equation, we have

$$u_1 = \cos x, \qquad u_2 = \sin x,$$
$$W = \begin{vmatrix} \cos x & \sin x \\ -\sin x & \cos x \end{vmatrix} = 1.$$
$$P = 1, \qquad S = \tan x,$$

From (7),

$$C_1 = -\int \tan x \sin x \, dx = \sin x - \ln|\sec x + \tan x|,$$

$$C_2 = \int \sin x \, dx = -\cos x,$$

so that

$$y_p = -\cos x \ln|\sec x + \tan x|, \tag{11}$$

and the general solution of (10) is

$$y = c_1 \cos x + c_2 \sin x - \cos x \ln|\sec x + \tan x|. \tag{12}$$

EXERCISES

Solve the differential equations of Exercises 1 through 9.

1. $y'' + 4y = \sec x$
2. $y'' + 3y = \sec x$
3. $y'' - y = 1/(1 + e^x)$
4. $y'' - 2y' + y = e^x \ln x$
5. $2x^2 y'' + 3xy' - y = 1/x$
6. $y'' + k^2 y = \tan x$
7. $x^2 y'' - 2xy' + 2y = x^3$
8. $x^2 y'' - 2xy' + 2y = x$
9. $(1 - x^2)y'' - xy' + y = f(x)$, given that $u_1 = x$, $u_2 = (1 - x^2)^{1/2}$

By using a formula for u_2 in terms of u_1, obtain the Wronskian W for the differential equations:

10. $y'' + x^{-1}y' + y = 0$
11. $(1 - x^2)y'' - 2xy' + p(p+1)y = 0$

3–11 Taylor series solution of homogeneous linear differential equations. We continue to study the second-order equation with variable coefficients. As we now know how to find particular integrals once the general solution of the associated homogeneous equation has been determined, we may restrict attention to the homogeneous equation

$$P(x)y'' + Q(x)y' + R(x)y = 0. \tag{1}$$

For some types of coefficients P, Q, and R it is, of course, possible to find solutions in terms of functions of an elementary nature. The equation with constant coefficients and the equidimensional equation are examples of this.

In those cases in which we do not see how to obtain the solution in terms of elementary functions, and there are many of these which occur in applications, it is natural to turn to series developments of one kind or another. We shall discuss here primarily one type of series development, namely, power series.

For the sake of convenience we shall in the following discuss series developments in powers of x. But all we do will equally well apply with obvious modifications to developments in powers of $(x - x_0)$, where x_0 has any finite value.

Let us consider the series

$$y = c_0 + c_1 x + c_2 x^2 + \cdots \tag{2}$$

and see in what circumstances we can determine the coefficients c_n in such a way that the expression (2) satisfies the differential equation (1).

It is, in general, possible to specify at will the values of y and dy/dx of a solution of a second-order differential equation at a given point $x = x_0$. This means that in general we shall be able to prescribe arbitrarily the values of c_0 and c_1 in (2). For the purpose of simplifying the following discussion it is advantageous to restrict attention here specifically to differential equations for which this is possible.*

The general coefficient c_n in the series (2) is given by

$$c_n = \frac{y^{(n)}(0)}{n!}. \tag{3}$$

Consequently, in order to have a development of the form (2) it is necessary that all the derivatives of the function y be finite for $x = 0$. Let us see what this means with reference to the coefficient functions P, Q, and R.

If we write (1) in the form

$$\frac{d^2y}{dx^2} + \frac{Q}{P}\frac{dy}{dx} + \frac{R}{P}y = 0, \tag{4}$$

---

* There are differential equations of the form (1) with solutions of the form (2) for which it is not possible to prescribe c_0 and c_1 arbitrarily. These, however, are best treated in a different connection.

then we see that for arbitrary values of $y(0)$ and $y'(0)$ we shall be able to determine $y''(0)$ as a finite quantity only if

$$\frac{Q(0)}{P(0)} \text{ is finite and } \frac{R(0)}{P(0)} \text{ is finite} \tag{5}$$

in the sense that $\lim_{x \to 0} Q/P$ and $\lim_{x \to 0} R/P$ exist.

This, then, is the first requirement for a series solution (2) with arbitrary values of c_0 and c_1.

We shall get the higher derivatives of y by successive differentiations of Eq. (4). Consequently, in order to have all the derivatives $y^{(n)}(0)$ finite, it will be necessary not only that Q/P and R/P be finite at $x = 0$, but also all their derivatives must have this property. If R/P and Q/P themselves are representable by series in positive integral powers of x these requirements will certainly be satisfied, and it is customary to designate the point $x = 0$ in these circumstances as an *ordinary point* of the differential equation.

In summary, we may say that *the differential equation*

$$Py'' + Qy' + Ry = 0$$

has the point $x = 0$ as an ordinary point whenever we can write the coefficient ratios Q/P and R/P as Taylor series:

$$\frac{Q}{P} = a_0 + a_1 x + a_2 x^2 + \cdots,$$

$$\frac{R}{P} = b_0 + b_1 x + b_2 x^2 + \cdots \tag{6}$$

Under these conditions the general solution of the differential equation is of the form $y = c_0 + c_1 x + c_2 x^2 + \cdots$, with c_0 and c_1 arbitrary.

As regards convergence of the solution series, it can be proved that its interval of convergence is at least as large as, and in general coincides with, the smaller one of the intervals of convergence of the series (6).

3–12 Three illustrative examples. As examples of the method described in the preceding section we consider in turn the following three differential equations:

$$y'' - y = 0, \tag{1}$$

$$y'' - xy = 0, \tag{2}$$

$$(1 - x^2)y'' - 2xy' + p(p + 1)y = 0. \tag{3}$$

In each of these, we write

$$y = c_0 + c_1x + c_2x^2 + \cdots + c_nx^n + \cdots, \tag{4}$$

$$y' = c_1 + 2c_2x + 3c_3x^2 + \cdots + nc_nx^{n-1} + \cdots, \tag{5}$$

and

$$y'' = 2c_2 + 3 \cdot 2c_3x + 4 \cdot 3c_4x^2 + \cdots + n(n - 1)c_nx^{n-2} + \cdots \tag{6}$$

EXAMPLE 1. Putting (4) and (6) into (1), we have

$$2c_2 + 3 \cdot 2c_3x + 4 \cdot 3c_4x^2 + \cdots = c_0 + c_1x + c_2x^2 + \cdots$$

Equating the coefficients of like powers of x on the two sides of this equation, we obtain the following conditions on the coefficients c_n:

$$2c_2 = c_0, \quad 4 \cdot 3c_4 = c_2, \ldots, \quad 2n(2n - 1)c_{2n} = c_{2n-2}, \ldots$$

$$3 \cdot 2c_3 = c_1, \quad 5 \cdot 4c_5 = c_3, \ldots, \quad (2n + 1)2nc_{2n+1} = c_{2n-1}, \ldots$$

We see that no conditions are imposed on the first two coefficients c_0 and c_1, and for the remaining ones we find

$$c_2 = \frac{c_0}{2}, \quad c_4 = \frac{c_2}{4 \cdot 3} = \frac{c_0}{4!}, \ldots, \quad c_{2n} = \frac{c_0}{(2n)!}, \ldots$$

$$c_3 = \frac{c_1}{3 \cdot 2}, \quad c_5 = \frac{c_3}{5 \cdot 4} = \frac{c_1}{5!}, \ldots, \quad c_{2n+1} = \frac{c_1}{(2n + 1)!}, \ldots$$

The general solution of the differential equation (1) is then

$$y = c_0\left(1 + \frac{x^2}{2!} + \frac{x^4}{4!} + \cdots\right) + c_1\left(x + \frac{x^3}{3!} + \frac{x^5}{5!} + \cdots\right),$$

where c_0 and c_1 are arbitrary. If we recall the series developments for $\cosh x$ and $\sinh x$, we see that this agrees with the solution obtained by another method (Exercise 3 of Section 3–6, with $\lambda = 1$).

EXAMPLE 2. Introduction of (4) and (6) into (2) gives

$$2c_2 + 3 \cdot 2c_3x + 4 \cdot 3c_4x^2 + \cdots = c_0x + c_1x^2 + c_2x^3 + \cdots$$

This leads to the conditions $2c_2 = 0$ and

$$3 \cdot 2c_3 = c_0, \qquad 4 \cdot 3c_4 = c_1, \qquad 5 \cdot 4c_5 = c_2, \qquad 6 \cdot 5c_6 = c_3, \ldots$$

From these conditions, we see first that c_0 and c_1 may be chosen arbitrarily, while c_2 as well as c_5, c_8, c_{11}, etc. must be zero. We also see that

$$c_3 = \frac{c_0}{3 \cdot 2}, \qquad c_4 = \frac{c_1}{4 \cdot 3}, \qquad c_6 = \frac{c_0}{6 \cdot 5 \cdot 3 \cdot 2}, \qquad c_7 = \frac{c_1}{7 \cdot 6 \cdot 4 \cdot 3},$$

$$c_9 = \frac{c_0}{9 \cdot 8 \cdot 6 \cdot 5 \cdot 3 \cdot 2}, \qquad c_{10} = \frac{c_1}{10 \cdot 9 \cdot 7 \cdot 6 \cdot 4 \cdot 3}, \ldots$$

Thus the general solution of (2) is

$$y = c_0 \left(1 + \frac{x^3}{3 \cdot 2} + \frac{x^6}{6 \cdot 5 \cdot 3 \cdot 2} + \frac{x^9}{9 \cdot 8 \cdot 6 \cdot 5 \cdot 3 \cdot 2} + \cdots \right)$$

$$+ c_1 \left(x + \frac{x^4}{4 \cdot 3} + \frac{x^7}{7 \cdot 6 \cdot 4 \cdot 3} + \cdots \right).$$

EXAMPLE 3. Equation (3) is a differential equation which occurs frequently in physical applications; it is called Legendre's differential equation. If we insert the series (4), (5), and (6) into (3), we obtain

$$[2c_2 + 3 \cdot 2c_3 x + 4 \cdot 3c_4 x^2 + \cdots + n(n - 1)c_n x^{n-2} + \cdots]$$

$$- [2c_2 x^2 + 3 \cdot 2c_3 x^3 + 4 \cdot 3c_4 x^4 + \cdots + n(n - 1)c_n x^n + \cdots]$$

$$- 2[c_1 x + 2c_2 x^2 + 3c_3 x^3 + \cdots + nc_n x^n + \cdots]$$

$$+ p(p + 1)[c_0 + c_1 x + c_2 x^2 + \cdots + c_n x^n + \cdots] = 0.$$

Collecting the terms containing like powers of x, we have

$$[2c_2 + p(p + 1)c_0] + [3 \cdot 2c_3 - 2c_1 + p(p + 1)c_1]x$$

$$+ [4 \cdot 3c_4 - 2c_2 - 4c_2 + p(p + 1)c_2]x^2 + \cdots$$

$$+ [(n + 2)(n + 1)c_{n+2} - n(n - 1)c_n - 2nc_n + p(p + 1)c_n]x^n$$

$$+ \cdots = 0.$$

Equating to zero the coefficient of each power of x, we find that no conditions are imposed upon c_0 and c_1 and that the remaining coefficients must satisfy the following recurrence conditions:

$$c_2 = -\frac{p(p+1)}{2} c_0,$$

$$c_3 = \frac{2 - p(p+1)}{3 \cdot 2} c_1 = -\frac{(p-1)(p+2)}{3!} c_1,$$

$$c_4 = \frac{2 + 4 - p(p+1)}{4 \cdot 3} c_2 = -\frac{(p-2)(p+3)}{4 \cdot 3} c_2$$

$$= \frac{p(p+1)(p-2)(p+3)}{4!} c_0,$$

$$c_5 = \frac{4 \cdot 3 - p(p+1)}{5 \cdot 4} c_3 = -\frac{(p-3)(p+4)}{5 \cdot 4} c_3$$

$$= \frac{(p-1)(p+2)(p-3)(p+4)}{5!} c_1, \cdots$$

$$c_{n+2} = \frac{n(n+1) - p(p+1)}{(n+2)(n+1)} c_n = \cdots, \cdots$$

The general solution of Legendre's differential equation, accordingly, is

$$y = c_0 \left[1 - \frac{p(p+1)}{2!} x^2 + \frac{p(p-2)(p+1)(p+3)}{4!} x^4 - \cdots \right]$$

$$+ c_1 \left[x - \frac{(p-1)(p+2)}{3!} x^3 + \frac{(p-1)(p-3)(p+2)(p+4)}{5!} x^5 - \cdots \right].$$

An inspection of the recurrence relation for c_{n+2} in terms of c_n shows that when p is a positive integer or zero, one of the series in brackets breaks off and becomes a polynomial. For example, if $p = 3$, we find that $c_5 = c_7 = c_9 = \cdots = 0$. In general, the two series are infinite.

EXERCISES

Obtain the first few terms in the series solution for the equations of Exercises 1 through 6.

1. $y'' + y' - xy = 0$ 2. $(1 - x^2)y'' - 2xy' + 6y = 0$

3. $y'' - (1 + x^2)^{-1}y = 0$ [Solve this problem in two ways, once by writing the differential equation in the form $(1 + x^2)y'' - y = 0$, and once by writing $y'' - (1 - x^2 + x^4 - x^6 + \cdots)y = 0$.]

4. $y'' - xy' - y = 0$ (For all $n > 1$, express c_n in terms of c_0 and c_1.)

5. $y'' + (x + 1)y' - x^2 y = 0$ 6. $y'' + x^2 y = 0$

7. Use the result of Exercise 11 of Section 3–3 and Example 2 of this section to obtain the general solution of the nonlinear equation $z' = x - z^2$ as the ratio of two power series in x.

8. By analogy with Example 2, obtain the first few terms in the series solution of the equation $y'' - kxy = 0$.

3–13 Power-series expansions at singular points. In Section 3–7 we considered a special case of the homogeneous differential equation $Py'' + Qy' + Ry = 0$, namely, the equidimensional equation

$$y'' + \frac{\gamma}{x} y' + \frac{\delta}{x^2} y = 0, \tag{1}$$

in which γ and δ are constants not both zero. We saw that the general solution of this equation was of the form

$$y = c_1 |x|^{r_1} + c_2 |x|^{r_2} \tag{2}$$

so long as $r_2 \neq r_1$, and when $r_1 = r_2$ this had to be replaced by

$$y = (c_1 + c_2 \ln |x|)|x|^{r_1}. \tag{3}$$

In Section 3–11 we said that the point $x = 0$ was an ordinary point of the differential equation

$$\frac{d^2 y}{dx^2} + \frac{Q}{P} \frac{dy}{dx} + \frac{R}{P} y = 0 \tag{4}$$

if Q/P and R/P were representable as Taylor series about $x = 0$. Now the equidimensional equation (1) is of the form (4), but the coefficients γ/x and δ/x^2 are obviously not representable in this fashion. Consequently, the point $x = 0$ is not an ordinary point of Eq. (1). This is in agreement with the fact that the solutions (2) or (3) cannot be written in the form $c_0 + c_1 x + c_2 x^2 + \cdots$, with c_0 and c_1 arbitrary.

If the coefficients Q/P and R/P are not representable as Taylor series about $x = 0$, the point $x = 0$, is called a *singular* point of the differential equation (4). We shall not treat this case in full generality but we shall consider an important class of such equations.

If we want to characterize a class of equations (4) which includes as a special case the equidimensional equation (1), we may replace the conditions previously imposed on Q/P and R/P [(6) of Section 3–11] by the following more inclusive conditions: *the functions Q/P and R/P are both* *representable by power series about $x = 0$ as follows:*

$$\frac{Q}{P} = \frac{\alpha_0 + \alpha_1 x + \alpha_2 x^2 + \cdots}{x},$$

$$\frac{R}{P} = \frac{\beta_0 + \beta_1 x + \beta_2 x^2 + \cdots}{x^2}. \tag{5}$$

For the equidimensional equation (1), we have $\alpha_0 = \gamma$, $\beta_0 = \delta$, while all the remaining coefficients of the two series (5) vanish.

The special case of an ordinary point is obtained when $\alpha_0 = 0$, $\beta_0 = 0$, and $\beta_1 = 0$ in Eq. (5).

When Eq. (5) holds, we call the point $x = 0$ a *regular singular point* of the differential equation (4). The word *regular* is used to distinguish between differential equations for which (5) is true and those for which the representation (5) is not possible. When (5) does not hold, the point $x = 0$ is called an *irregular singular point* and the method of this section is not applicable.

Examples of differential equations for which $x = 0$ is an irregular singular point, and thus outside the scope of the present treatment, are

$$y'' + \frac{1}{x^3} y = 0, \tag{6}$$

$$y'' + \frac{1}{x^2} y' + y = 0. \tag{7}$$

Another example is given by Exercise 1 of Section 3–9. The solution of this exercise illustrates what may happen at an irregular singular point.

Considering the form of the solutions (2) and (3) of the equidimensional equation (1), we might expect that Eq. (4) under the conditions (5) has, in general, two solutions of the form

$$y = x^r (c_0 + c_1 x + c_2 x^2 + \cdots), \tag{8}$$

or one of this form and one of the form

$$y = x^r \ln x (c_0 + c_1 x + c_2 x^2 + \cdots), \tag{9}$$

where we shall assume that $x > 0$.

It will be found that there are either two distinct solutions of the form (8) or one solution of the form (8) and one solution similar to (9) but somewhat more complicated. Because of the superposition principle, these may then be combined to give the general solution of (4). In (8) and (9) we assume that $c_0 \neq 0$, since otherwise we would have x^{r+1} multiplied by a Taylor's series in x. Since we shall apply the superposition principle to the two particular solutions which we obtain, we may assume a value of c_0 at will. It will often be convenient to set $c_0 = 1$.

Rather than working out the general formula with the coefficients of the differential equation (4) given by (5), let us consider the following equation (which was chosen so as to exemplify the case of two different values of r):

$$2x^2 y'' + 3xy' + (2x - 1)y = 0. \tag{10}$$

To see that this equation satisfies the condition (5), we write it in the form

$$y'' + \frac{\frac{3}{2}}{x} y' + \frac{-\frac{1}{2} + x}{x^2} y = 0. \tag{11}$$

We introduce the series (8) for y, and for the derivatives of y:

$$y' = x^{r-1}[c_0 r + c_1(r + 1)x + c_2(r + 2)x^2 + \cdots], \tag{12}$$

$$y'' = x^{r-2}[c_0 r(r - 1) + c_1(r + 1)rx + c_2(r + 2)(r + 1)x^2 + \cdots]. \tag{13}$$

After cancellation of the common factor x^{r-2}, we are left with the series relation

$$c_0 r(r - 1) + c_1(r + 1)rx + c_2(r + 2)(r + 1)x^2 + \cdots$$
$$+ \tfrac{3}{2}[c_0 r + c_1(r + 1)x + c_2(r + 2)x^2 + \cdots]$$
$$+ (-\tfrac{1}{2} + x)[c_0 + c_1 x + c_2 x^2 + c_3 x^3 + \cdots] = 0. \tag{14}$$

We combine corresponding powers of x and equate the coefficient of each power of x to zero. This gives us the following system of equations

$$c_0[r(r - 1) + \tfrac{3}{2}r - \tfrac{1}{2}] = 0,$$
$$c_1[(r + 1)r + \tfrac{3}{2}(r + 1) - \tfrac{1}{2}] + c_0 = 0,$$
$$c_2[(r + 2)(r + 1) + \tfrac{3}{2}(r + 2) - \tfrac{1}{2}] + c_1 = 0, \tag{15}$$
$$\vdots$$

It is evident that we may go on by simply writing the *recurrence relation*

$$c_k[(r + k)(r + k - 1) + \tfrac{3}{2}(r + k) - \tfrac{1}{2}] + c_{k-1} = 0 \tag{15'}$$

for all positive integral values of k. (The case $k = 0$ may be included if we agree that the quantity c_{-1}, so far undefined, shall be zero.)

We have agreed that $c_0 \neq 0$. Consequently the first of equations (15) requires that

$$r^2 + (\tfrac{3}{2} - 1)r - \tfrac{1}{2} = 0. \tag{16}$$

Equation (16) is called the *indicial equation* of the differential equation (10). Its solutions are

$$r_1 = \tfrac{1}{2}, \qquad r_2 = -1, \tag{17}$$

and these are the only possible choices for the so far undetermined exponent r. For either one of these values of r we can now use the remaining equations (15) to determine successively $c_1, c_2, c_3, \ldots$ in terms of c_0.

For $r_1 = \tfrac{1}{2}$, we obtain

$$c_1 = -\frac{c_0}{\frac{3}{2} \cdot \frac{1}{2} + \frac{3}{2} \cdot \frac{3}{2} - \frac{1}{2}} = -\tfrac{2}{5}c_0,$$

$$c_2 = -\frac{c_1}{\frac{5}{2} \cdot \frac{3}{2} + \frac{3}{2} \cdot \frac{5}{2} - \frac{1}{2}} = -\tfrac{1}{7}c_1 = \tfrac{2}{35}c_0, \tag{18}$$

$$c_3 = -\frac{c_2}{\frac{7}{2} \cdot \frac{5}{2} + \frac{3}{2} \cdot \frac{7}{2} - \frac{1}{2}} = -\tfrac{2}{27}c_2 = -\tfrac{4}{945}c_0,$$

$$\vdots$$

For $r_2 = -1$, we obtain

$$c_1 = -\frac{c_0}{-\frac{1}{2}} = 2c_0,$$

$$c_2 = -\frac{c_1}{\frac{3}{2} \cdot 1 - \frac{1}{2}} = -c_1 = -2c_0, \tag{19}$$

$$c_3 = -\frac{c_2}{2 + \frac{3}{2} \cdot 2 - \frac{1}{2}} = -\tfrac{2}{9}c_2 = \tfrac{4}{9}c_0,$$

$$\vdots$$

We thus have the following two solutions, in each of which we have set $c_0 = 1$:

$$u_1 = x^{1/2}[1 - \tfrac{2}{5}x + \tfrac{2}{35}x^2 - \tfrac{4}{925}x^3 + \cdots], \tag{20a}$$

$$u_2 = x^{-1}[1 + 2x - 2x^2 + \tfrac{4}{9}x^3 + \cdots]. \tag{20b}$$

By superposition, the general solution of the differential equation (10) is

$$y = C_1 x^{1/2}[1 - \tfrac{2}{5}x + \tfrac{2}{35}x^2 - \tfrac{4}{925}x^3 + \cdots]$$

$$+ C_2 x^{-1}[1 + 2x - 2x^2 + \tfrac{4}{9}x^3 + \cdots]. \tag{21}$$

From the conditions (15), we first determined two values of r, and then for each such value of r we determined the coefficients $c_1, c_2, c_3, \ldots$ in terms of c_0. The first equation in (15) gave us the indicial equation for the two values of r. By comparing this equation with the differential equation written in the form (11) we see that the values of r in this case depended only upon the constant terms $\frac{3}{2}$ and $-\frac{1}{2}$ which occur in the numerators of two coefficients Q/P and R/P.

The general form of the indicial equation for all functions P, Q, R for which (5) holds is readily found to be

$$r^2 + (\alpha_0 - 1)r + \beta_0 = 0. \tag{22}$$

In the example (11) this indicial equation had two unequal roots leading to the two different series (20a) and (20b). We might expect two such different series solutions whenever the indicial equation has two unequal roots. This is indeed true so long as the difference between r_1 and r_2 is not an integer. If, however, this difference is an integer, then usually (but not always) it turns out that one of the two series solutions does not, in fact, exist. In this case it is necessary, just as in the case $r_1 = r_2$, to obtain a second solution by an extension of the above procedure.

EXERCISES

1. Determine which of the following differential equations have the origin as a regular singular point. Find the roots of the indicial equation for each of those which have the origin as a regular singular point.

(a) $x^2 y'' + 3xy' + (x+1)y = 0$

(b) $x^3 y'' + 3x^2 y' + (x^2 + x + 1)y = 0$

(c) $x^2 y'' + \sin x \cdot y' - 4y = 0$

(d) $x^3 y'' + (\cos 2x - 1)y' + 2(e^x - 1)y = 0$

2. State the nature of the point $x = 0$ for the following differential equations:

(a) $y'' - (\sin^2 x)y = 0$ (b) $x^2 y'' - (\sin^2 x)y = 0$

(c) $x^4 y'' - (\sin^2 x)y = 0$ (d) $x^6 y'' - (\sin^2 x)y = 0$

3. The differential equation

$$\frac{d^2 y}{dx^2} + \frac{1}{x-1}\frac{dy}{dx} + \left(1 + \frac{2}{x-1} + \frac{3}{(x-1)^2}\right)y = 0$$

has the point $x = 1$ as regular singular point. Assuming a solution in the form $y = c_0(x-1)^r + c_1(x-1)^{r+1} + \cdots$, obtain the indicial equation and its roots

4. The equation

$$\frac{d^2 y}{dx^2} + \frac{1}{x(x-1)}\frac{dy}{dx} + y = 0$$

has the points $x = 0$ and $x = 1$ as regular singular points. Obtain the indicial equations corresponding to each of the two points.

Locate and identify the finite singular points of the differential equations of Exercises 5 through 8.

5. $x^2(1 - x^2)^2 y'' + 2x(1 - x)y' - y = 0$

6. $x^3(1 - x)^2 y'' - 2x^2(1 - x)y' + 3y = 0$

7. $x^2 y'' + (1 + 2x)y' = 0$ 8. $x^4 y'' + 2x^3 y' + x^2 y = 0$

Find the first three nonvanishing terms of each of the two solutions of the form

$$c_0 x^r + c_1 x^{r+1} + c_2 x^{r+2} + \cdots$$

of the differential equations of Exercises 9 through 12.

9. $2x^2 y'' + xy' - (x + 1)y = 0$

10. $x^2 y'' + xy' + (x^2 - \frac{1}{4})y = 0$

11. $xy'' + 2y' + xy = 0$

12. $xy'' + (c - x)y' - ay = 0$, c not an integer. (This equation is known as the *confluent hypergeometric equation*.)

13. Show that $xy'' + y' + xy = 0$ has *one* solution of the form $y = c_0 + c_1 x + \cdots$ with c_0 (but not c_1) arbitrary and obtain this solution.

14. Show that Legendre's differential equation

$$(1 - x^2)y'' - 2xy' + p(p + 1)y = 0 \tag{a}$$

has the point $x = 1$ as a regular singular point, and obtain the indicial equation for this point of the differential equation.

Hint. Substitute $\xi = x - 1$ and note that the differential equation (a) becomes

$$\frac{d^2 y}{d\xi^2} + \frac{2(\xi + 1)}{\xi^2 + 2\xi} \frac{dy}{d\xi} - \frac{p(p + 1)}{\xi^2 + 2\xi} y = 0. \tag{b}$$

Then use the series developments

$$\frac{2(\xi + 1)}{\xi^2 + 2\xi} = \frac{1}{\xi}\left[1 + \frac{\xi}{2} - \left(\frac{\xi}{2}\right)^2 + \left(\frac{\xi}{2}\right)^3 - \cdots\right],$$

and

$$-\frac{1}{\xi^2 + 2\xi} = -\frac{1}{2\xi}\left[1 - \frac{\xi}{2} + \left(\frac{\xi}{2}\right)^2 - \left(\frac{\xi}{2}\right)^3 + \cdots\right]$$

to show that the point $\xi = 0$ is a regular singular point of the differential equation (b), with indicial equation $r^2 = 0$.

15. Use the results of Exercise 14 to show that Legendre's differential equation (a) has a solution expressible as a Taylor series in powers of $x - 1$:

$$y = c_0 + c_1(x - 1) + c_2(x - 1)^2 + \cdots$$

with c_0 (but not c_1) arbitrary. Determine c_1 and c_2 in terms of c_0.

Hint. The differential equation (b) has a solution expressible in the form $y = c_0 + c_1\xi + c_2\xi^2 + \cdots$ with c_0 arbitrary. (Why?) Use the series given in the hint to Exercise 14 to obtain c_1 and c_2 in terms of c_0.

3–14 More on power-series expansions at a regular singular point. The following example has been constructed in order to clarify further what may happen in connection with power-series solutions at a regular singular point. We consider the equation

$$\frac{d^2y}{dx^2} + \left(a - \frac{2}{x}\right)\frac{dy}{dx} + \left(\frac{b}{x} + \frac{2}{x^2}\right)y = 0, \tag{1}$$

where a and b are constants.

We set

$$y = c_0 x^r + c_1 x^{r+1} + \cdots, \quad c_0 \neq 0, \tag{2}$$

with corresponding expressions for y' and y''. Introduction of (2) into (1) leaves us with the following system of relations for $r, c_0, c_1, \ldots$:

$c_0[r(r-1) - 2r + 2] = 0,$

$c_1[(r+1)r - 2(r+1) + 2] + c_0[ar + b] = 0,$

$c_2[(r+2)(r+1) - 2(r+2) + 2] + c_1[a(r+1) + b] = 0, \tag{3}$

$\vdots$

$c_n[(r+n)(r+n-1) - 2(r+n) + 2] + c_{n-1}[a(r+n-1) + b] = 0.$

$\vdots$

The indicial equation, which allows c_0 to be arbitrary, is

$$r^2 - 3r + 2 = 0, \tag{4}$$

with roots

$$r_1 = 2, \quad r_2 = 1. \tag{5}$$

We see that these roots differ by an integer, so that difficulties may be expected.

Consider next the *second* of Eqs. (3), which may be written in the form

$$c_1[r^2 - r] + c_0[ar + b] = 0. \tag{6}$$

We see that when $r = r_1 = 2$, then c_1 may always be expressed in terms of c_0. Inspection of the *remaining* equations in (3) shows that when $r = 2$ *all* coefficients c_n may successively be determined in terms of c_0.

This means that we have always one solution of the differential equation (1), which we may designate by u_1, of the form

$$u_1 = x^2 - (a + \tfrac{1}{2}b)x^3 + \cdots \tag{7}$$

The remaining case, $r = r_2 = 1$, is somewhat less simple. We see that for $r = 1$ the coefficient of c_1 in Eq. (6) vanishes. We now have two possibilities in regard to the coefficient of c_0 in (6). Either

$$a + b \neq 0 \tag{i}$$

or

$$a + b = 0. \tag{ii}$$

When $(a + b) \neq 0$, then Eq. (6), with $r = 1$, requires that $c_0 = 0$. This is not compatible with our initial assumption (2). Accordingly, we do not have a solution of the form (2) corresponding to the second root $r = 1$ of the indicial equation. We have thus confirmed our earlier statement that if the roots of the indicial equation differ by an integer, then there *may* be only one and not two solutions of the form (2).

We now turn to the second possibility, $a + b = 0$. In this case, Eq. (6) with $r = 1$ imposes no condition on either c_0 or c_1. Since c_0 occurs only in the first two relations in (3), we conclude that c_0 is arbitrary. However, c_1 is also arbitrary, since the remaining relations in (3) impose no conditions on c_1. In particular, the third equation in (3) gives us

$$c_2 = -\tfrac{1}{2}ac_1,$$

and the remaining coefficients c_n may successively be determined in terms of c_1. We have then, as a solution of the given differential equation, *so long as $a + b = 0$,*

$$y = c_0x + c_1[x^2 - \tfrac{1}{2}ax^3 + \cdots]. \tag{8}$$

We may note that if $a + b = 0$, the function u_1 given by (7) coincides with the expression in brackets in (8), and we can say that in the exceptional case $a + b = 0$ the solution corresponding to the root $r = 1$ includes the solution corresponding to $r = 2$ and represents the general solution of the given problem.

We now resume consideration of case (i), for which we have so far only the solution u_1. To obtain u_2, we use the method of variation of parameters. We have, according to Eq. (10) of Section 3-9,

$$u_2 = u_1 \int \frac{e^{-\int (Q/P)dx}}{u_1^2} \, dx = u_1 \int \frac{e^{-\int [a - 2/x]dx}}{u_1^2} \, dx \tag{9}$$

$$= u_1 \int \frac{x^2 e^{-ax} \, dx}{[x^2 - (a + \tfrac{1}{2}b)x^3 + \cdots]^2} = u_1 \int \frac{e^{-ax} \, dx}{x^2[1 - (a + \tfrac{1}{2}b)x + \cdots]^2}.$$

We now introduce for e^{-ax} and also for $[1 - (a + \frac{1}{2}b)x + \cdots]^{-2}$ their Taylor series. Therewith

$$u_2 = u_1 \int x^{-2}[1 - ax + \frac{1}{2}a^2x^2 + \cdots][1 + 2(a + \frac{1}{2}b)x + \cdots]\,dx$$

or

$$u_2 = u_1 \int [x^{-2} + (a + b)x^{-1} + \alpha_0 + \alpha_1 x + \cdots]\,dx,$$

where the coefficients α_n are constants which may be expressed in terms of the constants a and b. We now integrate term by term and obtain

$$u_2(x) = u_1(x)[-x^{-1} + (a + b)\ln x + \alpha_0 x + \frac{1}{2}\alpha_1 x^2 + \cdots]$$

or

$$u_2(x) = (a + b)u_1(x)\ln x + \beta_1 x + \beta_2 x^2 + \cdots, \tag{10}$$

where $\beta_1, \beta_2, \ldots$ are constants which may be obtained by multiplying the series (7) for u_1 into the part of u_2 which is free of the logarithm.

We add the following remarks. (a) Note that the logarithmic term in u_2 cancels out when $a + b = 0$. This is in accordance with the result expressed by Eq. (8). (b) Note that the part of the solution having a logarithmic term is, in fact, more complicated than an expression of the form (9) of Section 3–13.

EXERCISES

1. Show that $y = c_1x + c_2 \ln x$ is the general solution of the differential equation $(\ln x - 1)y'' - x^{-1}y' + x^{-2}y = 0$. Is $x = 0$ a regular singular point of the differential equation?

2. Given the differential equation

$$\frac{d^2y}{dx^2} + \left(\alpha + \frac{\beta}{x} + \frac{\gamma}{x^2}\right)y = 0.$$

(a) Show that the roots of the indicial equation differ by an integer whenever $\gamma = \frac{1}{4}(1 - m^2)$, where m is an arbitrary integer. (b) If $\gamma = \frac{1}{4}(1 - m^2)$, with m a positive integer, show that the smaller one of the two roots of the indicial equation makes equal to zero both the coefficient of c_0 in the first recurrence relation and the coefficient of c_m in the $(m + 1)$st recurrence relation.

3. Obtain a general solution in the form of power series of the equation $y'' + (1 + \frac{3}{16}x^{-2})y = 0$. (Determine the first three nonvanishing terms in each of the two linearly independent solutions.)

4. Given the equation

$$y'' + (\alpha + \beta x^{-1} - \frac{3}{4}x^{-2})y = 0.$$

Show that there is only one solution of the form $c_0x^r + c_1x^{r+1} + \cdots$, $c_0 \neq 0$, unless $\beta^2 + \alpha = 0$. When $\beta^2 + \alpha = 0$, show that the smaller of the two roots of the indicial equation leads to a general solution of the differential equation. What is the form of this general solution?

5. Given that $y'' - y' + x^{-1}y = 0$ has the solution $u_1 = x$, find u_2 by the method of variation of parameters in the form $x \ln |x| + v_2$ and expand v_2 in a series in powers of x.

6. Given that $y(x)$ satisfies a differential equation

$$y'' + (a_0 + a_1 x + \cdots)y' + (b_0 + b_1 x + \cdots)y = 0.$$

Show that the differential equation satisfied by $z(\xi) = y(x)$ with $x = \xi^k$ is

$$\frac{d^2 z}{d\xi^2} + \frac{1 - k + k\xi^k(a_0 + a_1\xi^k + \cdots)}{\xi}\frac{dz}{d\xi} + \frac{k^2\xi^{2k}(b_0 + b_1\xi^k + \cdots)}{\xi^2}z = 0.$$

For what values of k is the point $\xi = 0$ a regular singular point of the differential equation for z and for what values of k is it an ordinary point?

3–15 Bessel's differential equation of the zeroth order. Bessel functions of the first kind.

In this section and the next we consider the series solutions of Bessel's differential equation

$$\frac{d^2 y}{dx^2} + \frac{1}{x}\frac{dy}{dx} + y = 0. \tag{1}$$

The indicial equation (22) of Section 3–13 becomes here

$$r^2 = 0, \tag{2}$$

and we have an example in which the two roots r_1 and r_2 are equal. By Section 3–13, since $r_1 = 0$, we know that one solution is of the form

$$u_1 = c_0 + c_1 x + c_2 x^2 + \cdots \tag{3}$$

Inserting this into (1), we find that c_0 (but not c_1!) is arbitrary and that the remaining coefficients satisfy the following system of equations

$$c_1 = 0, \quad (2 \cdot 1 + 2)c_2 + c_0 = 0, \quad (3 \cdot 2 + 3)c_3 + c_1 = 0,$$

$$(4 \cdot 3 + 4)c_4 + c_2 = 0, \quad (5 \cdot 4 + 5)c_5 + c_3 = 0, \ldots$$

It is seen that we have

$$c_1 = c_3 = \cdots = 0 \tag{5}$$

and that the coefficients with even subscripts all obey the recurrence relation

$$n^2 c_n + c_{n-2} = 0, \quad n = 2, 4, 6, \ldots \tag{6}$$

From this,

$$c_2 = \frac{-c_0}{2^2}, \quad c_4 = \frac{c_0}{2^2 \cdot 4^2}, \quad c_6 = \frac{-c_0}{2^2 \cdot 4^2 \cdot 6^2}, \cdots,$$

$$c_{2n} = \frac{(-1)^n c_0}{2^{2n}(n!)^2}, \cdots \quad (7)$$

These conditions lead us to a particular solution u_1 which, with $c_0 = 1$, is given by

$$u_1 = 1 - \frac{1}{(1!)^2}\left(\frac{x}{2}\right)^2 + \frac{1}{(2!)^2}\left(\frac{x}{2}\right)^4 - \frac{1}{(3!)^2}\left(\frac{x}{2}\right)^6 + \cdots \quad (8a)$$

The function u_1 is called *Bessel's function of the first kind and of the zeroth order* and is customarily denoted by $J_0(x)$. We may write

$$J_0(x) = \sum_{n=0}^{\infty} \frac{(-1)^n}{(n!)^2}\left(\frac{x}{2}\right)^{2n}. \quad (8b)$$

The reason for calling the solution (8b) a Bessel function of the zeroth order is the following. Equation (1) is a special case of the more general equation

$$\frac{d^2y}{dx^2} + \frac{1}{x}\frac{dy}{dx} + \left(1 - \frac{p^2}{x^2}\right)y = 0, \quad (9)$$

which is also of importance for the applications. To distinguish between the solutions of this equation for different values of p, it is customary to call the corresponding solutions of this equation *Bessel functions of the pth order*.

EXERCISES

1. By differentiation of the differential equation for Bessel functions of order zero,

$$\frac{d^2y}{dx^2} + \frac{1}{x}\frac{dy}{dx} + y = 0,$$

show that $J_0'(x)$ satisfies Bessel's differential equation (9) with $p = 1$.

2. (a) Obtain a solution for the differential equation

$$y'' + x^{-1}y' - y = 0$$

in the form

$$1 + c_1x + c_2x^2 + \cdots$$

(b) The solution obtained in (a) is usually designated by $I_0(x)$ and is called the *modified Bessel function* of the zeroth order. Show that

$$I_0(x) = J_0(ix).$$

3. Show that $y = J_0(kx)$, where k is any constant, satisfies $y'' + x^{-1}y' + k^2y = 0$.

4. Obtain a solution of $y'' + x^{-1}y' + (1 - x^{-2})y = 0$ in the form $y = \frac{1}{2}x + c_1x^2 + c_2x^3 + \cdots$. This function is designated as $J_1(x)$. Show that $J_1(x) = -J_0'(x)$.

5. Show that the substitution $y(x) = x^{-1/2}u(x)$ reduces Bessel's equation (9) to the form $u'' + [1 + (\frac{1}{4} - p^2)x^{-2}]u = 0$. Use this fact to solve Bessel's equation of order $\frac{1}{2}$.

3–16 A second solution of Bessel's equation.

We now obtain a second particular solution of Bessel's differential equation of the zeroth order, $y'' + x^{-1}y' + y = 0$. We know that if $u_1(x)$ is a particular solution of the differential equation $Py'' + Qy' + Ry = 0$, then a second solution is given by

$$u_2(x) = u_1(x) \int \frac{e^{-\int(Q/P)dx}}{u_1^2} \, dx. \tag{1}$$

For the zeroth-order Bessel equation with the particular solution $u_1 = J_0(x)$, this means that a second solution is given by

$$u_2(x) = J_0(x) \int \frac{e^{-\int(dx/x)}}{[J_0(x)]^2} \, dx = J_0(x) \int \frac{dx}{x[J_0(x)]^2}. \tag{2}$$

To see what type of series expansion to expect for u_2 we proceed as follows.

By an appropriate application of the binomial theorem, we have

$$\frac{1}{[J_0(x)]^2} = \frac{1}{[1 - (\frac{1}{4}x^2 - \frac{1}{64}x^4 + \cdots)]^2}$$

$$= 1 + 2(\frac{1}{4}x^2 - \frac{1}{64}x^4 + \cdots) + 3(\frac{1}{4}x^2 - \frac{1}{64}x^4 + \cdots)^2 + \cdots \tag{3}$$

Combining like powers of x, we obtain, with suitable coefficients α_n,

$$\frac{1}{[J_0(x)]^2} = 1 + \alpha_2x^2 + \alpha_4x^4 + \cdots \tag{4}$$

We put (4) into (2) and have

$$u_2(x) = J_0(x) \int (x^{-1} + \alpha_2x + \alpha_4x^3 + \cdots) \, dx$$

$$= J_0(x) [\ln x + \tfrac{1}{2}\alpha_2x^2 + \tfrac{1}{4}\alpha_4x^4 + \cdots]. \tag{5}$$

We see that u_2 is of the form $J_0(x) \ln x$ plus a product of two Taylor series in x. This means that if we introduce suitable new coefficients β_n, we may write

$$u_2(x) = J_0(x) \ln x + \beta_2x^2 + \beta_4x^4 + \cdots \tag{6}$$

In practice, the above procedure is used only to give us the *form* of the second particular solution. The values of the coefficients β_n are more conveniently obtained by direct substitution of (6) in the differential equation $y'' + x^{-1}y' + y = 0$. To this end, we calculate

$$u_2' = x^{-1}J_0(x) + \ln x \, J_0'(x) + 2\beta_2 x + 4\beta_4 x^3 + \cdots,$$

$$u_2'' = -x^{-2}J_0(x) + 2x^{-1}J_0'(x) + \ln x \, J_0''(x) + 2\beta_2 + 4 \cdot 3\beta_4 x^2 + \cdots \quad (7)$$

Setting $u_2'' + x^{-1}u_2' + u_2 = 0$ and rearranging terms slightly, we have then

$$\ln x \{J_0'' + x^{-1}J_0' + J_0\} + 2x^{-1}J_0'(x) + \{2\beta_2 + 4 \cdot 3\beta_4 x^2 + \cdots\}$$

$$+ x^{-1}\{2\beta_2 x + 4\beta_4 x^3 + \cdots\} + \{\beta_2 x^2 + \beta_4 x^4 + \cdots\} = 0. \quad (8)$$

The term multiplying $\ln x$ vanishes, since J_0 is a solution of the given differential equation. Regrouping the remainder of (8) according to ascending powers of x, we are left with the following relation:

$$(2 + 2)\beta_2 + (3 \cdot 4\beta_4 + 4\beta_4 + \beta_2)x^2 + \cdots$$

$$+ [(2n - 1)2n\beta_{2n} + 2n\beta_{2n} + \beta_{2n-2}]x^{2n-2} + \cdots = -\frac{2}{x}J_0'(x)$$

$$= 1 - \frac{2 \cdot 4}{4 \cdot 16}x^2 + \cdots + \frac{2(-1)^{n+1}2n}{(n!)^2 2^{2n}}x^{2n-2} + \cdots \quad (9)$$

From this, we obtain immediately

$$4\beta_2 = 1, \qquad 16\beta_4 + \beta_2 = -\tfrac{1}{8}, \quad (10)$$

and the general relation for the coefficients β_{2n} may be written

$$(2n)^2\beta_{2n} + \beta_{2n-2} = \frac{(-1)^{n+1}n}{(n!)^2 \, 2^{2n-2}}, \qquad n = 2, 3, \ldots \quad (11)$$

To see what the general form of the coefficient β_{2n} might be, let us calculate a few of them. From (10),

$$\beta_2 = \tfrac{1}{4}, \quad (12a)$$

$$\beta_4 = \tfrac{1}{16}(-\tfrac{1}{8} - \tfrac{1}{4}) = -\tfrac{1}{16} \cdot \tfrac{1}{4}(\tfrac{1}{2} + 1). \quad (12b)$$

From (11),

$$\beta_6 = \tfrac{1}{36}[\tfrac{3}{36 \cdot 16} + \tfrac{1}{16} \cdot \tfrac{1}{4}(\tfrac{1}{2} + 1)] = \tfrac{1}{36} \cdot \tfrac{1}{16} \cdot \tfrac{1}{4}(\tfrac{1}{3} + \tfrac{1}{2} + 1). \quad (12c)$$

From this sequence of formulas, we might guess that the general term β_{2n} is of the form

$$\beta_{2n} = \frac{(-1)^{n+1}}{(2n)^2(2n-2)^2(2n-4)^2\cdots 2^2}\left(\frac{1}{n} + \frac{1}{n-1} + \cdots + \frac{1}{2} + 1\right)$$

$$= \frac{(-1)^{n+1}}{2^{2n}(n!)^2}\left(\frac{1}{n} + \frac{1}{n-1} + \cdots + \frac{1}{2} + 1\right). \tag{12d}$$

The correctness of this result may be seen by direct substitution in (11).

With (12), our particular solution u_2 as written in (6) is now determined. It happens that a linear combination of this u_2 and of $u_1 = J_0$ is generally taken as the second particular solution. This linear combination is denoted by $Y_0(x)$ and is called Bessel's function of the *second kind* and of zeroth order. It is of the form

$$Y_0(x) = \frac{2}{\pi}[u_2(x) + (\gamma - \ln 2)J_0(x)]$$

$$= \frac{2}{\pi}\left[\left(\ln\frac{x}{2} + \gamma\right)J_0(x)\right. \tag{13}$$

$$\left. + \left\{\frac{x^2}{2^2} - \left(\frac{1}{2}+1\right)\frac{x^4}{2^4(2!)^2} + \left(\frac{1}{3}+\frac{1}{2}+1\right)\frac{x^6}{2^6(3!)^2} - \cdots\right\}\right].$$

In (13) the quantity γ is a number, called Euler's constant, which is defined as follows:

$$\gamma = \lim_{n\to\infty}\left(\frac{1}{n} + \frac{1}{n-1} + \cdots + \frac{1}{2} + 1 - \ln n\right) = 0.5772\ldots \tag{14}$$

Both the function J_0 and the function Y_0 have been tabulated. The nature of their dependence on x may be seen from Fig. 3–1. We note in particular the wavy nature of the graphs of the two functions and the fact that $Y_0(x)$ becomes logarithmically infinite as x approaches zero.

The general solution of the zeroth-order Bessel equation (1) of Section 3–15, with two arbitrary constants C_1 and C_2, is now

$$y = C_1 J_0(x) + C_2 Y_0(x). \tag{15}$$

The properties of the functions $J_0(x)$ and $Y_0(x)$ have been studied in great detail. For purposes of the applications, J_0 and Y_0 are often used in ways which are similar to the way in which the solutions $\cos x$ and $\sin x$ of the equation $y'' + y = 0$ are used.

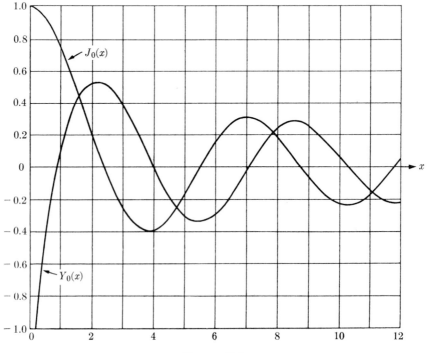

FIGURE 3–1

EXERCISES

1. Express the solution of the differential equation

$$y'' + x^{-1}y' + \lambda^2 y = 0,$$

where λ^2 is a constant, in terms of Bessel functions. Obtain a transcendental equation determining possible values of λ such that y satisfies the two conditions

(a) $y'(0) = 0, \quad y(1) = 0$ (b) $y(\tfrac{1}{2}) = 0, \quad y(1) = 0$

2. By reference to Exercise 7 in Section 3–3 show that when $0 < x$ the Wronskian

$$W = J_0(x)Y_0'(x) - J_0'(x)Y_0(x)$$

must be of the form cx^{-1}. Determine the value of the constant c by considering, with the help of the series in Eq. (13) and in Eq. (8) of the preceding section, the form of W as x approaches zero.

3. Obtain a solution of $y'' + x^{-1}y' + y = 0$ in the interval $0 < a < x$ which satisfies the conditions $y(a) = y_a, y'(a) = y_a'$.

4. By making the changes of variables $\xi = \lambda x^b$, $y(\xi) = x^{-a}z(x)$ in the differential equation

$$y''(\xi) + \xi^{-1}y'(\xi) + y(\xi) = 0,$$

show that

$$z = c_1 x^a J_0(\lambda x^b) + c_2 x^a Y_0(\lambda x^b),$$

where a, b and λ are constants, is the general solution of

$$\frac{d^2z}{dx^2} + \frac{1 - 2a}{x}\frac{dz}{dx} + \frac{a^2 + \lambda^2 b^2 x^{2b}}{x^2} z = 0.$$

5. Derive the particular solution

$$y_p = \frac{\pi}{2} Y_0(x) \int_0^x \xi^m J_0(\xi) \, d\xi + \frac{\pi}{2} J_0(x) \int_x^c \xi^m Y_0(\xi) \, d\xi$$

for the nonhomogeneous differential equation

$$y''(x) + x^{-1}y'(x) + y(x) = x^{m-1}.$$

MISCELLANEOUS EXERCISES. CHAPTER 3

In Exercises 1 through 4 determine a second-order differential equation with the solution indicated

1. (a) $y = c_1 e^x + c_2 e^{2x}$ (b) $y = c_1 \cos x + c_2 \sin x$

    (c) $y = c_1 \cos (x + c_2)$ (d) $y = c_1 \cos (x + c_2) + 3$

    (e) $y = c_1 e^{2x} + c_2 e^{3x} + 2x + 4$ (f) $y = c_1 e^{2x} + c_2 x e^{2x} + x^2$

2. (a) $y^3 = c_1 + c_2 x$ (b) $y = x^4 + c_1 x^2 + c_2$

    (c) $y = (c_1 + c_2 x^2)e^x$ (d) $y = c_1 e^x + c_2 e^{1/x}$

3. (a) $y = c_1 x + c_2 x^2$ (b) $y^2 = c_1 x + c_2 x^2$

4. $y = c_1 \cos x + c_2 \cos 2x$

Solve the following differential equations:

5. $yy'' + (y')^2 = 1$ 6. $y'' + y = \csc x$

7. $x^2 y'' + (y')^2 = 0$ 8. $y'' - 2(1 + i)y' + 2iy = 0$

9. $x^2 y'' - 2xy' + 2y = 0$ 10. $x^2 y'' + 3xy' + y = 0$

11. $x^2 y'' - 3xy' + 3y = 0$

12. $x^2 y'' - 2xy' + 2y = x^n$ $(n \neq 1, n \neq 2)$

13. $x^2 y'' - nxy' + ny = 0$ 14. $x^2 y'' + xy' + 4y = 0$

15. $y'' + y = 2e^{-x} + 3x$ 16. $y'' - 2y' + y = 2e^x + x$

17. $y'' - 5y' + 4y = 2xe^x + 3e^x + x^2$

18. $y'' + y = 2 \sin 2x + e^x$

19. $y'' + y = 2 \sin x + e^{2x}$

20. $2x^2y'' + 2xy' - y = 1$

21. $y'' = x(y')^3$

22. $(1 - x^2)y'' - xy' = 0$

23. $y'' + y = \cot x$

24. $y'' + 4y = \csc 2x$

25. $y'' + 3y' + 2y = \sin e^x$

26. $y'' + y' - 2y = 3 \ln x$

27. $x^2y'' + 3xy' + 2y = \ln x$

28. $y'' - y' = 3x^2 + 2e^x - e^{-x} + 5$

29. $x^2y'' - 2xy' + 2y = 3x^2$

30. $xy'' + 4x(y')^2 - y' = 0$

31. $xy'' + y' = 2x$

32. $xy'' + y' = x^2 + 3$

33. $y'' - xy' + y = 0$

34. $yy'' - y^2y' - (y')^2 = 0$

In Exercises 35 through 38 solve the differential equations with the given initial conditions.

35. $y'' + 2xy'^2 = 0;$ $y(0) = 0,\ y'(0) = 1$

36. $y'' + 2xy'^2 = 0;$ $y(0) = 0,\ y'(0) = -1$

37. $xy'' + 2y' = 4x^2;$ $y(1) = 0,\ y'(1) = 1$

38. $y'' - 2y' + y = 0;$ $y(0) = 1,\ y'(0) = 0$

39. Solve the differential equation $xy'' + ny' = f(x)$ for

(a) $n = 1,\ f(x) = x^3$, (b) $n = 2,\ f(x) = e^x/x$, (c) $n = -1,\ f(x) = 0$.

40. Obtain a second-order linear differential equation satisfied by $z = f[g(s)]$, where g is a given function and $y = f(x)$ satisfies the equation

$$y'' + 2ay' + by = 0.$$

41. Given that

$$\left(\frac{z}{h}\right)'' - \frac{g''}{g'}\left(\frac{z}{h}\right)' - (g')^2\frac{z}{h} = 0$$

has the solution $z = [c_1 \cosh g(s) + c_2 \sinh g(s)]h(s)$. What are the coefficients $p(s)$ and $q(s)$ in the equation $z'' + pz' + qz = 0$ with the same solution?

42. By reference to the preceding exercise obtain the solution of

$$\frac{d^2z}{ds^2} + \frac{2m - n + 1}{s}\frac{dz}{ds} + \left[\frac{(n - 3m)m}{s^2} - n^2\lambda^2s^{2n-2}\right]z = 0.$$

43. Determine a constant α so that the differential equation

$$x^3y'' + 2xy' - y = 12x^4 + \alpha x^2 + 2x - 7$$

has a particular solution of the form $y = ax^3 + bx^2 + cx + d$, where $a, b, c,$ and d are constants. For this value of α determine the values of $a, b, c,$ and d.

44. Show that the differential equation $xy'' - (x + 2)y' + 2y = 0$ has a solution of the form $y = ax^2 + bx + c$. Determine $a, b,$ and c and use this result to obtain the general solution.

45. Show that $y = J_0(2ix)$ is a solution of the differential equation

$$x^2 y'' + xy' - 4x^2 y = 0.$$

46. Show that

$$[xJ_1(x)]' = xJ_0(x).$$

In Exercises 47 and 48 show that the function indicated is a particular solution of the given differential equation, and use that fact to solve the differential equation.

47. $(1 + x^2)y'' - 2xy' + 2y = 0;$ $y = x$

48. $xy'' + 2y' - xy = 0;$ $y = e^x/x$

49. Use the result of Exercise 48 to solve the differential equation

$$xy'' + 2y' - xy = x^3 - 6x.$$

Solve Exercises 50 through 56 by means of series of the form

$$y = c_0 + c_1 x + c_2 x^2 + \cdots,$$

with c_0 and c_2 arbitrary in Exercise 50, and c_0 and c_1 arbitrary in each of the other exercises. In Exercises 50 and 51 check your series solution by obtaining an exact solution.

50. $xy'' - (x + 1)y' + y = 0$ 51. $(1 + x^2)y'' + xy' - y = 0$

52. $y'' - (1 + x^2)y = 0$ 53. $y'' + xy' + y = 0$

54. $y'' + y' + xy = 0$ 55. $(x + 2)y'' + xy' - y = 0$

56. $y'' + x^2 y' + xy = 0$

Find the first three nonvanishing terms of each of the two solutions of the form

$$y = c_0 x^r + c_1 x^{r+1} + c_2 x^{r+2} + \cdots$$

of the differential equations of Exercises 57 through 61.

57. $4xy'' + 2y' + y = 0$ 58. $5xy'' + y' + 2y = 0$

59. $2xy'' + y' - 2xy = 0$ 60. $x^2 y'' + x^2 y' - 2y = 0$

61. $2xy'' + y' - 2x(1 + x^2)y = 0$

Solve Exercises 62 and 63 by means of series of the form

$$y = c_0 + c_1(x - 1) + c_2(x - 1)^2 + \cdots$$

In Exercise 62 check your result by obtaining an exact solution.

62. $y'' + y = 0;$ $y(1) = 1,\ y'(1) = 0$

63. $y'' = x + y^2;$ $y(1) = 1,\ y'(1) = 2$

64. Solve

$$x^2 y'' - 3xy' + (2 + x)y = 0; \qquad y(2) = 0, \ y'(2) = 1$$

by means of a series of the form

$$y = c_0 + c_1(x - 2) + c_2(x - 2)^2 + \cdots$$

65. Reduce $x^{q+2}y'' = f(x^{q+1}y', x^q y)$ by the substitutions $x^q y(x) = z(t)$, $t = \ln x$ to a differential equation for z in which the independent variable t does not occur explicitly.

CHAPTER 4

HIGHER-ORDER DIFFERENTIAL EQUATIONS

4-1 Introduction. In this chapter we shall concern ourselves with the class of differential equations of the form

$$y^{(n)} = f(x, y, y', \ldots, y^{(n-1)}) \tag{1}$$

or with equations readily reducible to this form. While the solution of such nth-order equations for $n > 2$ will generally be more laborious than solutions of second- or first-order equations, the *methods* which may be employed are frequently rather direct extensions of the methods used in connection with second-order equations. This is particularly so for linear differential equations of the nth order.

To see what generality to expect from a solution $y = y(x)$ of the nth-order equation (1), let us make the following observation. If we select some fixed point $x = x_0$, it appears that we may, in general, preassign arbitrarily the values of the n quantities $y(x_0), y'(x_0), \ldots, y^{(n-1)}(x_0)$, and Eq. (1) then furnishes the value of $y^{(n)}(x_0)$. For example, in

$$y''' = 1 - xyy' - 2(y'')^2 \tag{2}$$

we may choose $x_0 = 1$ and assign

$$y(1) = \tfrac{1}{2}, \qquad y'(1) = 2, \qquad y''(1) = 3, \tag{3}$$

and then the differential equation gives the value of $y'''(1)$ as

$$y'''(1) = -18. \tag{4}$$

It is customary to designate a set of conditions of the form

$$y(x_0) = y_0, \quad y'(x_0) = y_0', \quad \ldots, \quad y^{(n-1)}(x_0) = y_0^{(n-1)}, \tag{5}$$

where $y_0, y_0', \ldots, y_0^{(n-1)}$ are given quantities, as *initial conditions* for the nth-order differential equation (1). As an example, Eqs. (3) are a set of initial conditions for the differential equation (2).

The same set (3) of initial conditions is evidently not admissible if we modify the differential equation (2) to read

$$y''' = \sqrt{1 - xyy' - 2(y'')^2} \tag{6}$$

145

and require that y be a real-valued function. In this sense, we must always restrict ourselves to sets of initial conditions which are compatible with the given differential equation.

Just as in the case of the second-order equation $y'' = f(x, y, y')$, there is a general existence and uniqueness theorem for the nth-order equation (1), where f is a function of $n + 1$ real variables $x, y, z_1, \ldots, z_{n-1}$ which is defined and continuous in a region R of $(x, y, z_1, \ldots, z_{n-1})$-space, and which is such that the partial derivatives $\partial f/\partial y$, $\partial f/\partial z_1, \ldots, \partial f/\partial z_{n-1}$ are also continuous in R. Under these conditions the theorem guarantees for every $(x_0, y_0, y_0', \ldots, y_0^{(n-1)})$ in R the existence of a unique solution $y = y(x)$ which satisfies the initial conditions (5). This solution is defined in some x-interval containing x_0.

With this in mind, we now define the concept of a general solution of $y^{(n)} = f(x, y, y', \ldots, y^{(n-1)})$. We shall call $y = g(x; c_1, c_2, \ldots, c_n)$ the general solution of this equation in some x-interval if it contains all solutions in this interval.

To illustrate, the differential equation

$$y''' = 0 \tag{7}$$

has the solution

$$y = c_1 + c_2 x + c_3 x^2 \tag{8}$$

and this is its general solution, since we know from the fundamental theorem of integral calculus that all solutions of (7) will be of the form (8).

As a further illustration, observe that Eq. (2) satisfies all the conditions necessary for the validity of the existence and uniqueness theorem, for all values of x, y, y', and y''. Consequently any solution which is general enough to allow satisfaction of the condition $y(x_0) = y_0$, $y'(x_0) = y_0'$, $y''(x_0) = y_0''$ for arbitrary x_0, y_0, y_0', y_0'' will be the general solution of (2) in some interval including x_0.

For the sake of defining the notion of general solution, it is customary to deal with the set of initial conditions (5). In practice, conditions referring to *both* endpoints of an interval in which the differential equation is to be solved often occur. In such cases, one speaks of *boundary conditions* rather than of initial conditions.

EXERCISES

Determine the differential equations of lowest order which have the solutions stated in Exercises 1 through 4.

1. $y = x^2 + c_1 + c_2 x + c_3 e^x + c_4 e^{2x}$ 2. $y^2 = c_1 e^x + c_2 x + c_3$

3. $e^y = c_0 + c_1 x + c_2 x^2 + x^3$ 4. $y = x + c_1 e^x + c_2 x^2 + c_3$

5. To every second-order differential equation with solution $c_1u_1(x) + c_2u_2(x)$ corresponds a third-order differential equation with solution $C_1u_1^2 + C_2u_2^2 + C_3u_1u_2$. Determine the third-order equation wich corresponds in this sense to the second-order equation $y'' + y = 0$.

6.
7. Show that the given solutions in Exercises 1 through 4 are general solu-
8. tions.
9.

10. Determine all values of a, b, and c for which the initial conditions $y(1) = a$, $y'(1) = b$, $y''(1) = c$ can be satisfied with the solution of Exercise 4.

4–2 The homogeneous linear differential equation with constant coefficients.

The simplest class of nth-order differential equations is the class of linear, homogeneous equations with constant coefficients:

$$\frac{d^n y}{dx^n} + a_1 \frac{d^{n-1} y}{dx^{n-1}} + \cdots + a_{n-1} \frac{dy}{dx} + a_n y = 0. \tag{1}$$

Equation (1) evidently has solutions of the form e^{rx}, for suitable values of r. Introducing e^{rx} into (1) and dividing out the common factor e^{rx}, we are left with the algebraic equation

$$r^n + a_1 r^{n-1} + \cdots + a_{n-1} r + a_n = 0. \tag{2}$$

Equation (2) is called the *auxiliary equation* of the differential equation (1). The polynomial on the left of (2) is equivalent to a product of n linear factors, and Eq. (2) is then equivalent to

$$(r - r_1)(r - r_2) \cdots (r - r_{n-1})(r - r_n) = 0. \tag{3}$$

The constants r_k are the roots of the auxiliary equation (2).

If these roots are all distinct, then we have n distinct solutions $e^{r_1 x}$, $e^{r_2 x}, \ldots, e^{r_n x}$ of the differential equation (1).

Since the superposition principle which we proved for second-order linear differential equations also holds for nth-order linear equations,

$$y = c_1 e^{r_1 x} + c_2 e^{r_2 x} + \cdots + c_n e^{r_n x} \tag{4}$$

is also a solution.

To see whether (4) is the general solution, we consider the initial value problem

$$y^{(m)}(x_0) = y_0^{(m)}, \qquad m = 0, \ldots, n - 1, \tag{5}$$

where the quantities $y_0^{(m)}$ are arbitrarily prescribed. Introduction of (4) into (5) leads to the following system of simultaneous linear equations for the constant coefficients c_m:

$$
\begin{aligned}
c_1 e^{r_1 x_0} \quad &+ \cdots + c_n e^{r_n x_0} \quad = y_0, \\
c_1 r_1 e^{r_1 x_0} \quad &+ \cdots + c_n r_n e^{r_n x_0} \quad = y_0', \\
&\vdots \\
c_1 r_1^{n-1} e^{r_1 x_0} &+ \cdots + c_n r_n^{n-1} e^{r_n x_0} = y_0^{(n-1)}.
\end{aligned} \tag{6}
$$

A necessary and sufficient condition for the solvability of (6) with arbitrary terms on the right is that the determinant

$$
\Delta \equiv
\begin{vmatrix}
1 & 1 & \cdots & 1 \\
r_1 & r_2 & \cdots & r_n \\
r_1^2 & r_2^2 & \cdots & r_n^2 \\
\vdots & & & \\
r_1^{n-1} & r_2^{n-1} & \cdots & r_n^{n-1}
\end{vmatrix} \tag{7}
$$

have a value different from zero. In algebra it is shown that this determinant, which is called Vandermonde's determinant, is different from zero if the r_m are all distinct. If we accept this fact, then we have shown that the solution (4) is the general solution of (1) so long as all the r_m are distinct.

If the roots r_m of (2) are not all distinct, then the solution (4) no longer contains n constants of integration in such a way that the initial conditions (5) can be satisfied. For example, if $r_1 = r_2$, then the part of the solution $c_1 e^{r_1 x} + c_2 e^{r_2 x}$ becomes $(c_1 + c_2)e^{r_1 x}$ and the two constants of integration c_1 and c_2 become one constant of integration $c_1 + c_2$. In the case of the second-order equation, where we had only r_1 and r_2, we found that the solution $c_1 e^{r_1 x} + c_2 e^{r_2 x}$ was replaced by $(c_1 + c_2 x)c^{r_1 x}$. It may be verified by direct substitution that if $r_1 = r_2$ for the nth-order equation (1), this same expression becomes part of the general solution.

We briefly state various other facts relating to the nth-order equation with constants coefficients. If

$$
r_1 = r_2 = \cdots = r_m \tag{8}
$$

is an m-fold root of the auxiliary equation (2), then the first m terms in the general solution (4) must be replaced by

$$
(c_1 + c_2 x + \cdots + c_m x^{m-1})e^{r_1 x}.
$$

We prove this in Section 4–8.

The roots r_m may be complex numbers. If the coefficients a_k are real, then all nonreal roots occur in conjugate complex pairs $\alpha + i\beta$ and $\alpha - i\beta$. As in the case of the second-order equation, the part of the solution (4) corresponding to two such roots may be written in the alternative form

$$e^{\alpha x}(A \cos \beta x + B \sin \beta x),$$

where A and B are constants of integration. If $\alpha + i\beta$ and $\alpha - i\beta$ are roots of multiplicity m, then we have

$$e^{\alpha x}[(A_1 + A_2 x + \cdots + A_m x^{m-1}) \cos \beta x$$
$$+ (B_1 + B_2 x + \cdots + B_m x^{m-1}) \sin \beta x]$$

as part of our general solution.

EXAMPLE 1. The differential equation

$$y^{(iv)} - 5y'' + 4y = 0$$

has the auxiliary equation

$$r^4 - 5r^2 + 4$$
$$= (r^2 - 1)(r^2 - 4) = (r - 1)(r + 1)(r - 2)(r + 2) = 0.$$

Consequently, the general solution is

$$y = c_1 e^x + c_2 e^{-x} + c_3 e^{2x} + c_4 e^{-2x}.$$

EXAMPLE 2.
$$y^{(iv)} - 2y'' + y = 0,$$
$$r^4 - 2r^2 + 1 = (r^2 - 1)^2 = (r - 1)^2 (r + 1)^2 = 0,$$
$$y = (c_1 + c_2 x)e^x + (c_3 + c_4 x)e^{-x}.$$

EXAMPLE 3.
$$y^{(iv)} + 4a^4 y = 0, \qquad r^4 + 4a^4 = 0,$$
$$r_1 = (1 + i)a, \quad r_2 = (1 - i)a, \quad r_3 = (-1 + i)a, \quad r_4 = (-1 - i)a,$$
$$y = (c_1 \cos ax + c_2 \sin ax)e^{ax} + (c_3 \cos ax + c_4 \sin ax)e^{-ax}.$$

EXAMPLE 4.
$$y^{(iv)} + 2y'' + y = 0,$$
$$r^4 + 2r^2 + 1 = (r^2 + 1)^2 = (r - i)^2 (r + i)^2,$$
$$y = (c_1 + c_2 x) \cos x + (c_3 + c_4 x) \sin x.$$

In each of the foregoing examples the determination of the roots of the auxiliary equation was readily possible in an explicit manner. It is evident, however, that often the most difficult part of the problem will be the determination of the roots of the auxiliary equation. In practice, this will often have to be done by numerical approximation methods.

EXERCISES

Solve the differential equations of Exercises 1 through 12.

1. $y''' + 3y'' + 3y' + y = 0$ 2. $y''' + y = 0$

3. $y''' - y = 0$ 4. $y^{\text{iv}} - k^4 y = 0$

5. $y^{(8)} + k^8 y = 0$ 6. $y^{(\text{iv})} - 2k^2 y'' + k^4 y = 0$

7. $y^{(8)} + 2a^4 y^{(\text{iv})} - y = 0$

8. $y^{\text{iv}} - 4y''' + 6y'' - 4y' + y = 0$

9. $y^{(\text{iv})} + 2a^2 y'' + a^4 y = 0$ 10. $y''' - 6y'' + 11y' - 6y = 0$

11. $y^{(\text{v})} - 6y^{(\text{iv})} - 8y''' + 48y'' + 16y' - 96y = 0$

12. $y^{(\text{v})} - a^2 y''' + y'' - a^2 y = 0$

Determine the fourth-order linear differential equation with constant coefficients with the following roots of the auxiliary equation:

13. $r_1 = 1,$ $r_2 = 2,$ $r_3 = 3,$ $r_4 = 4$

14. $r_1 = \frac{1}{2},$ $r_2 = \frac{3}{2},$ $r_3 = -\frac{1}{2} + i,$ $r_4 = -\frac{1}{2} - i$

15. $r_1 = -0.35,$ $r_2 = -0.83,$ $r_3 = 0.25 + 0.70i,$ $r_4 = 0.25 - 0.70i$

16. Show that the substitution $x = e^t$ reduces the equidimensional equation $x^n y^{(n)} + a_1 x^{n-1} y^{(n-1)} + \cdots + a_n y = 0$ to a differential equation with constant coefficients.

4–3 The nth-order linear differential equation. We now turn to the consideration of the nth-order linear differential equation

$$p_0(x) \frac{d^n y}{dx^n} + p_1(x) \frac{d^{n-1} y}{dx^{n-1}} + \cdots + p_{n-1}(x) \frac{dy}{dx} + p_n(x) y = f(x) \quad (1)$$

and the associated homogeneous equation

$$p_0 y^{(n)} + p_1 y^{(n-1)} + \cdots + p_{n-1} y' + p_n y = 0 \quad (2)$$

in an interval $a < x < b$ in which the variable coefficients p_m are continuous and $p_0 \neq 0$.

Let $u_1, u_2, \ldots, u_m$ be m solutions of the homogeneous equation (2). Then, because of the superposition principle, the linear combination $c_1 u_1 + c_2 u_2 + \cdots + c_m u_m$ also satisfies (2).

Since the general solution of an nth-order differential equation is to contain n constants of integration, we may expect, in analogy to what we encountered for the differential equation with constant coefficients, that the general solution of (2) is of the form

$$y = c_1 u_1 + c_2 u_2 + \cdots + c_n u_n. \tag{3}$$

If this is to be the general solution, the set of particular solutions $u_1, \ldots, u_n$ which occur in (3) must be such that we can solve the initial value problem

$$y^{(m)}(x_0) = y_0^{(m)}, \qquad m = 0, 1, \ldots, n - 1, \tag{4}$$

for given values of $x_0, y_0, \ldots, y_0^{(n-1)}$ with $a < x_0 < b$. (The existence and uniqueness theorem which we have stated in Section 1 guarantees that the solution of (2) and (4) is unique. This means that (3) contains all solutions in (a, b) whenever (4) can be satisfied.)

Introduction of (3) into (4) gives the following system of equations for the determination of the coefficients c_m:

$$
\begin{aligned}
c_1 u_1(x_0) &\quad + \cdots + c_n u_n(x_0) &= y_0, \\
c_1 u_1'(x_0) &\quad + \cdots + c_n u_n'(x_0) &= y_0', \\
&\;\;\vdots \\
c_1 u_1^{(n-1)}(x_0) &+ \cdots + c_n u_n^{(n-1)}(x_0) &= y_0^{(n-1)}.
\end{aligned}
\tag{5}
$$

A necessary and sufficient condition for the solvability of (5) for arbitrarily given values $y_0, \ldots, y_0^{(n-1)}$ is that the determinant

$$
W(x) \equiv
\begin{vmatrix}
u_1(x) & \cdots & u_n(x) \\
u_1'(x) & \cdots & u_n'(x) \\
\vdots & & \\
u_1^{(n-1)}(x) & \cdots & u_n^{(n-1)}(x)
\end{vmatrix}
\tag{6}
$$

have a value different from zero when $x = x_0$.

The determinant $W(x)$ is called the *Wronskian* of the system $u_1(x), \ldots, u_n(x)$.

We do not yet know how to obtain a system $u_1(x), \ldots, u_n(x)$ of particular solutions with the property that $W(x_0) \neq 0$. It can, however, be shown that if $W(x_0) \neq 0$ for a single point x_0 in (a, b) and if $p_0(x) \neq 0$

in (a, b), then $W(x) \neq 0$ throughout the interval (a, b) and consequently the linear combination (3) represents the general solution in the entire interval.

The fact that the Wronskian is different from zero in an interval as soon as it is different from zero at one point x_0 may be illustrated by means of the differential equation with constant coefficients. If $u_m(x) = e^{r_m x}$, then

$$W(x) = e^{(r_1 + r_2 + \cdots + r_n)x} \Delta, \tag{7}$$

where Δ is the determinant defined by Eq. (7) of Section 4–2. We see that if $\Delta \neq 0$, then also $W(x) \neq 0$ for all finite x.

Turning now to the problem of the general solution of the nonhomogeneous equation (1), the following facts may be observed. Let y_p be any particular solution of the nonhomogeneous differential equation. Then, as one may verify by direct substitution, $y_p + c_1 u_1 + \cdots + c_n u_n$ also satisfies this differential equation. Since this expression is sufficiently general to solve the initial value problem so long as $c_1 u_1 + \cdots + c_n u_n$ is the general solution of the homogeneous equation, we have the result that the general solution of the nonhomogeneous equation is

$$y = y_p + c_1 u_1 + \cdots + c_n u_n, \tag{8}$$

where y_p is any particular solution of the given nonhomogeneous equation.

Exercises

Given the solution $y = (c_1 + c_2 x)e^x + (c_3 + c_4 x)e^{-x}$ of the differential equation $y^{\text{iv}} - 2y'' + y = 0$, show that each of the following initial or boundary value problems leads to the determination of the constants of integration c_j:

1. $y(0) = 1, \qquad y'(0) = y''(0) = y'''(0) = 0$
2. $y(0) = 1, \qquad y'(0) = y(1) = y'(1) = 0$

3. Given the solution $y = c_1 \cos kx + c_2 \sin kx + c_3 e^{kx} + c_4 e^{-kx}$ of the differential equation $y^{\text{iv}} - k^4 y = 0$, $k \neq 0$, obtain those exceptional values of k for which the boundary value problem

$$y(0) = 1, \qquad y''(0) = 0, \qquad y(a) = 0, \qquad y''(a) = 0$$

does not have a solution. Show that if the first of the four conditions is replaced by $y(0) = 0$, the resultant *homogeneous* system of boundary conditions leads to a solution $y \neq 0$ if and only if k assumes one of the exceptional values.

4. Calculate the Wronskian for each of the following systems of solutions of the differential equations indicated:

(a) $1, e^x, e^{-x};\quad y''' - y' = 0$ (b) $1, x, e^{-x};\quad y''' + y'' = 0$

(c) $1, x, e^x, e^{-x};\quad y^{(\text{iv})} - y'' = 0$

5. Show that the Wronskian $W(x)$ defined in (6) for the differential equation (2) satisfies the differential equation

$$p_0(x)W' + p_1(x)W = 0.$$

6. Use the result of Exercise 5 to show that if $W(x_0) \neq 0$ for a single point x_0 in (a, b) and if $p_0(x) \neq 0$ in (a, b), then $W(x) \neq 0$ throughout the interval (a, b).

4–4 The method of variation of parameters. Let

$$y_h = c_1 u_1 + \cdots + c_n u_n \tag{1}$$

be the general solution of the homogeneous differential equation

$$p_0 y^{(n)} + p_1 y^{(n-1)} + \cdots + p_{n-1} y' + p_n y = 0. \tag{2}$$

To find the general solution of the nonhomogeneous equation

$$p_0 y^{(n)} + p_1 y^{(n-1)} + \cdots + p_n y = f(x), \tag{3}$$

one may proceed as follows, in extension of what was done earlier for second-order differential equations.

Write

$$y = C_1(x)u_1 + \cdots + C_n(x)u_n. \tag{4}$$

Then

$$y' = C_1 u_1' + \cdots + C_n u_n' + C_1' u_1 + \cdots + C_n' u_n. \tag{5}$$

As a first condition on the n functions C_m, set

$$C_1' u_1 + \cdots + C_n' u_n = 0. \tag{6}$$

Having done this, y'' becomes

$$y'' = C_1 u_1'' + \cdots + C_n u_n'' + C_1' u_1' + \cdots + C_n' u_n'. \tag{7}$$

As a second condition on the n functions C_m, set

$$C_1' u_1' + \cdots + C_n' u_n' = 0. \tag{8}$$

Continuing in this way on to the $(n - 1)$st derivative of y, we obtain

$$y^{(m)} = C_1 u_1^{(m)} + \cdots + C_n u_n^{(m)}, \qquad m = 0, 1, \ldots, n - 1, \tag{9}$$

with the following set of conditions on the unknown functions $C_1, \ldots, C_n$:

$$C_1' u_1^{(m-1)} + \cdots + C_n' u_n^{(m-1)} = 0, \qquad m = 1, \ldots, n - 1. \tag{10}$$

Finally, we have

$$y^{(n)} = C_1 u_1^{(n)} + \cdots + C_n u_n^{(n)} + C_1' u_1^{(n-1)} + \cdots + C_n' u_n^{(n-1)}. \quad (11)$$

We now introduce (9) and (11) into the differential equation (2). The resulting equation may be written in the form

$$C_1(x)[p_0 u_1^{(n)} + \cdots + p_{n-1} u_1' + p_n u_1]$$

$$+ C_2(x)[p_0 u_2^{(n)} + \cdots + p_{n-1} u_2' + p_n u_2] + \cdots$$

$$+ C_n(x)[p_0 u_n^{(n)} + \cdots + p_{n-1} u_n' + p_n u_n]$$

$$+ p_0(x)[C_1' u_1^{(n-1)} + \cdots + C_n' u_n^{(n-1)}] = f(x). \quad (12)$$

Since the functions u_m are solutions of the homogeneous equation (1), everything except the last line in (12) vanishes and we are left with the relation

$$p_0(x)[C_1' u_1^{(n-1)} + \cdots + C_n' u_n^{(n-1)}] = f(x). \quad (13)$$

Equation (13), together with the $n - 1$ equations (10), is seen to be a system of n simultaneous linear equations for the n functions C_m'.

After division of (13) by $p_0(x)$ (here we use the fact that $p_0(x) \neq 0$), the determinant of the system is the Wronskian $W(x)$ defined in (6) of Section 4–3. Since we know that the Wronskian does not vanish in this case, we are sure that Eqs. (10) and (13) may be used to obtain the functions C_m'. Having C_m', we find C_m by direct integration and therewith we have the general solution of the given differential equation.

EXAMPLE.

$$y^{\text{iv}} - y = f(x).$$

The general solution of the homogeneous equation is $c_1 e^x + c_2 e^{-x} + c_3 e^{ix} + c_4 e^{-ix}$. Setting

$$y = C_1(x)e^x + C_2(x)e^{-x} + C_3(x)e^{ix} + C_4(x)e^{-ix},$$

Eqs. (10) and (13) provide the following equations for C_1', C_2', C_3', and C_4':

$$C_1' e^x + C_2' e^{-x} + C_3' e^{ix} + C_4' e^{-ix} = 0,$$

$$C_1' e^x - C_2' e^{-x} + iC_3' e^{ix} - iC_4' e^{-ix} = 0,$$

$$C_1' e^x + C_2' e^{-x} - C_3' e^{ix} - C_4' e^{-ix} = 0,$$

$$C_1' e^x - C_2' e^{-x} - iC_3' e^{ix} + iC_4' e^{-ix} = f(x).$$

The determinant of this system is

$$W = \begin{vmatrix} e^x & e^{-x} & e^{ix} & e^{-ix} \\ e^x & -e^{-x} & ie^{ix} & -ie^{-ix} \\ e^x & e^{-x} & -e^{ix} & -e^{-ix} \\ e^x & -e^{-x} & -ie^{ix} & ie^{-ix} \end{vmatrix} = 16i.$$

We shall omit the actual determination of the coefficient functions C_1, C_2, C_3, and C_4.

4–5 The method of undetermined coefficients. Considering the fact that actual application of the method of variation of parameters to nth-order differential equations may involve quite lengthy calculations, it is worth while to note that when the right member of the differential equation is of suitable form we have again at our disposal the method of undetermined coefficients which we previously considered for second-order equations.

We restrict ourselves here to applying the method to the differential equation with constant coefficients:

$$y^{(n)} + a_1 y^{(n-1)} + \cdots + a_n y = f(x). \tag{1}$$

Let us first take the case

$$f(x) = e^{kx} \tag{2}$$

and see under what conditions we have a particular integral of the form

$$y_p = A e^{kx}. \tag{3}$$

Substitution of (2) and (3) into (1) and cancellation of the common factor e^{kx} leave us with the following equation for the undetermined coefficient A:

$$A(k^n + a_1 k^{n-1} + \cdots + a_{n-1} k + a_n) = 1. \tag{4}$$

We see that this determines A, provided k is *not* a root of the auxiliary equation (2) of Section 4–2.

It is possible to show that if k *is* a root of the auxiliary equation, say of order m, then instead of (3) we shall have a particular integral of the form $y_p = A x^m e^{kx}$.

In the same manner, we may obtain particular integrals when $f(x)$ is either $\cos kx$ or $\sin kx$, by writing

$$\cos kx = \frac{1}{2}(e^{ikx} + e^{-ikx}), \qquad \sin kx = \frac{1}{2i}(e^{ikx} - e^{-ikx}).$$

A third class of functions $f(x)$ for which the method of undetermined coefficients is applicable is the class of functions

$$f(x) = x^m, \qquad m \text{ a positive integer.} \tag{5}$$

When $f(x)$ is given by (5), we choose

$$y_p = A_1 x^m + A_2 x^{m-1} + \cdots + A_m. \tag{6}$$

We introduce (5) and (6) into (1) and find that we may determine the coefficients A_j by equating coefficients of corresponding powers of x on the left and right sides of the resulting equation. This will always work provided the coefficient a_n in (1) is different from zero.

When a_n is zero, we may replace Eq. (1) by its integrated form

$$\frac{d^{n-1}y}{dx^{n-1}} + a_1 \frac{d^{n-2}y}{dx^{n-2}} + \cdots + a_{n-1}y = \frac{x^{m+1}}{m+1} \tag{7}$$

and then apply the foregoing procedure. [Note that the constant of integration which we might add on the right of (7) would contribute a term to the particular solution y_p which is already contained in the general solution of the homogeneous equation (1) of Section 4–2. It may therefore be omitted.] It should be clear how to extend this procedure if in addition to $a_n = 0$ we further have $a_{n-1} = a_{n-2} = \cdots = a_{n-q} = 0$.

As is the case with the second-order equation, it is possible to use the method of undetermined coefficients for the differential equation with constant coefficients for somewhat more general types of functions $f(x)$ than the cases here considered. These, however, are of little practical importance.

EXERCISES

Obtain particular solutions of the differential equations of Exercises 1 through 8.

1. $y^{iv} - 2y'' + y = 3 \sin kx + 4 \cos kx$
2. $y^{iv} + 4y = 2 \sin 2x + 1 + 3x^2 + 4e^x$
3. $y^{iv} - 2y'' + y' = 2x$
4. $y''' - y'' + y' - y = x^2 + 3e^x$
5. $y^{iv} - k^4 y = K_1 e^{kx} + K_2 \cos kx$
6. $y^{iv} - 2k^2 y'' + k^4 y = K_1 e^{kx} + K_2 \cos kx$
7. $y''' - 9y' = 2x + 3 + 5e^{3x}$
8. $y^{(vi)} + 2y^{(iv)} + y'' = 2$

4–6 The Laplace transform of the linear differential equation with constant coefficients. A useful method for solving the nonhomogeneous nth-order equation with constant coefficients,

$$y^{(n)} + a_1 y^{(n-1)} + \cdots + a_n y = f(x), \tag{1}$$

is basically as follows. We multiply (1) by a factor e^{-px}, where p is a parameter, and integrate the resulting equation from zero to infinity:

$$\int_0^\infty e^{-px}[y^{(n)} + a_1 y^{(n-1)} + \cdots + a_n y]\, dx = \int_0^\infty e^{-px} f(x)\, dx. \tag{2}$$

We call $\int_0^\infty e^{-px} f(x)\, dx$ the *Laplace transform* of $f(x)$ and write

$$\int_0^\infty e^{-px} f(x)\, dx = F(p). \tag{3}$$

We restrict attention to such functions $f(x)$ for which the integral in (3) exists for real values of p greater than some constant p_0. We similarly write for the last term on the left of (2)

$$\int_0^\infty e^{-px} y(x)\, dx = Y(p), \tag{4}$$

and we shall not, at this point, worry whether or not the solution function $y(x)$ is of such form that the integral in (4) exists.

We turn next to the integral $\int_0^\infty e^{-px} y'(x)\, dx$, the Laplace transform of the derivative y'. We can express this Laplace transform of y' in terms of the transform of y itself by integration by parts, as follows:

$$\int_0^\infty e^{-px} y'(x)\, dx = e^{-px} y(x)\Big|_0^\infty + p \int_0^\infty e^{-px} y(x)\, dx. \tag{5}$$

At this stage in the development we make a further restrictive assumption, namely, that $y(x)$ is such as to make the integrated portion vanish at the upper limit:

$$\lim_{x \to \infty} e^{-px} y(x) = 0. \tag{6}$$

We then have

$$\int_0^\infty e^{-px} y'(x)\, dx = -y(0) + p Y(p). \tag{7}$$

We can similarly express the Laplace transforms of all the derivatives

$y^{(m)}$ in terms of $Y(p)$, by repeated integration by parts. We have as a result the important formula

$$\int_0^\infty e^{-px} y^{(m)}(x)\, dx$$
$$= -[p^{m-1}y(0) + p^{m-2}y'(0) + \cdots + y^{(m-1)}(0)] + p^m Y(p). \quad (8)$$

For its validity this formula requires in addition to the limiting relation (6) the following limiting relations:

$$\lim_{x \to \infty} e^{-px} y^{(k)}(x) = 0, \qquad k = 1, 2, \ldots, m-1. \quad (9)$$

We now substitute (8), (4), and (3) in the *transformed* equation (2) and write this equation in the following form:

$$(p^n + a_1 p^{n-1} + \cdots + a_{n-1}p + a_n) Y(p)$$
$$- (p^{n-1} + a_1 p^{n-2} + \cdots + a_{n-2}p + a_{n-1})y(0)$$
$$- (p^{n-2} + a_1 p^{n-3} + \cdots + a_{n-3}p + a_{n-2})y'(0) - \cdots$$
$$- y^{(n-1)}(0) = F(p). \quad (10)$$

In (10) we now make use of initial conditions of the form

$$y^{(m)}(0) = y_0^{(m)}, \qquad m = 0, 1, \ldots, n-1, \quad (11)$$

where the quantities $y_0^{(m)}$ are given constants. This means that Eq. (10) gives us the Laplace transform $Y(p)$ of the solution-function $y(x)$, in terms of the Laplace transform of the right member $f(x)$ and in terms of the initial values of y and its derivatives, as follows:

$$(p^n + a_1 p^{n-1} + \cdots + a_{n-1}p + a_n) Y(p)$$
$$= F(p) + y_0 p^{n-1} + (y_0' + a_1 y_0)p^{n-2} + \cdots$$
$$+ (y_0^{(n-1)} + a_1 y_0^{(n-2)} + \cdots + a_{n-1}y_0). \quad (12)$$

We note that while the original relations between $y(x)$ and $f(x)$ and the initial values $y_0^{(m)}$ are relations involving various derivatives of the unknown functions, the corresponding relation between the Laplace transforms of y and f is of an algebraic nature. We shall see that it is this fact which is responsible for the effectiveness of the Laplace transform method.

EXAMPLE. Obtain $Y(p)$ for

$$y^{iv} - y = f(x),$$

with

$$y(0) = y_0, \qquad y'(0) = y''(0) = y'''(0) = 0.$$

Equation (12), with $n = 4$, $y_0' = y_0'' = y_0''' = 0$, and $a_1 = a_2 = a_3 = 0$, $a_4 = -1$ becomes

$$Y(p) = \frac{F(p) + y_0 p^3}{p^4 - 1}.$$

4–7 Some Laplace transform formulas. In order to apply the Laplace transform method, one needs what amounts to a catalogue of frequently occurring Laplace transforms. Some of these are very simply obtained from Eq. (3) of Section 4–6.

For example, when

$$f(x) = 1, \quad \text{then} \quad F(p) = \int_0^\infty e^{-px}\,dx = \frac{1}{p}, \qquad 0 < p, \qquad (1)$$

and when

$$f(x) = e^{ax}, \quad \text{then} \quad F(p) = \int_0^\infty e^{(a-p)x}\,dx = \frac{1}{p-a}, \qquad a < p. \quad (2)$$

Furthermore, when

$$f(x) = \cos bx = \tfrac{1}{2}(e^{ibx} + e^{-ibx}), \qquad (2a)$$

then

$$F(p) = \frac{1}{2}\left(\frac{1}{p-ib} + \frac{1}{p+ib}\right) = \frac{p}{p^2 + b^2}, \qquad 0 < p. \qquad (2b)$$

The latter formula is a simple illustration of the general fact that if

$$f = c_1 f_1 + c_2 f_2, \quad \text{then} \quad F = c_1 F_1 + c_2 F_2. \qquad (3)$$

A formula which will be particularly useful in solving differential equations with constant coefficients is the following:

$$f(x) = x^n e^{ax}, \quad F(p) = \frac{n!}{(p-a)^{n+1}}, \qquad a < p, \qquad (4)$$

where $n = 0, 1, 2, \ldots$

A general result of importance is a formula for the Laplace transform of the following integral:

$$h(x) = \int_0^x f(x - s)g(s)\,ds. \qquad (5a)$$

We state here without proof that the transform $H(p)$ of h is given by the product

$$H(p) = F(p)G(p). \tag{5b}$$

To illustrate the use of (5) let us find a function $h(x)$ with Laplace transform

$$H(p) = \frac{1}{(p - a)(p - b)}.$$

If

$$F(p) = \frac{1}{p - a}, \qquad G(p) = \frac{1}{p - b},$$

then, according to (2),

$$f(x) = e^{ax}, \qquad g(x) = e^{bx},$$

and, according to (5a),

$$h(x) = \int_0^x e^{a(x-s)}e^{bs}\,ds = e^{ax}\int_0^x e^{(b-a)s}\,ds = e^{ax}\frac{e^{(b-a)s}}{b - a}\bigg|_0^x = \frac{e^{bx} - e^{ax}}{b - a}.$$

In this particular case we can find the same result directly by writing

$$\frac{1}{(p - a)(p - b)} = \left(\frac{1}{p - b} - \frac{1}{p - a}\right)\frac{1}{b - a}$$

and using (3) and (2).

EXERCISES

Determine the Laplace transform $F(p)$ for the functions $f(x)$ in Exercises 1 through 7.

1. $\sin bx$ 2. $\cosh ax$ 3. $\sinh ax$ 4. $\displaystyle\int_0^x g(\xi)\,d\xi$

5. 1 for $0 \le x \le a$, 0 for $a < x$ 6. $e^{-ax}\cos bx$ 7. $e^{-ax}\sin bx$

Determine a function $f(x)$ the Laplace transform $F(p)$ of which is given in each of Exercises 8 through 12.

8. $\dfrac{3}{p + 4}$ 9. $\dfrac{1}{p(p - 1)}$ 10. $\dfrac{1}{p^2 + a^2}$

11. $\dfrac{b^2}{p(p^2 + b^2)} = \dfrac{1}{p} - \dfrac{p}{p^2 + b^2}$

12. $\dfrac{2a^2}{p^4 - a^4} = \dfrac{1}{p^2 - a^2} - \dfrac{1}{p^2 + a^2}$

4–8 Laplace transform solutions. Use of the transform formulas of the preceding section enables us to solve differential equations with constant coefficients by going from the transform of the solution, as obtained in Section 4–6, to the solution itself. This will be illustrated by a number of examples. A short table of appropriate transforms is given below.

$f(x)$	$F(p)$
1	$\dfrac{1}{p}$
x^n	$\dfrac{n!}{p^{n+1}}$
e^{ax}	$\dfrac{1}{p - a}$
$x^n e^{ax}$	$\dfrac{n!}{(p - a)^{n+1}}$
$e^{ax} \cos bx$	$\dfrac{p - a}{(p - a)^2 + b^2}$
$e^{ax} \sin bx$	$\dfrac{b}{(p - a)^2 + b^2}$
$\cosh ax$	$\dfrac{p}{p^2 - a^2}$
$\sinh ax$	$\dfrac{a}{p^2 - a^2}$
$\displaystyle\int_0^x f(x - s)g(s)\, ds$	$F(p)G(p)$
$f^{(n)}(x)$	$p^n F(p) - p^{n-1}f(0) - p^{n-2}f'(0) - \cdots - f^{(n-1)}(0)$

EXAMPLE 1. Solve

$$y'' - y = 1, \qquad y_0 = 1, \qquad y_0' = 0.$$

From Eq. (12), Section 4–6,

$$(p^2 - 1)Y = p^{-1} + p$$

or

$$Y = \frac{1 + p^2}{p(p^2 - 1)} = -\frac{1}{p} + \frac{2p}{p^2 - 1}.$$

From the table of transforms,

$$y(x) = -1 + 2 \cosh x.$$

EXAMPLE 2. Solve the homogeneous equation

$$y'' - 2ay' + a^2y = 0.$$

We leave y_0 and y_0' arbitrary and have then, from Eq. (12), Section 4–6,

$$(p^2 - 2ap + a^2)Y = y_0p + y_0' - 2ay_0$$

or

$$Y = \frac{y_0p + y_0' - 2ay_0}{(p - a)^2}.$$

We notice that in order to use our transform table we must decompose $p/(p - a)^2$ into partial fractions, as follows:

$$\frac{p}{(p - a)^2} = \frac{a}{(p - a)^2} + \frac{1}{p - a}.$$

From

$$Y = \frac{-ay_0 + y_0'}{(p - a)^2} + \frac{y_0}{p - a}$$

it follows then that

$$y = (-ay_0 + y_0')xe^{ax} + y_0e^{ax}.$$

This gives us an additional derivation of our earlier solution for the case of a double root of the auxiliary equation. Also, the present form of the solution incorporates the initial conditions explicitly, instead of the arbitrary constants c_1 and c_2 which earlier had to be determined separately.

EXAMPLE 3. Solve

$$y^{iv} - k^4y = 0,$$

with the initial conditions

$$y_0 = 1, \qquad y_0' = y_0'' = y_0''' = 0.$$

From Eq. (12), Section 4–6,

$$Y = \frac{p^3}{p^4 - k^4} = \frac{1}{2}\left(\frac{p}{p^2 - k^2} + \frac{p}{p^2 + k^2}\right),$$

and then

$$y = \tfrac{1}{2}(\cosh kx + \cos kx).$$

EXAMPLE 4. Solve the nonhomogeneous equation

$$y^{iv} - k^4y = f(x),$$

with the homogeneous initial conditions

$$y_0 = y_0' = y_0'' = y_0''' = 0.$$

From Eq. (12), Section 4–6,

$$Y = \frac{F(p)}{p^4 - k^4}.$$

We write this expression for Y in the form

$$Y = F(p)G(p),$$

and we know that

$$G = \frac{1}{p^4 - k^4} = \frac{1}{2k^2}\left(\frac{1}{p^2 - k^2} - \frac{1}{p^2 + k^2}\right)$$

is the transform of

$$g(x) = \frac{1}{2k^3}(\sinh kx - \sin kx).$$

We now use Eq. (5), Section 4–7, for the product of two transforms to conclude from the form of $Y(p)$ that the solution $y(x)$ is given by means of the integral

$$y(x) = \frac{1}{2k^3}\int_0^x f(s)\,[\sinh k(x - s) - \sin k(x - s)]\,ds.$$

or

$$y(x) = \frac{1}{2k^3}\int_0^x [\sinh ks - \sin ks]f(x - s)\,ds.$$

The same result may of course also be found, with somewhat lengthier calculations, by means of the method of variation of parameters.

EXAMPLE 5. Given that the auxiliary equation

$$r_n + a_1 r^{n-1} + \cdots + a_{n-1}r + a_n = 0$$

of the differential equation

$$y^{(n)} + a_1 y^{(n-1)} + \cdots + a_{n-1}y' + a_n y = 0$$

has an m-fold root $r_1 = r_2 = \cdots = r_m$, show that the general solution of the differential equation includes an expression of the form

$$(c_1 + c_2 x + \cdots + c_m x^{m-1})e^{r_1 x}.$$

According to Eq. (12) of Section 4–6, if r_1 is an m-fold root of the auxiliary equation

$$Y(p) = \frac{y_0 p^{n-1} + (y_0' + a_1 y_0)p^{n-2} + \cdots + (y_0^{(n-1)} + \cdots + a_{n-1}y_0)}{(p - r_1)^m (p^{n-m} + b_1 p^{n-m-1} + \cdots + b_{n-m})}.$$

Decomposing into partial fractions insofar as the factor $(p - r_1)^m$ is concerned, we have further, with suitable constants A_k,

$$Y(p) = \frac{A_1}{(p - r_1)^m} + \frac{A_2}{(p - r_1)^{m-1}} + \cdots + \frac{A_m}{p - r_1}$$

$$+ \frac{A_{m+1}p^{n-m-1} + A_{m+2}p^{n-m-2} + \cdots + A_n}{p^{n-m} + b_1 p^{n-m-1} + \cdots + b_{n-m}}.$$

By referring to the fourth formula in our short table of Laplace transforms we find that the function $y(x)$ which corresponds to the above $Y(p)$ includes a portion

$$\left(\frac{A_1}{(m-1)!} x^{m-1} + \frac{A_2}{(m-2)!} x^{m-2} + \cdots + \frac{A_m}{0!} \right) e^{r_1 x},$$

which is of the predicted form.

We note that our consideration proves a result which earlier, in Section 4–2, had been stated without proof.

EXERCISES

Solve Exercises 1 through 7 by the Laplace transform method.

1. $y' + ay = 1$, $y_0 = 0$
2. $y' + ay = e^{-ax}$, $y_0 = 1$
3. $y'' + a^2 y = 0$, $y_0 = 1$, $y_0' = 0$
4. $y'' + 2ay' + by = f(x)$, $y_0 = y_0' = 0$
5. $y''' - y = 0$, $y_0 = y_0'' = 0$, $y_0' = 1$
6. $y''' - 3y'' + 3y' - y = 0$, $y_0 = y_0' = 0$
7. $y' - ay = g(x)$, $y_0 = 0$
8. The Laplace transform Y of the solution of $y^{iv} + 4k^4 y = 0$ in terms of y_0, y_0', y_0'', y_0''' is given by

$$(p^4 + 4k^4)Y = y_0 p^3 + y_0' p^2 + y_0'' p + y_0'''.$$

Obtain y by means of formulas in the short table of Laplace transforms, through recognition of the fact that $p^4 + 4k^4 = [(p - k)^2 + k^2][(p + k)^2 + k^2]$.

4-9 Power-series solutions of nth-order linear differential equations. The ordinary point. Application of power series to nth-order linear differential equations proceeds in a manner which is entirely analogous to what we encountered in the treatment of second-order equations. We may therefore be quite brief.

Given the differential equation

$$p_0(x)\frac{d^n y}{dx^n} + p_1(x)\frac{d^{n-1}y}{dx^{n-1}} + \cdots + p_{n-1}(x)\frac{dy}{dx} + p_n(x)y = 0, \quad (1)$$

let us first assume that the nature of the coefficients p_m is such that we may write

$$\frac{p_m(x)}{p_0(x)} = \sum_{k=0}^{\infty} a_{mk}x^k, \quad (2)$$

where the series on the right are convergent in some interval $|x| < R$. When (2) is valid, Eq. (1) is solvable for arbitrarily given values of $y(0)$, $y'(0), \ldots, y^{(n-1)}(0)$. Therefore, in a power-series solution of the form

$$y = \sum_{j=0}^{\infty} c_j x^j, \quad (3)$$

we will be able to assume arbitrarily the values of the first n coefficients $c_0, c_1, \ldots, c_{n-1}$, and the remaining coefficients will be expressible in terms of the first n coefficients.

In extension of what we did for second-order equations, we shall call the point $x = 0$ an *ordinary point* of the differential equation (1) so long as the coefficient functions $p_m(x)$ are restricted as in (2).

Substitution of (2) and (3) into (1) gives us

$$\sum_{j=0}^{\infty} c_j j(j-1)\ldots(j-n+1)x^{j-n}$$

$$+ \sum_{k=0}^{\infty} a_{1k}x^k \sum_{j=0}^{\infty} c_j j(j-1)\ldots(j-n+2)x^{j-n+1}$$

$$+ \sum_{k=0}^{\infty} a_{2k}x^k \sum_{j=0}^{\infty} c_j j(j-1)\ldots(j-n+3)x^{j-n+2} + \cdots$$

$$+ \sum_{k=0}^{\infty} a_{nk}x^k \sum_{j=0}^{\infty} c_j x^j = 0. \quad (4)$$

We satisfy (4) by combining corresponding powers of x and by setting the coefficient of each power of x equal to zero. In this way we obtain from the terms multiplying x^0:

$$c_n n! + a_{10} c_{n-1}(n - 1)! + a_{20} c_{n-2}(n - 2)! + \ldots + a_{n0} c_0 = 0. \quad (5a)$$

We shall not write out explicitly the corresponding relations coming from the terms with x^i, where $i = 1, 2, \ldots$, but we may observe that these relations are of the form

$$c_{n+i} = \text{linear combination of } c_0, c_1, \ldots, c_{n+i-1}. \quad (5b)$$

We see from (5a) and (5b) that $c_0, c_1, \ldots, c_{n-1}$ may indeed be chosen arbitrarily, and $c_n, c_{n+1}, \ldots$ may successively be expressed in terms of the first n coefficients of the solution series.

EXAMPLE.

$$y^{\text{iv}}(x) - xy = 0.$$

Substitution of

$$y = c_0 + c_1 x + c_2 x^2 + \cdots$$

results in the relation

$$\left[c_4 4! + c_5 5! x + c_6 \frac{6!}{2!} x^2 + \cdots \right] - [c_0 x + c_1 x^2 + \cdots] = 0.$$

From this,

$$c_4 4! = 0, \qquad c_5 5! = c_0, \qquad c_6 \frac{6!}{2!} = c_1, \qquad c_7 \frac{7!}{3!} = c_2,$$

$$c_8 \frac{8!}{4!} = c_3, \quad \ldots, \quad c_n \frac{n!}{(n - 4)!} = c_{n-5}, \quad \ldots$$

We see that $c_0, c_1, c_2,$ and c_3 are arbitrary, and that the solution series assumes the form

$$y = c_0 \left[1 + \frac{x^5}{5!} + \frac{6!}{10!5!} x^{10} + \frac{6!11!}{15!10!5!} x^{15} + \cdots \right]$$

$$+ c_1 \left[x + \frac{2!}{6!} x^6 + \frac{2!7!}{11!6!} x^{11} + \cdots \right]$$

$$+ c_2 \left[x^2 + \frac{3!}{7!} x^7 + \frac{3!8!}{12!7!} x^{12} + \cdots \right]$$

$$+ c_3 \left[x^3 + \frac{4!}{8!} x^8 + \frac{4!9!}{8!13!} x^{13} + \cdots \right].$$

EXERCISES

For each of the following differential equations determine the first few non-vanishing coefficients in the power series solution of the form (3).

1. $y''' - xy = 0$ 2. $y^{iv} - x^2 y = 0$

3. $(1 - x)y''' + 2xy' + 3y = 0$

4. By a suitable change of the independent variable reduce the problem of solving the differential equations

$$\text{(a) } y''' - kxy = 0, \quad \text{(b) } y^{(iv)} - kx^2 y = 0$$

to Exercises 1 and 2, respectively.

4-10 The regular singular point. We next define a *regular singular point* of the differential equation (1) of the preceding section. Again in analogy to what we did for the second-order equation, we say that the point $x = 0$ is a regular singular point if the nature of the coefficient functions p_m is such that we may write

$$\frac{p_m(x)}{p_0(x)} = \frac{1}{x^m} \sum_{k=0}^{\infty} b_{mk} x^k, \tag{1}$$

where the series on the right are convergent in some interval $|x| < R$.

We now no longer have the possibility of arbitrarily prescribing the values of $y(0), y'(0), \ldots, y^{(n-1)}(0)$. Consequently, we cannot in general expect a series solution of the form (3) of Section 4-9. We can, however, by analogy with the second-order case, expect that we shall encounter series solutions of the form

$$y = \sum_{j=0}^{\infty} c_j x^{j+s}, \quad c_0 \neq 0, \tag{2}$$

where s is a suitably determined constant, and solutions including terms of the form

$$(\ln x)^m \sum_{j=0}^{\infty} d_j x^{j+s}, \quad d_0 \neq 0, \tag{3}$$

where we shall assume $x > 0$.

Possible values of s are obtained by substituting the solution series (2) and the expressions (1) for the coefficients p_m into the differential equation (1) of Section 4-9 and by equating to zero the coefficients of the different power of x in the resultant equation. The lowest power of x which occurs is x^{s-n}. The coefficient of x^{s-n} is

$$c_0[s(s - 1) \ldots (s - n + 1) + b_{10}s(s - 1) \ldots (s - n + 2)$$

$$+ b_{20}s(s - 1) \ldots (s - n + 3) + \cdots + b_{n0}] = 0. \tag{4}$$

Since $c_0 \neq 0$, the contents of the bracket must vanish. This means that possible values of s are solutions of an nth-degree polynomial equation, called the *indicial equation*. This equation has n roots which may or may not be all distinct.

If multiple roots occur, then we will certainly not have n distinct solutions of the form (2) and the general solution will always contain expressions of the form (3). If all roots are distinct, one might expect n distinct solutions of the form (2). This, however, is not always so. It can be shown that only if no two of the n distinct roots differ by an integer is one assured of n distinct solutions of the form (2). If two or more of the distinct roots do differ by an integer, then there may or may not be n distinct solutions of the form (2). In the latter case, it is again necessary to search for solutions including terms of the form (3).

EXAMPLE 1.
$$y''' - x^{-2}y = 0.$$

Introduction of

$$y = c_0 x^s + c_1 x^{s+1} + \cdots,$$

$$y''' = c_0 s(s-1)(s-2)x^{s-3} + c_1(s+1)s(s-1)x^{s-2} + \cdots$$

leads to the following relations:

$$c_0 s(s-1)(s-2) = 0,$$

$$c_1(s+1)s(s-1) - c_0 = 0,$$

$$c_2(s+2)(s+1)s - c_1 = 0,$$

$$\vdots$$

$$c_n(s+n)(s+n-1)(s+n-2) - c_{n-1} = 0,$$

$$\vdots$$

The indicial equation is

$$s(s-1)(s-2) = 0,$$

with the roots

$$s_1 = 0, \qquad s_2 = 1, \qquad s_3 = 2.$$

We find that when $s = 0$ and $s = 1$ we cannot have $c_0 \neq 0$, since the second condition requires that $c_0 = 0$. Accordingly, we have just one particular solution of the assumed form, namely,

$$y = c_0\left[x^2 + \frac{x^3}{3!} + \frac{x^4}{4!3!} + \frac{2!x^5}{5!4!3!} + \frac{3!2!}{6!5!4!3!}x^6 + \cdots\right].$$

To obtain the general solution of the given differential equation, it will be necessary to consider expressions involving logarithms. This we shall not carry out here. We remark that we have encountered a case for which the roots of the indicial equation, while being distinct, differ by integers.

EXAMPLE 2.
$$y''' - (\alpha x^{-3} - x^{-2})y = 0.$$

Taking y as in Example 1, we have

$$c_0 s(s-1)(s-2)x^{s-3} + c_1(s+1)(s)(s-1)x^{s-2} + \cdots$$

$$-\alpha[c_0 x^{s-3} + c_1 x^{s-2} + \cdots] + [c_0 x^{s-2} + c_1 x^{s-1} + \cdots] = 0.$$

From this,

$$c_0[s(s-1)(s-2) - \alpha] = 0,$$

$$c_1[(s+1)s(s-1) - \alpha] + c_0 = 0,$$

$$c_2[(s+2)(s+1)s - \alpha] + c_1 = 0,$$

$$\vdots$$

$$c_n[(s+n)(s+n-1)(s+n-2) - \alpha] + c_{n-1} = 0,$$

$$\vdots$$

The indicial equation is

$$s(s-1)(s-2) - \alpha = 0.$$

To avoid having to solve a general cubic, let us choose α such that one of the three roots has a given value other than 0, 1, 2, say

$$s_1 = \tfrac{1}{2}.$$

Then

$$\alpha = \tfrac{3}{8}$$

and

$$s_2 = \tfrac{1}{4}(5 - \sqrt{13}), \qquad s_3 = \tfrac{1}{4}(5 + \sqrt{13}).$$

The general solution is

$$y = C_1\left[x^{1/2} + \frac{4}{3}x^{3/2} + \cdots\right]$$

$$+ C_2\left[x^{(5-\sqrt{13})/4} + \frac{1}{\tfrac{3}{8} - (s_2+1)s_2(s_2-1)}x^{1+(5-\sqrt{13})/4} + \cdots\right]$$

$$+ C_3\left[x^{(5+\sqrt{13})/4} + \frac{1}{\tfrac{3}{8} - (s_3+1)s_3(s_3-1)}x^{1+(5+\sqrt{13})/4} + \cdots\right].$$

EXERCISES

1. Solve the differential equation $y''' - \frac{3}{8}x^{-3}y = 0$.

2. Given the differential equation $y''' - \alpha x^{-3}y = 0$, show that if $\alpha = 2\sqrt{3}/9$ the indicial equation has a double root $\beta = 1 - (\sqrt{3}/3)$ and a single root $\gamma = 1 + (2\sqrt{3}/3)$ and that the solution is $y = c_1 x^\gamma + c_2 x^\beta + c_3 x^\beta \ln x$.

3. Given that the differential equation

$$\frac{d^3 y}{dx^3} + \frac{A_0 + A_1 x + \cdots}{x} \frac{d^2 y}{dx^2} + \frac{B_0 + B_1 x + \cdots}{x^2} \frac{dy}{dx} + \frac{C_0 + C_1 x + \cdots}{x^3} y = 0$$

has a general solution of the form

$$y = c_1 x^{\alpha_1}(1 + \cdots) + c_2 x^{\alpha_2}(1 + \cdots) + c_3 x^{\alpha_3}(1 + \cdots)$$

with $\alpha_1 \neq \alpha_2$, $\alpha_1 \neq \alpha_3$, $\alpha_2 \neq \alpha_3$, show that the coefficients A_0, B_0, and C_0 must be solutions of the system of linear equations

$$\alpha_i(\alpha_i - 1)(\alpha_i - 2) + \alpha_i(\alpha_i - 1)A_0 + \alpha_i B_0 + C_0 = 0, \qquad i = 1, 2, 3.$$

4–11 Factorization of differential operators. A procedure which is sometimes useful for solving linear differential equations may be introduced as follows. We consider the equation

$$\frac{d}{dx}\left(\frac{dy}{dx} - r_1 y\right) - r_2\left(\frac{dy}{dx} - r_1 y\right) = 0, \tag{1}$$

where r_1 and r_2 are constants. Equation (1) is equivalent to

$$\frac{d^2 y}{dx^2} - (r_1 + r_2)\frac{dy}{dx} + r_1 r_2 y = 0 \tag{1a}$$

and has the solution $y = c_1 e^{r_1 x} + c_2 e^{r_2 x}$ when $r_1 \neq r_2$, and $y = (c_1 + c_2 x)e^{r_1 x}$ when $r_1 = r_2$.

Equation (1) may also be written in the form

$$\left(\frac{d}{dx} - r_2\right)\left(\frac{d}{dx} - r_1\right)y = 0 \tag{1b}$$

or, with the symbol d/dx replaced by a symbol D, in the form

$$(D - r_2)(D - r_1)y = 0. \tag{1c}$$

It is readily seen that so long as r_2 and r_1 are constants the operations $(D - r_2)$ and $(D - r_1)$ are interchangeable and the solution y consists of two parts,

$$y = y_1 + y_2, \tag{2}$$

where, provided $r_1 \neq r_2$, the functions y_1 and y_2 are obtained from the two first-order equations

$$(D - r_1)y_1 = 0, \qquad (D - r_2)y_2 = 0. \tag{3}$$

The exceptional case $r_1 = r_2$ may be treated as follows. We write

$$(D - r_1)^2 y = 0 \tag{4}$$

in the form

$$(D - r_1)z = 0, \qquad z = (D - r_1)y \tag{5}$$

and find first z and then y by solving two successive first-order equations. We note that this is in fact the method which has been used in Section 3–5 for solving Eq. (4).

In either case, factorization of the second-order differential operator $D^2 - (r_1 + r_2)D + r_1 r_2$ into a product of two first-order operators, $(D - r_1)(D - r_2)$, meant that the solution of the given second-order equation could be obtained in terms of the solution of two first-order equations.

It is a simple matter to generalize this result to the case of the nth-order equation with constant coefficients:

$$(D^n + a_1 D^{n-1} + \cdots + a_{n-1}D + a_n)y = 0. \tag{6}$$

The nth-order operator may be factored in exactly the same way as the auxiliary equation of the differential equation (6) is factored:

$$(D - r_1)(D - r_2) \cdots (D - r_n)y = 0 \tag{6'}$$

and, so long as the constants r_k are distinct, the solution of (6) is given by

$$y = y_1 + y_2 + \cdots + y_n, \tag{7}$$

where y_1, y_2, etc. are solutions of

$$(D - r_1)y_1 = 0, \qquad (D - r_2)y_2 = 0, \qquad \ldots, \qquad (D - r_n)y_n = 0. \tag{8}$$

If $r_1 = r_2 = \cdots = r_m$ is an m-tuple root of the auxiliary equation, then part of the solution of (6) is given by the solution of

$$(D - r_1)^m y = 0, \tag{9}$$

and this is readily seen to be equivalent to a sequence of m successive first-order equations.

We will not, in what follows, be concerned with additional applications of the differential-operator method to equations with constant coefficients.

Results which can be obtained in this way are analogous to results which can also be obtained by the Laplace transform method. Instead, we shall be concerned with the possibility of using the method of factoring differential operators for differential equations with variable coefficients.

Second-order equations with variable coefficients. Given the second-order differential equation

$$PD^2y + QDy + Ry = 0, \tag{10}$$

where P, Q, and R are functions of x, we attempt a factorization of the form

$$(p_1D + q_1)(p_2D + q_2)y = 0. \tag{11}$$

Upon carrying out the indicated differentiations in (11) this equation appears in the form

$$[p_1p_2D^2 + (q_1p_2 + p_1q_2 + p_1p_2')D + (q_1q_2 + p_1q_2')]y = 0. \tag{11a}$$

Equation (11a) shows that, in general, the order of applying the operators $p_1D + q_1$ and $p_2D + q_2$ is not interchangeable; that is, these operators do not *commute.*

The developed form of

$$(p_2D + q_2)(p_1D + q_1)y = 0 \tag{12}$$

is

$$[p_1p_2D^2 + (q_1p_2 + p_1q_2 + p_2p_1')D + (q_1q_2 + p_2q_1')]y = 0. \tag{12a}$$

The second-order differential equation (11) is equivalent to two successive first-order equations. We may write, with an auxiliary function z,

$$(p_1D + q_1)z = 0, \qquad (p_2D + q_2)y = z. \tag{13}$$

Since we know the explicit solution of any linear first-order equation, we have then a method for the explicit solution of any second-order equation (10) as soon as we have succeeded in factoring (10) in the form (11).

To obtain conditions for the existence of this factorization, we compare Eqs. (10) and (11a). We find that the functions p and q in (11) must be related to the functions P, Q, R in (10) through two equations of the form

$$\frac{q_1}{p_1} + \frac{q_2}{p_2} + \frac{p_2'}{p_2} = \frac{Q}{P}, \qquad \frac{q_1q_2}{p_1p_2} + \frac{q_2'}{p_2} = \frac{R}{P}. \tag{14}$$

Setting for an example

$$p_1 = p_2 = x, \qquad q_1 = \alpha_1 x + \beta_1, \qquad q_2 = \alpha_2 x + \beta_2, \tag{15}$$

where α_j and β_j are constants, we find that the differential equation

$$D^2y + \left(\alpha_1 + \alpha_2 + \frac{1 + \beta_1 + \beta_2}{x}\right) Dy$$

$$+ \left(\alpha_1\alpha_2 + \frac{\alpha_2 + \alpha_1\beta_2 + \alpha_2\beta_1}{x} + \frac{\beta_1\beta_2}{x^2}\right) y = 0 \quad (16)$$

is equivalent to

$$(xD + \alpha_1 x + \beta_1)(xD + \alpha_2 x + \beta_2)y = 0. \quad (17)$$

Regrettably, Eq. (16) does not represent the entire class of equations

$$x^2 D^2 y + (a_0 + a_1 x) Dy + (b_0 + b_1 x + b_2 x^2)y = 0, \quad (18)$$

but only a subclass of this equation, since the five coefficients a_0, a_1, b_0, b_1, b_2 in (18) must be given in terms of the four coefficients α_1, α_2, β_1, β_2 in (17) and (16).

We now consider conditions under which the operators $p_1 D + q_1$ and $p_2 D + q_2$ commute. A comparison of Eqs. (11) and (12) indicates that we shall have that

$$(p_1 D + q_1)(p_2 D + q_2) = (p_2 D + q_2)(p_1 D + q_1),$$

provided the coefficients p_j and q_j satisfy the following two relations:

$$p_1 p_2' = p_2 p_1', \qquad p_1 q_2' = p_2 q_1'. \quad (19)$$

Equations (19) are obviously satisfied when the quantities p_j and q_j are constants. They are also satisfied provided

$$\frac{p_1}{p_2} = \frac{q_1'}{q_2'} = k, \quad (20)$$

with any constant k.

For the case that the two operators in (11) commute, we have that the solutions of both

$$(p_1 D + q_1)y_1 = 0, \qquad (p_2 D + q_2)y_2 = 0 \quad (21)$$

satisfy the second-order equation (11) and then, so long as the equations for y_1 and y_2 are not identical, we have that $y = y_1 + y_2$ is the general solution of (11). When the two equations are identical, that is, when $p_1 = p_2$ and $q_1 = q_2$, then the general solution must again be obtained from the two successive first-order equations (13).

Fourth-order differential equations. Of particular interest in physical applications are classes of fourth-order differential equations of the form

$$(P_0 D^4 + P_1 D^3 + P_2 D^2 + P_3 D + P_4)y = 0, \tag{22}$$

for which the solution may be expressed in terms of the solution of two second-order equations.

As an example of such an equation, we consider

$$(D^2 + x^{-1}D)^2 y = y. \tag{23}$$

In developed form, Eq. (23) reads

$$(D^4 + 2x^{-1}D^3 - x^{-2}D^2 + 2x^{-3}D)y = y. \tag{23a}$$

It is apparent that $x = 0$ is a regular singular point for this differential equation and that power-series solutions may be obtained, following the procedure indicated in Section 4–10. A simpler result is obtained by factoring differential operators in (23) as follows:

$$[(D^2 + x^{-1}D)^2 - 1]y = (D^2 + x^{-1}D + 1)(D^2 + x^{-1}D - 1)y = 0. \tag{23b}$$

The two second-order operators in (23b) commute and the solution of (23b) is of the form

$$y = y_1 + y_2, \tag{24}$$

where

$$(D^2 + x^{-1}D + 1)y_1 = 0, \qquad (D^2 + x^{-1}D - 1)y_2 = 0. \tag{25}$$

In (25) we have two Bessel equations as discussed in Sections 3–15 and 3–16. Accordingly, the solution (24) of the fourth-order equation (23) is given by the expression

$$y = c_1 J_0(x) + c_2 Y_0(x) + c_3 J_0(ix) + c_4 Y_0(ix). \tag{26}$$

We have previously noted that it is customary to write $J_0(ix) = I_0(x)$. A corresponding change in notation concerning Y_0 is to write $Y_0(ix) = -(2/\pi)K_0(x) + iI_0(x)$, where the real-valued function $K_0(x)$ is designated as the modified zeroth-order Bessel function of the second kind.

In order to express the solution of more general fourth-order equations in terms of the solution of second-order equations, we consider fourth-order equations of the form

$$[(PD^2 + QD + R)^2 - (\lambda_1 + \lambda_2)(PD^2 + QD + R) + \lambda_1\lambda_2]y = 0. \tag{27}$$

Equation (27), in factored form, is,

$$(PD^2 + QD + R - \lambda_1)(PD^2 + QD + R - \lambda_2)y = 0. \qquad (27a)$$

It follows from (27a), so long as $\lambda_1 \neq \lambda_2$, that $y = y_1 + y_2$, where y_j satisfies the second-order equation $(P D^2 + QD + R - \lambda_j)y_j = 0$. When $\lambda_1 = \lambda_2 = \lambda$, then the solution of (27) is given by setting $(P D^2 + QD + R - \lambda)y = z$ and by solving the second-order non-homogeneous equation for y in terms of the auxiliary function z which in turn is the solution of the homogeneous second-order equation $(P D^2 + QD + R - \lambda)z = 0$.

We do not wish to consider the complete problem of trying to reduce the general fourth-order equation (22) to the factorable form (23), but rather consider the following special class of equations:

$$x^n D^2(x^m D^2)y = y. \qquad (28)$$

It is evident that (28) may be factored directly into two second-order equations when the two exponents m and n are equal to each other. What we wish to show is that when $n \neq m$ we may still have a factorization of this nature. Inspection of the form of (28) indicates that this factorization, if it exists, should appear as

$$(x^k D^2 + ax^{k-1}D + bx^{k-2})^2 y = y, \qquad (29)$$

where a and b are constants and the exponent k is given in terms of the exponents m and n as $k = \frac{1}{2}(m + n)$.

Expanding (28) and (29) and comparing coefficients, we find that in order for (29) and (28) to be the same differential equations, the following five algebraic relations must hold:

$$n + m = 2k, \qquad m = k + a,$$
$$(m - 1)m = (k - 1)(k + 3a) + a + a^2 + 2b,$$
$$0 = a(k - 1)(a + k - 2) + 2b(k - 2) + 2ab, \qquad (30)$$
$$0 = b(k - 2)(k - 3) + ab(k - 2) + b^2.$$

Since for given m and n we have only three quantities, k, a, and b, at our disposal, it is evident that the factorization (29) will not be possible for every m and n. We have already observed that factorization exists in the original equation (28), when $m = n$. This is equivalent to stating that the five algebraic equations for k, a, b are satisfied when $m = n$ if we set $k = m$, $a = b = 0$.

Additional cases for which factorization is possible are obtained from the solution of the algebraic system (30). We find that there are two classes of such cases. The first class of cases is given by

$$k = 1, \quad b = 0, \quad m = 1 + a, \quad n = 1 - a, \quad a \text{ arbitrary.} \quad (31)$$

The second class of cases is given by

$$a = 4 - 2k, \quad b = 2 - 3k + k^2, \quad m = 4 - k, \quad n = 3k - 4. \quad (32)$$

Equations (31) and (32) show that we have factorability whenever m and n in Eq. (28) are related in the form

$$m + n = 2 \quad \text{or} \quad 3m + n = 8. \quad (33)$$

When $m + n = 2$ we have

$$x^{2-m} D^2(x^m D^2) = [x D^2 + (m - 1)D]^2, \quad (34a)$$

and when $3m + n = 8$ we have

$$x^{8-3m} D^2(x^m D^2)$$
$$= [x^{4-m} D^2 + (2m - 4)x^{3-m}D + (m^2 - 5m + 6)x^{2-m}]^2. \quad (34b)$$

In both cases the solution y of Eq. (28) is given in the form $y = y_1 + y_2$, where y_1 and y_2 are determined from second-order equations $(x^k D^2 + ax^{k-1}D + bx^{k-2})y_j = \pm y_j$, which we shall not consider further here.

EXERCISES

1. Solve

$$x^2 D^2 y + (1 + \beta_1 + \beta_2)x Dy + [\beta_1\beta_2 + \alpha(1 + \beta_1 - \beta_2)x - a^2 x]y = 0.$$

2. Solve $xD^2 y + (1 + \beta + \alpha x) Dy + \alpha\beta y = 0$.

3. Show that $y = y_1 + y_2$ where $(pD + q + \lambda_j)y_j = 0$, with $\lambda_1 \neq \lambda_2$, is the general solution of $(pD + q)^2 y + (\lambda_1 + \lambda_2)(pD + q)y + \lambda_1\lambda_2 y = 0$.

4. Show that in order that $PD^2 + QD + R = (pD + q)^2$ we must have $2pp'' - (p')^2 + [4(R/P) - (Q/P)^2 - 2(Q/P)']p^2 = 0$ and $2q = (Q/P)p - p'$.

5. Show that in order that $D^2 + QD + R = (D + q)^2$ we must have $2q = Q$ and $4R = Q^2 + 2Q'$.

6. Determine functions p, q, r for which $(pD + q)^2 = rD^2$.

7. Solve $x^4 D^2 y = y$, using the answer to Exercise 6.

8. Find first-order equations for y_1 and y_2 such that $y = y_1 + y_2$ is the solution of $x^4 D^2 y - (\lambda_1 + \lambda_2)x^2 Dy + (\lambda_1 x + \lambda_2 x + \lambda_1\lambda_2)y = 0$.

9. Show that $PD^2 + QD + R = (pD + q)^2 + (\lambda_1 + \lambda_2)(pD + q) + \lambda_1\lambda_2$ whenever

$$p = \sqrt{P}, \qquad q = \frac{2Q - P'}{4\sqrt{P}} - \frac{\lambda_1 + \lambda_2}{2},$$

$$R = \frac{Q^2}{4P} + \frac{Q'}{2} - \frac{QP'}{2P} + \frac{5(P')^2}{16P} - \frac{P''}{4} + \frac{(\lambda_1 - \lambda_2)^2}{4}.$$

10. Verify that $(pD + q)^2 ry = (PD^2 + QD + R)y$ provided that

$$P = p^2r, \qquad Q = 2p^2r' + p(p' + 2q)r,$$
$$R = p^2r'' + p(p' + 2q)r' + (pq' + q^2)r.$$

11. Show that the contents of Exercise 10 imply the identity

$$[x^k D + (m - \tfrac{1}{2}k)x^{k-1}]^2 x^m y = x^{2k+m} D^2 y$$

for suitable values of constant k.

12. What relation must hold among the constants k, m, n, l and a in order that the following identity be valid?

$$x^n D(x^m D x^k y) = (x^l D + ax^{l-1})^2 y.$$

13. Determine values of m for which the solution of $D^2(x^{3m} D^2 y) + x^m y = 0$ may be expressed in terms of solutions of second-order equations and state these second-order equations.

14. Obtain necessary and sufficient conditions in order that the equation $PD^2 y + QDy + Ry = 0$ has solutions of the form $y = pDz + qz$, where

$$(p_1 D + q_1)(P_1 D^2 + Q_1 D + R_1)z = 0.$$

MISCELLANEOUS EXERCISES. CHAPTER 4

Determine the differential equations of lowest order which have the solutions stated in Exercises 1, 2 and 3.

1. $y = x^2 + c_1 \cos x + c_2 x + c_3$ 2. $y = (c_1 + c_2 x + c_3 x^2)e^x + 2$

3. $\sin y = c_1 + c_2 x + c_3 x^2 + e^x$

4. Show that the solutions given in Exercises 1 and 2 are general solutions.

Solve the following:

5. $y^{(iv)} - 3y''' + y'' - 3y' = 0$ 6. $y^{(iv)} - y'' = 0$

7. $y''' - y = x$ 8. $y^{(iv)} + y'' = 0$

9. $y^{(v)} + y^{(iv)} = 0$ 10. $xy''' - 3y'' = x^4$

11. $y^{(vii)} - 8y^{(iv)} - y''' + 8y = 0$ 12. $y''' - 3y'' + 4y = 4x$

13. $y''y''' = 1$ 14. $y'''y^{(iv)} = 1$

15. $y''' - y'' - y' + y = 8(x - 1)e^{-x}$

16. $y''' + y'' - y' - y = x^2 + 4e^x$

17. $y''' + y'' = 6x$

19. $y''' - 6y'' + 5y' = 0$

21. $y''' - y' = 2e^x - 4x$

23. $y^{(iv)} - y = \cos 2x$

25. $y^{(vi)} - y^{(iv)} - y'' + y = 5e^{2x}$

18. $y''' + y' = 2x$

20. $xy^{(iv)} + y''' = 1$

22. $y''' - 3y'' + 4y = 6e^{2x}$

24. $y''' + 4y' + 16y = e^x$

26. $y^{(iv)} + 2y'' + y = 3x^2$

27. $2x^2 y''' + 3xy'' - y' = 0$ [*Hint.* Use Exercise 3 of Section 3–7.]

28. Show that

$$y = \tfrac{1}{2} \int f(x)\, dx - e^x \int f(x)e^{-x}\, dx + \tfrac{1}{2} e^{2x} \int f(x)e^{-2x}\, dx$$

is a particular solution of the differential equation $y''' - 3y'' + 2y' = f(x)$.

29. Determine three distinct values of m such that $y = x^m$ is a solution of the differential equation $x^3 y''' + 2x^2 y'' - 4xy' + 4y = 0$. Using this information, determine the general solution.

30. Using the Laplace transform method, solve the differential equation $y''' - y' = e^{-x}$ with the initial conditions $y(0) = y'(0) = y''(0) = 0$.

For the differential equations in Exercises 31 through 33 determine the first few nonvanishing coefficients in the series solution $y = c_0 + c_1 x + c_2 x^2 + \cdots$

31. $y''' - x^2 y = 0$

32. $y^{(iv)} - x^3 y = 0$

33. $y''' + yy' - x^2 y = 12 + 3x$, $y(0) = y'(0) = 0$, $y''(0) = 1$

34. Solve the equation

$$y'' + (2\lambda x - x^{-1})y' + (\lambda^2 - 1)x^2 y = 0$$

by using the fact that it may be written in the form

$$\left(\frac{1}{x} \frac{d}{dx} + \lambda \right)^2 y = y.$$

CHAPTER 5

SYSTEMS OF FIRST-ORDER DIFFERENTIAL EQUATIONS

5–1 Introduction. Related to the problem of the differential equation of nth order but somewhat more general is the problem of a system of n simultaneous first-order equations. The theory of systems of simultaneous equations is usually developed for systems in which the derivatives y'_k are explicitly given as functions of x and of the unknown functions $y_1, \ldots, y_n$:

$$
\begin{aligned}
y'_1 &= f_1(x, y_1, \ldots, y_n), \\
&\;\;\vdots \\
y'_n &= f_n(x, y_1, \ldots, y_n).
\end{aligned}
\tag{1}
$$

The single nth-order equation $y^{(n)} = f(x, y, y', \ldots, y^{(n-1)})$ may be seen to be a special case of (1) by writing in it

$$
y = y_1, \qquad y' = y_2, \qquad y'' = y_3, \qquad \ldots, \qquad y^{(n-1)} = y_n. \tag{2}
$$

Equation (1) of Section 4–1 now becomes one of the simultaneous equations, namely,

$$
y'_n = f(x, y_1, y_2, \ldots, y_n), \tag{3a}
$$

while the remaining equations of the system follow from (2) in the form

$$
y'_1 = y_2, \qquad y'_2 = y_3, \qquad \ldots, \qquad y'_{n-1} = y_n \tag{3b}
$$

If we select some fixed point $x = x_0$, we may evidently preassign arbitrarily the values of the n quantities $y_1(x_0), \ldots, y_n(x_0)$ so long as these values are in the range for which the functions f_k are defined. Equations (1) then furnish the values of the derivatives $y'_1(x_0), \ldots, y'_n(x_0)$.

For the solution of the system (1) with initial conditions

$$
y_1(x_0) = y_{1,0}, \qquad \ldots, \qquad y_n(x_0) = y_{n,0} \tag{4}
$$

we have again a general existence and uniqueness theorem. In this book we do not prove this theorem. Its contents may be stated as follows:

Assume that the functions $f_1, f_2, \ldots, f_n$ are defined and continuous in a region R of $(x, y_1, y_2, \ldots, y_n)$-space. Further assume that the partial derivatives $\partial f_1/\partial y_1, \partial f_1/\partial y_2, \ldots, \partial f_1/\partial y_n, \partial f_2/\partial y_1, \ldots, \partial f_n/\partial y_n$ are also continuous in R. Under these conditions the theorem guarantees for every $(x_0, y_{1,0}, y_{2,0}, \ldots, y_{n,0})$ in R the existence of a unique solution $y_1 = y_1(x)$,

179

$y_2 = y_2(x), \ldots, y_n = y_n(x)$ which satisfies the initial conditions (4). This solution is defined in some x-interval containing x_0.

As before, we call a solution of the system (1) the general solution in some interval if it contains all solutions in the interval.

For systems which are such that the existence and uniqueness theorem applies, the general solution must contain n constants of integration c_1, $c_2, \ldots, c_n$ in such a way that the initial conditions (4) can all be satisfied.

EXERCISES

1. Write the differential equation $y'' + 2ay' + by = f(x)$ as a system of two first-order equations.

2. Write the system of two second-order differential equations

$$x''(t) = ax + by, \qquad y''(t) = \alpha x + \beta y$$

as a system of four first-order differential equations, using the substitution $dx/dt = u$, $dy/dt = v$.

Obtain a system of two simultaneous first-order differential equations for y and z with the solutions given in Exercises 3 through 7.

3. $y = A_1 e^x + A_2 e^{-x}, \qquad z = 2A_1 e^x - A_2 e^{-x}$

4. $y = (A_1 + A_2 x)e^x, \qquad z = (3A_1 + 5A_2 x)e^x$

5. $y + z^2 + c_1 x + c_2 = 0, \qquad z^3 + z + y^3 + y + c_2 x + c_1 = 0$

6. $y = c_1 + c_2 x, \qquad z = c_1 x + c_2$

7. $y = c_1 u_1 + c_2 u_2, \qquad z = c_1 v_1 + c_2 v_2$

8. Use the answer to Exercise 6 to obtain the general solution of the system

$$(1 - x^2)y' = z - xy, \qquad (1 - x^2)z' = y - xz,$$

and show that the general initial-value problem for this system is solvable for all x_0 except $x_0 = \pm 1$.

9, 10. Show that the given solutions in Exercises 3 and 4 are the general solutions.

5–2 Two simultaneous first-order equations with constant coefficients.

We now consider as the simplest example of a system of differential equations the two equations

$$y' = a_1 y + a_2 z, \qquad z' = b_1 y + b_2 z, \tag{1}$$

where a_1, a_2, b_1, and b_2 are given constants.

Recalling that the exponential function has the property of having derivatives which are constant multiples of this function and remembering our previous work on the single differential equation with constant co-efficients, we expect to find solutions of (1) for which both y and z contain terms of the form e^{rx}. Since now, however, both y and z occur in one and the same equation, we must modify our previous work on the single equation with constant coefficients in such a way that we can keep track of both y and z separately. We do this by assuming as trial particular solutions of (1) the expressions

$$y = Ae^{rx}, \qquad z = Be^{rx}, \tag{2}$$

where A and B are suitable constant factors.

Combination of (2) and (1) leaves us, after omission of the common factor e^{rx} in both of equations (1), with the following two simultaneous algebraic equations:

$$(a_1 - r)A + a_2B = 0,$$
$$b_1A + (b_2 - r)B = 0. \tag{3}$$

In order that this homogeneous system of equations for A and B have solutions other than the trivial solution $A = B = 0$, it is necessary that the determinant of the system vanish:

$$\begin{vmatrix} a_1 - r & a_2 \\ b_1 & b_2 - r \end{vmatrix} = 0. \tag{4}$$

This means that r must be a solution of the quadratic equation

$$r^2 - (a_1 + b_2)r + (a_1b_2 - a_2b_1) = 0. \tag{5}$$

In analogy to our previous work, we call this the auxiliary equation of the system (1).

We denote the roots of (5) by r_1 and r_2 and assume first that $r_1 \neq r_2$. If we set $r = r_1$ in the simultaneous equations (3) for A and B, the two equations are compatible and consequently one of the corresponding constants A_1 and B_1 can be chosen arbitrarily and the other will be determined. We have the same situation for the other root r_2 and the corresponding constants A_2 and B_2.

Since the superposition principle holds for the linear system (1), the sum of the two particular solutions obtained is also a solution, and we have

$$y = A_1e^{r_1x} + A_2e^{r_2x}, \qquad z = B_1e^{r_1x} + B_2e^{r_2x}, \tag{6}$$

where exactly two of the four constants A_1, A_2, B_1, and B_2 are arbitrary.

As for the single linear equation, the case of equal roots of the auxiliary equation requires special consideration. In the case of the single equation it was always necessary to introduce new types of solutions when the auxiliary equation had equal roots. It is important to note that with a system of equations it may or may not be necessary to introduce new types of solutions. This may be seen as follows. If one of the A's and one of the B's can be chosen arbitrarily, then even if $r_1 = r_2$, we still have two arbitrary constants in the solution (6), which is all we can expect. If, however, only A_1 and A_2 (or B_1 and B_2) can be chosen arbitrarily, then the solution (6) clearly involves only one arbitrary constant $A_1 + A_2$ (or $B_1 + B_2$). Consequently, in this case it will be necessary to look for a second solution of some other form. From our experience with the single linear equation, we expect that the general solution will be of the form

$$y = (A_1 x + A_2)e^{r_1 x}, \qquad z = (B_1 x + B_2)e^{r_1 x} \qquad (7)$$

and this is, in fact, true.

EXAMPLE 1.

$$y' = 4y - 2z, \qquad z' = 3y - z,$$

$$(4 - r)A - 2B = 0,$$

$$3A + (-1 - r)B = 0,$$

$$r^2 - 3r + 2 = 0, \qquad r_1 = 1, \qquad r_2 = 2,$$

$$3A_1 - 2B_1 = 0, \qquad 2A_2 - 2B_2 = 0,$$

$$3A_1 - 2B_1 = 0, \qquad 3A_2 - 3B_2 = 0.$$

In this case, which is the usual one, we may choose arbitrarily either A_1 or B_1 in the first pair and either A_2 or B_2 in the second. We may write the solution, for instance, in the form

$$y = A_1 e^x + A_2 e^{2x}, \qquad z = \tfrac{3}{2} A_1 e^x + A_2 e^{2x}.$$

EXAMPLE 2.

$$y' = y, \qquad z' = 2y + 5z.$$

This example is one in which certain pairs of the constants of integration cannot be chosen arbitrarily. Instead of going through the steps of the general procedure, we can solve this system directly by first determining y in the form

$$y = A_1 e^x$$

and then determining z from the second equation $z' - 5z = 2A_1 e^x$. This gives

$$z = -\tfrac{1}{2} A_1 e^x + B_2 e^{5x}.$$

Evidently, we could not choose A_2 arbitrary in this example, since it has to be zero.

EXAMPLE 3. $y' = ay, \quad z' = az.$

This is an example where the two roots are equal, $r_1 = r_2 = a$, but where it is clearly unnecessary to introduce any new type of solution, the general solution being

$$y = Ae^{ax}, \quad z = Be^{ax}.$$

This example is very special but it is the *only* example which illustrates the case of two equal roots with no new type of solution. When we come to systems of more than two simultaneous equations, we shall see that this behavior can occur for systems which are not of such special nature.

EXAMPLE 4. $y' = y, \quad z' = 3y + z.$

Again, we could first solve for y and then for z. It will be more instructive, however, not to take advantage of this possibility, but rather to follow the method outlined at the beginning of this section. We have

$$(1 - r)A + 0 \cdot B = 0,$$

$$3A + (1 - r)B = 0,$$

and therewith

$$(1 - r)^2 = 0, \quad r_1 = r_2 = 1.$$

From this we see that B_1 and B_2 are arbitrary and that $A_1 = A_2 = 0$. The solutions of this form are then

$$y = 0, \quad z = (B_1 + B_2)e^x.$$

It is apparent that we have here a case where solutions of a different form must be introduced in order to have two constants of integration. In accordance with (7), we assume the general solution of the form

$$y = (A_1x + A_2)e^x, \quad z = (B_1x + B_2)e^x,$$

where, of course, the four constants A_1, A_2, B_1, B_2 must be determined anew. By substitution in our given system of differential equations, we find

$$A_1x + A_1 + A_2 = A_1x + A_2,$$

$$B_1x + B_1 + B_2 = 3A_1x + 3A_2 + B_1x + B_2.$$

From this,

$$A_1 + A_2 = A_2, \qquad B_1 = 3A_1 + B_1, \qquad B_1 + B_2 = 3A_2 + B_2,$$

and consequently

$$A_1 = 0, \qquad B_2 \text{ arbitrary}, \qquad B_1 \text{ arbitrary}, \qquad A_2 = \tfrac{1}{3}B_1.$$

The general solution containing two arbitrary constants is seen to be

$$y = \tfrac{1}{3}B_1 e^x, \qquad z = (B_1 x + B_2)e^x.$$

For later use, let us observe that in each of these examples the solutions y and z may be written in the form

$$y = c_1 u_1(x) + c_2 u_2(x), \qquad z = c_1 v_1(x) + c_2 v_2(x), \tag{8}$$

where the pairs of functions u_1, v_1 and u_2, v_2 separately satisfy the given system of differential equations and where c_1 and c_2 are arbitrary constants.

In Example 1, we evidently have

$$u_1 = e^x, \qquad v_1 = \tfrac{3}{2}e^x,$$

$$u_2 = e^{2x}, \qquad v_2 = e^{2x},$$

and the results for the remaining examples can be written in an analogous manner.

EXERCISES

Solve the equations of Exercises 1 through 6.

1. $y' = -y + 2z, \qquad z' = 4y + z$ 2. $y' = 2y + z, \qquad z' = 2z$

3. $y' = z, \qquad z' = y$ 4. $y' = 4y - z, \qquad z' = 2y + z$

5. $y' = 4z, \qquad z' = y$ 6. $y' = 2z, \qquad z' = y + z$

7. Show that the equidimensional system of linear differential equations

$$xy' = a_1 y + a_2 z, \qquad xz' = a_3 y + a_4 z,$$

where the a_n are constants, is transformed into a system with constant coefficients by the substitution $x = e^t$.

8. Given that the system of linear differential equations

$$y' = a_1(x)y + a_2(x)z, \qquad z' = b_1(x)y + b_2(x)z,$$

has the pair of solutions

$$y = u_1, \quad z = v_1; \qquad y = u_2, \quad z = v_2,$$

where u_2 is not a constant multiple of u_1 and v_2 is not a constant multiple of v_1. Show the validity of the superposition principle for the given linear system by showing that $y = c_1 u_1 + c_2 u_2$, $z = c_1 v_1 + c_2 v_2$, where c_1 and c_2 are arbitrary constants, are also solutions of the system.

9. Show that the determinant

$$W(x) = \begin{vmatrix} u_1 & v_1 \\ u_2 & v_2 \end{vmatrix}$$

of the functions u_n and v_n in Exercise 8 satisfies the first-order differential equation

$$W' = (a_1 + b_2) W.$$

5–3 Three simultaneous first-order equations with constant coefficients. Let us next consider the system of differential equations

$$y'_1 = a_{11} y_1 + a_{12} y_2 + a_{13} y_3,$$
$$y'_2 = a_{21} y_1 + a_{22} y_2 + a_{23} y_3, \qquad (1)$$
$$y'_3 = a_{31} y_1 + a_{32} y_2 + a_{33} y_3,$$

where the coefficients a_{mn} are given constants. We look for solutions of the form

$$y_1 = A e^{rx},$$
$$y_2 = B e^{rx}, \qquad (2)$$
$$y_3 = C e^{rx}.$$

Combination of (1) and (2) leads to the following three simultaneous equations for the constants A, B, and C:

$$(a_{11} - r)A + a_{12}B + a_{13}C = 0,$$
$$a_{21}A + (a_{22} - r)B + a_{23}C = 0, \qquad (3)$$
$$a_{31}A + a_{32}B + (a_{33} - r)C = 0.$$

A necessary condition for these three equations to have solutions other than $A = B = C = 0$ is the vanishing of the determinant of the system:

$$\begin{vmatrix} a_{11} - r & a_{12} & a_{13} \\ a_{21} & a_{22} - r & a_{23} \\ a_{31} & a_{32} & a_{33} - r \end{vmatrix} = 0. \qquad (4)$$

Development of the determinant leads to a cubic for the quantity r which will have three roots, r_1, r_2, and r_3. Corresponding to these values of r, we will have coefficients A_1, B_1, C_1; A_2, B_2, C_2; A_3, B_3, C_3, which will be related by Eqs. (3), with r replaced by r_1, r_2, and r_3 respectively. Since the determinant of the system (3) vanishes for each of these values of r, we are sure that one coefficient out of each set A_1, B_1, C_1; A_2, B_2, C_2; A_3, B_3, C_3 can be chosen arbitrarily.

This means that if the three roots r_1, r_2, and r_3 are all distinct, we have in the combinations

$$y_1 = A_1 e^{r_1 x} + A_2 e^{r_2 x} + A_3 e^{r_3 x},$$
$$y_2 = B_1 e^{r_1 x} + B_2 e^{r_2 x} + B_3 e^{r_3 x}, \tag{5}$$
$$y_3 = C_1 e^{r_1 x} + C_2 e^{r_2 x} + C_3 e^{r_3 x},$$

altogether three arbitrary constants of integration.

If the roots are not distinct, it may still happen that we are left with three arbitrary constants. On the other hand, it may happen that only one or two arbitrary constants are left. We then must again find new types of solutions. We may distinguish the following two cases:

(i) $\qquad\qquad\qquad\qquad r_1 = r_2 \neq r_3,$

(ii) $\qquad\qquad\qquad\qquad r_1 = r_2 = r_3.$

In the first of these, the general solution may contain terms of the form $xe^{r_1 x}$ and be of the form

$$y_1 = (A_1 x + A_2)e^{r_1 x} + A_3 e^{r_3 x},$$
$$y_2 = (B_1 x + B_2)e^{r_1 x} + B_3 e^{r_3 x}, \tag{6}$$
$$y_3 = (C_1 x + C_2)e^{r_1 x} + C_3 e^{r_3 x}.$$

In the second case, the general solution may contain terms of the form $x^2 e^{r_1 x}$ and $xe^{r_1 x}$ and be of the form

$$y_1 = (A_1 x^2 + A_2 x + A_3)e^{r_1 x},$$
$$y_2 = (B_1 x^2 + B_2 x + B_3)e^{r_1 x}, \tag{7}$$
$$y_3 = (C_1 x^2 + C_2 x + C_3)e^{r_1 x}.$$

We shall always be safe in assuming the solutions in the forms (6) or (7) when case (i) or case (ii) is given, although it may turn out that the coefficients of all terms with $xe^{r_1 x}$ and $x^2 e^{r_1 x}$ become zero in the actual solution.

Exercises

Solve the following systems of differential equations.

1. $dx/dt = 2y, \quad dy/dt = 2z, \quad dz/dt = 2x$

2. $dx/dt = 2x, \quad dy/dt = 3x - 2y, \quad dz/dt = 2y + 3z$

3. $dx/dt = x + y, \quad dy/dt = z - x, \quad dz/dt = y + z$

4. $dy_1/dx = y_1 + 2y_2 + 3y_3, \quad dy_2/dx = 2y_1 + y_2 + y_3,$

   $dy_3/dx = 3y_1 + y_2 + 2y_3$ [*Hint.* Determine one real root of the auxiliary equation numerically or graphically within two-figure accuracy and
   find the other two roots from a remaining quadratic.]

5. Show that the expressions

$$y_1 = \alpha_{11}A_1 e^{r_1 x} + \alpha_{12}A_2 e^{r_2 x} + \alpha_{13}A_3 e^{r_3 x},$$
$$y_2 = \alpha_{21}A_1 e^{r_1 x} + \alpha_{22}A_2 e^{r_2 x} + \alpha_{23}A_3 e^{r_3 x},$$
$$y_3 = \alpha_{31}A_1 e^{r_1 x} + \alpha_{32}A_2 e^{r_2 x} + \alpha_{33}A_3 e^{r_3 x},$$

in which the quantities r_m and α_{mn} are given constants and the quantities A_m
are arbitrary constants, satisfy the system of differential equations

$$\begin{vmatrix} \alpha_{11} & \alpha_{12} & \alpha_{13} \\ \alpha_{21} & \alpha_{22} & \alpha_{23} \\ \alpha_{31} & \alpha_{32} & \alpha_{33} \end{vmatrix} \frac{dy_m}{dx} = \begin{vmatrix} \alpha_{m1}r_1 & \alpha_{m2}r_2 & \alpha_{m3}r_3 \\ \alpha_{21} & \alpha_{22} & \alpha_{23} \\ \alpha_{31} & \alpha_{32} & \alpha_{33} \end{vmatrix} y_1$$

$$+ \begin{vmatrix} \alpha_{11} & \alpha_{12} & \alpha_{13} \\ \alpha_{m1}r_1 & \alpha_{m2}r_2 & \alpha_{m3}r_3 \\ \alpha_{31} & \alpha_{32} & \alpha_{33} \end{vmatrix} y_2 + \begin{vmatrix} \alpha_{11} & \alpha_{12} & \alpha_{13} \\ \alpha_{21} & \alpha_{22} & \alpha_{23} \\ \alpha_{m1}r_1 & \alpha_{m2}r_2 & \alpha_{m3}r_3 \end{vmatrix} y_3.$$

**5–4 Laplace transform solution of simultaneous linear first-order
equations with constant coefficients.** The method of the Laplace transform, which we introduced in the preceding chapter, is as suitable for
systems of linear differential equations with constant coefficients as it is
for the single equation.

Let us consider the system

$$\frac{dy_j}{dx} = \sum_{k=1}^{n} a_{jk} y_k + f_j(x), \quad j = 1, \ldots, n \tag{1}$$

with initial conditions

$$y_j(0) = y_{j,0}. \tag{2}$$

Multiplication of (1) by e^{-px} and integration from zero to infinity leads to
a system of algebraic equations for the Laplace transforms

$$Y_j(p) = \int_0^\infty y_j(x) e^{-px} \, dx, \tag{3}$$

which read, under the assumption that $\lim\limits_{x\to\infty} e^{-px}y_j(x) = 0$,

$$pY_j - y_{j,0} = \sum_{k=1}^{n} a_{jk}Y_k + F_j$$

or

$$\sum_{k=1}^{n} (a_{jk} - p\,\delta_{jk})Y_k = -F_j - y_{j,0}, \qquad j = 1, 2, \ldots, n, \qquad (4)$$

where

$$\delta_{jk} = \begin{cases} 1, & j = k, \\ 0, & j \neq k. \end{cases} \qquad (5)$$

Equations (4) are linear algebraic equations for the transforms Y_k. We note, by a consideration of Cramer's rule, that the solution of (4) will be of the form

$$Y_k = \frac{\sum_j (F_j + y_{j,0})\,\Delta_{jk}(p)}{\Delta(p)}, \qquad (6)$$

where Δ is an nth-degree polynomial in p and the Δ_{jk} are $(n - 1)$st-degree polynomials in p.

We may go from the transforms $Y_k(p)$ to the solution functions $y_k(x)$ if we can find the right side of (6) in a transform table or if we can break down this right side into portions, each of which can be found in a transform table. It is clear that the process of partial fraction decomposition and Eq. (5), Section 4–7, for the product of two Laplace transforms have an important part in this method of solution.

EXAMPLE. The system of differential equations

$$y_1' = 4y_1 - 2y_2 + 1,$$
$$y_2' = 3y_1 - y_2,$$

with the initial conditions $y_{1,0} = 1$, $y_{2,0} = 2$, corresponds to the algebraic system

$$pY_1 - 1 = 4Y_1 - 2Y_2 + p^{-1},$$
$$pY_2 - 2 = 3Y_1 - Y_2.$$

The solution of the algebraic system is

$$Y_1 = \frac{(p-1)^2}{p(p-1)(p-2)} = \frac{p-1}{p(p-2)} = \frac{1}{2p} + \frac{1}{2(p-2)},$$
$$Y_2 = \frac{2p^2 - 5p + 3}{p(p-1)(p-2)} = \frac{3}{2p} + \frac{1}{2(p-2)}.$$

From the transform table in Section 4-8,

$$y_1 = \tfrac{1}{2} + \tfrac{1}{2}e^{2x}, \qquad y_2 = \tfrac{3}{2} + \tfrac{1}{2}e^{2x}.$$

EXERCISES

Solve the systems of differential equations in Exercises 1 through 6.

1. $y_1' = y_2, \quad y_2' = y_1; \qquad y_{1,0} = 1, \quad y_{2,0} = 0$

2. $y_1' = y_2, \quad y_2' = y_1 + e^{2x}; \qquad y_{1,0} = y_{2,0} = 0$

3. $y_1' = y_2, \quad y_2' = y_1 + e^{x}; \qquad y_{1,0} = y_{2,0} = 0$

4. $y_1' = 2y_2, \quad y_2' = 2y_3, \quad y_3' = 2y_1; \qquad y_{1,0} = 1, \quad y_{2,0} = y_{3,0} = 0$

5. $y_1' = 4y_1 - y_2, \quad y_2' = 2y_1 + y_2; \qquad y_{1,0} = 0, \quad y_{2,0} = 1$

6. $y_1' = 4y_2, \quad y_2' = y_1; \qquad y_{1,0} = 1, \quad y_{2,0} = 1$

5-5 General properties of solutions of systems of linear differential equations. We turn now to the consideration of the following system of differential equations

$$y_1' = p_{11}(x)y_1 + \cdots + p_{1n}(x)y_n + f_1(x),$$
$$\vdots \tag{1}$$
$$y_n' = p_{n1}(x)y_1 + \cdots + p_{nn}(x)y_n + f_n(x),$$

where p_{jk} and f_j are given continuous functions of x, and to the associated *homogeneous* system

$$y_1' = p_{11}y_1 + \cdots + p_{1n}y_n,$$
$$\vdots \tag{2}$$
$$y_n' = p_{n1}y_1 + \cdots + p_{nn}y_n.$$

Let

$$y_1 = u_{1k}, \quad y_2 = u_{2k}, \quad \ldots, \quad y_n = u_{nk} \tag{3}$$

be a set of particular solutions of the homogeneous system (2) and let us assume that we have n such sets $(k = 1, \ldots, n)$. It is then easy to show that the linear combinations

$$y_1 = c_1 u_{11} + c_2 u_{12} + \cdots + c_n u_{1n},$$
$$\vdots \tag{4}$$
$$y_n = c_1 u_{n1} + c_2 u_{n2} + \cdots + c_n u_{nn},$$

with arbitrary values of the constants $c_1, \ldots, c_n$ also satisfy (2). This is the form which the superposition principle assumes for the linear homogeneous system (2).

Since the set of solutions (4) contains n arbitrary constants, we expect that if the particular solutions u_{jk} are of sufficient generality we have in (4) the general solution of the given system (2). We shall now establish a condition which the functions u_{jk} must satisfy in order that (4) does, in fact, represent the general solution.

We shall assume as a given fact that the initial value problem consisting of the differential equations (2) and the initial conditions $y_k(x_0) = y_{k,0}$ has a unique solution in some interval $a < x < b$. (This is a consequence of the general existence and uniqueness theorem mentioned in Section 1.) This means that Eqs. (4) represent the general solution of the given system of differential equations (2) provided that the following set of simultaneous equations for the determination of the constants c_j:

$$c_1 u_{11}(x_0) + \cdots + c_n u_{1n}(x_0) = y_{1,0},$$
$$\vdots \tag{5}$$
$$c_1 u_{n1}(x_0) + \cdots + c_n u_{nn}(x_0) = y_{n,0},$$

has a solution for every x_0 in the interval (a, b).

A necessary and sufficient condition for the solvability of (5) with arbitrarily given terms on the right is the nonvanishing of the determinant of the system (5). If we write

$$W(x) = \begin{vmatrix} u_{11}(x) & \cdots & u_{1n}(x) \\ \cdots & \cdots & \cdots \\ u_{n1}(x) & \cdots & u_{nn}(x) \end{vmatrix} \tag{6}$$

(we call this the Wronskian of the system), then we must have $W(x_0) \neq 0$, and this must be so for all values of x_0 in the range in which Eq. (4) represents the general solution.

The necessary and sufficient condition for (4) to be the general solution of (2) in an interval $a < x < b$ is then the condition

$$W(x) \neq 0, \qquad a < x < b. \tag{7}$$

An important fact in this connection is the following. *If the individual solution functions u_{jk} are differentiable in an interval $a < x < b$, and if in the same interval the sum $p_{11} + p_{22} + \cdots + p_{nn}$ is continuous, then $W(x) \neq 0$ in the entire interval, provided $W(x_0) \neq 0$ for some single point x_0 in the interval (a, b).* We are then merely required, in order to see whether (4) is the general solution of (2), to establish the nonvanishing of W at some conveniently chosen point x_0 in the interval in which the functions p_{jk} are continuous.

The proof of the foregoing is accomplished by obtaining a differential equation for W and by interpreting the explicit solution of this differential equation.

The derivative of W is given by a sum of n determinants, as follows:

$$\frac{dW}{dx} = \begin{vmatrix} u'_{11} & \cdots & u'_{1n} \\ u_{21} & \cdots & u_{2n} \\ \cdots & \cdots & \cdots \\ u_{n1} & \cdots & u_{nn} \end{vmatrix} + \begin{vmatrix} u_{11} & \cdots & u_{1n} \\ u'_{21} & \cdots & u'_{2n} \\ \cdots & \cdots & \cdots \\ u_{n1} & \cdots & u_{nn} \end{vmatrix} + \cdots + \begin{vmatrix} u_{11} & \cdots & u_{1n} \\ u_{21} & \cdots & u_{2n} \\ \cdots & \cdots & \cdots \\ u'_{n1} & \cdots & u'_{nn} \end{vmatrix}.$$

In this we write the derivatives u'_{jk} as linear combinations of u_{rs}, in accordance with the differential equations (2). In this way, each of the n determinants becomes in turn the sum of n determinants. Of these $n - 1$ are zero, since the corresponding elements of two rows are equal, except for a common factor. The result is

$$\frac{dW}{dx} = (p_{11} + p_{22} + \cdots + p_{nn}) \begin{vmatrix} u_{11} & \cdots & u_{1n} \\ u_{21} & \cdots & u_{2n} \\ \cdots & \cdots & \cdots \\ u_{n1} & \cdots & u_{nn} \end{vmatrix}$$

or

$$\frac{dW}{dx} = (p_{11} + p_{22} + \cdots + p_{nn})W. \tag{8}$$

From this,

$$W(x) = W(x_0)e^{\int_{x_0}^{x} (p_{11}+p_{22}+\cdots+p_{nn})dx}, \tag{9}$$

where x_0 may be any fixed point in the interval (a, b). We see that if $W(x_0) \neq 0$ then $W(x) \neq 0$ throughout this interval. And that is what we intended to prove.

We return now to the system of nonhomogeneous equations (1). In the same manner as above, we show that if we add to the general solution (4) of the associated homogeneous system (2) *any* set of particular solutions $y_{1,p}, y_{2,p}, \ldots, y_{n,p}$ of the nonhomogeneous system, we will have obtained the general solution of the given nonhomogeneous system.

EXAMPLE. The system of differential equations

$$y'_1 = 4y_1 - 2y_2, \qquad y'_2 = 3y_1 - y_2$$

has the solution

$$y_1 = c_1 u_{11} + c_2 u_{12}, \qquad y_2 = c_1 u_{21} + c_2 u_{22},$$

where

$$u_{11} = e^x, \qquad u_{12} = e^{2x}, \qquad u_{21} = \tfrac{3}{2}e^x, \qquad u_{22} = e^{2x}.$$

The Wronskian of the system is

$$W = \begin{vmatrix} e^x & e^{2x} \\ \frac{3}{2}e^x & e^{2x} \end{vmatrix} = -\frac{1}{2}e^{3x} \neq 0,$$

and this satisfies the first-order equation $W' = (4 - 1)W$.

The values of the constants c_1 and c_2 may be determined from assumed initial conditions. For example, if

$$y_1(0) = 1, \qquad y_2(0) = 0,$$

then

$$c_1 + c_2 = 1, \qquad \tfrac{3}{2}c_1 + c_2 = 0$$

and

$$c_1 = -2, \qquad c_2 = 3.$$

EXERCISES

1, 2, 3. Determine the constants of integration in the general solution of Exercises 1, 2, 3 of Section 5–2 by requiring that the solutions satisfy the initial conditions

(a) $y(0) = 0, \qquad z(0) = 1$ \qquad (b) $y(1) = 1, \qquad z(1) = 2.$

4. Show that the system of differential equations

$$y_1' = a_{11}y_1 + a_{12}y_2, \qquad y_2' = a_{21}y_1 + a_{22}y_2,$$

where $a_{12} \neq 0$, $a_{21} \neq 0$ and $(a_{11} - a_{22})^2 + 4a_{12}a_{21} \neq 0$, has solutions of the form

$$y_1 = c_1 u_{11} + c_2 u_{12}, \qquad y_2 = c_1 u_{21} + c_2 u_{22},$$

where

$$u_{11} = e^{r_1 x}, \qquad\qquad u_{12} = e^{r_2 x},$$

$$u_{21} = \frac{r_1 - a_{11}}{a_{12}} e^{r_1 x}, \qquad u_{22} = \frac{r_2 - a_{11}}{a_{12}} e^{r_2 x},$$

and where

$$r_{1,2} = \tfrac{1}{2}\left(a_{11} + a_{22} \pm \sqrt{(a_{11} - a_{22})^2 + 4a_{12}a_{21}}\right).$$

5. Show that the solution in Exercise 4 is the general solution of the given system of differential equations.

6, 7, 8. Determine the constants of integration in the general solution of Exercises 1, 2, 3 of Section 5–3 by requiring that the solutions satisfy the initial conditions $x(0) = 1$, $y(0) = 0$, $z(0) = 0$.

5–6 The method of variation of parameters. To obtain the general solution of the nonhomogeneous system (1) of the preceding section, we proceed as follows. We modify the general solution of the homogeneous system by writing

$$y_1 = C_1(x)u_{11} + C_2(x)u_{12} + \cdots + C_n(x)u_{1n},$$
$$\vdots \tag{1}$$
$$y_n = C_1(x)u_{n1} + C_2(x)u_{n2} + \cdots + C_n(x)u_{nn}.$$

From this, by differentiation,

$$y_1' = C_1'u_{11} + \cdots + C_n'u_{1n} + C_1u_{11}' + \cdots + C_nu_{1n}',$$
$$\vdots \tag{2}$$
$$y_n' = C_1'u_{n1} + \cdots + C_n'u_{nn} + C_1u_{n1}' + \cdots + C_nu_{nn}'.$$

We introduce (2) into the given system (1) of the preceding section and make use of the fact that the sets $u_{1j}, u_{2j}, \ldots, u_{nj}$ represent solutions of the associated homogeneous system. This leaves us with the following equations for the determination of the coefficient functions $C_1, \ldots, C_n$:

$$C_1'u_{11} + \cdots + C_n'u_{1n} = f_1,$$
$$\vdots \tag{3}$$
$$C_1'u_{n1} + \cdots + C_n'u_{nn} = f_n.$$

Since the determinant of this system, $W(x)$, does not vanish, we may solve (3) for the quantities $C_1', \ldots, C_n'$. The coefficient functions $C_1, \ldots, C_n$, themselves are obtained from this by integration.

It is worth noting that, in contrast to what we encountered in treating a single nth-order differential equation, the n conditions imposed on the coefficient functions C_j are all a direct consequence of the given differential equations. The method of variation of parameters appears thus in a somewhat simpler form for systems of first-order equations than it appears for the single nth-order equation.

EXAMPLE.

$$y_1' = 4y_1 - 2y_2 + f_1(x), \qquad y_2' = 3y_1 - y_2 + f_2(x).$$

From Example 1 of Section 5–2,

$$y_1 = C_1e^x + C_2e^{2x}, \qquad y_2 = \tfrac{3}{2}C_1e^x + C_2e^{2x}.$$

From Eq. (3),

$$C_1'e^x + C_2'e^{2x} = f_1, \qquad \tfrac{3}{2}C_1'e^x + C_2'e^{2x} = f_2,$$

and then

$$C_1 = \int \frac{e^{2x}(f_1 - f_2)}{W}\, dx, \qquad C_2 = \int \frac{e^x(f_2 - \tfrac{3}{2}f_1)}{W}\, dx,$$

where $W = -\tfrac{1}{2}e^{3x}$.

Exercises

Using the known solutions of the associated reduced systems, solve the following equations.

1. $y_1' = -y_1 + 2y_2 - e^{3x}$, $y_2' = 4y_1 + y_2$ (see Ex. 1, Sec. 5–2)

2. $y_1' = y_2$, $y_2' = y_1 + \cos x + 2e^x$ (see Ex. 3, Sec. 5–2)

3. $xy_1' = y_2$, $xy_2' = y_1 + x$ (see Exs. 3 and 7, Sec. 5–2)

4. $y_1' = 4y_2 + 2e^{2x}$, $y_2' = y_1$ (see Ex. 5, Sec. 5–2)

5. $y_1' = 2y_1 + x$, $y_2' = 3y_1 - 2y_2$, $y_3' = 2y_2 + 3y_3$ (see Ex. 2, Sec. 5–3)

5–7 Taylor series solutions for systems of linear differential equations with variable coefficients. We found in Chapter 3 that the linear differential equation

$$y'' + p(x)y' + q(x)y = 0 \tag{1}$$

possesses a general solution of the form

$$y = c_0 + c_1 x + c_2 x^2 + \cdots, \tag{2}$$

where c_0 and c_1 are arbitrary constants of integration, provided the coefficient functions p and q could be written in the form

$$p(x) = p_0 + p_1 x + p_2 x^2 + \cdots, \quad q(x) = q_0 + q_1 x + q_2 x^2 + \cdots \tag{3}$$

In these circumstances, the point $x = 0$ was called an ordinary point of the differential equation (1). The corresponding results for the single nth-order equation were stated in Section 4–9.

The foregoing is readily extended to systems of ordinary linear differential equations. We shall show this for the system of two simultaneous linear differential equations

$$y' = P(x)y + Q(x)z, \qquad z' = R(x)y + S(x)z. \tag{4}$$

We call the point $x = 0$ an *ordinary point* for the system (4) if all the coefficient functions may be developed into Taylor series about the point $x = 0$:

$$P(x) = p_0 + p_1 x + p_2 x^2 + \cdots, \quad Q(x) = q_0 + q_1 x + q_2 x^2 + \cdots,$$
$$R(x) = r_0 + r_1 x + r_2 x^2 + \cdots, \quad S(x) = s_0 + s_1 x + s_2 x^2 + \cdots \tag{5}$$

Under these conditions we will be able to determine solutions of (4) by writing

$$y = a_0 + a_1 x + a_2 x^2 + \cdots, \quad z = b_0 + b_1 x + b_2 x^2 + \cdots, \tag{6}$$

where a_0 and b_0 are arbitrary constants of integration.

Introduction of (5) and (6) into the system (4) gives us

$$
\begin{aligned}
a_1 + 2a_2 x &+ 3a_3 x^2 + \cdots \\
&= (p_0 + p_1 x + p_2 x^2 + \cdots)(a_0 + a_1 x + a_2 x^2 + \cdots) \\
&\quad + (q_0 + q_1 x + q_2 x^2 + \cdots)(b_0 + b_1 x + b_2 x^2 + \cdots), \\
b_1 + 2b_2 x &+ 3b_3 x^2 + \cdots \\
&= (r_0 + r_1 x + r_2 x^2 + \cdots)(a_0 + a_1 x + a_2 x^2 + \cdots) \\
&\quad + (s_0 + s_1 x + s_2 x^2 + \cdots)(b_0 + b_1 x + b_2 x^2 + \cdots).
\end{aligned}
\tag{7}
$$

We now multiply term by term on the right of Eqs. (7) and equate coefficients of corresponding powers of x on the left and on the right. In this way, we obtain the following system of conditions:

$$a_1 = p_0 a_0 + q_0 b_0, \quad b_1 = r_0 a_0 + s_0 b_0, \tag{8}$$

$$
\begin{aligned}
2a_2 &= p_0 a_1 + p_1 a_0 + q_0 b_1 + q_1 b_0, \\
2b_2 &= r_0 a_1 + r_1 a_0 + s_0 b_1 + s_1 b_0,
\end{aligned}
\tag{9}
$$

$$
\begin{aligned}
3a_3 &= p_0 a_2 + p_1 a_1 + p_2 a_0 + q_0 b_2 + q_1 b_1 + q_2 b_0, \\
3b_3 &= r_0 a_2 + r_1 a_1 + r_2 a_0 + s_0 b_2 + s_1 b_1 + s_2 b_0,
\end{aligned}
\tag{10}
$$

$$\vdots$$

$$
\begin{aligned}
(n+1)a_{n+1} &= p_0 a_n + p_1 a_{n-1} + \cdots + p_n a_0 \\
&\quad + q_0 b_n + q_1 b_{n-1} + \cdots + q_n b_0, \\
(n+1)b_{n+1} &= r_0 a_n + r_1 a_{n-1} + \cdots + r_n a_0 \\
&\quad + s_0 b_n + s_1 b_{n-1} + \cdots + s_n b_0,
\end{aligned}
\tag{11}
$$

$$\vdots$$

Equations (8) through (11) show that the solution coefficients a_0 and b_0 remain arbitrary and that the other coefficients a_1, b_1; a_2, b_2; ... ; a_{n+1}, b_{n+1}; ... may be determined successively in terms of a_0 and b_0.

The extension of this procedure to systems of n equations of the form (2) of Section 5–5, where each of the coefficient functions p_{jk} can be developed in powers of x as in (5) above, is a simple matter. The actual calculations, however, will often require a good deal of time.

EXAMPLE.

$$y' = y + xz, \qquad z' = 2xy + z,$$
$$y = a_0 + a_1 x + \cdots, \qquad z = b_0 + b_1 x + \cdots,$$

$$a_1 = a_0, \qquad\qquad b_1 = b_0,$$
$$2a_2 = a_1 + b_0 = a_0 + b_0, \qquad 2b_2 = 2a_0 + b_1 = 2a_0 + b_0,$$
$$3a_3 = a_2 + b_1 = \tfrac{1}{2}a_0 + \tfrac{3}{2}b_0, \qquad 3b_3 = 2a_1 + b_2 = 3a_0 + \tfrac{1}{2}b_0,$$

$$\vdots \qquad\qquad\qquad \vdots$$

$$(n+1)a_{n+1} = a_n + b_{n-1}, \qquad (n+1)b_{n+1} = 2a_{n-1} + b_n,$$

$$\vdots \qquad\qquad\qquad \vdots$$

$$y = a_0\left(1 + x + \frac{x^2}{2} + \frac{x^3}{6} + \cdots\right) + b_0\left(\frac{x^2}{2} + \frac{x^3}{2} + \cdots\right),$$

$$z = a_0\left(x^2 + x^3 + \cdots\right) + b_0\left(1 + x + \frac{x^2}{2} + \frac{x^3}{6} + \cdots\right).$$

EXERCISES

For each of the following three systems of differential equations, determine a_1, a_2, a_3, b_1, b_2, b_3 in terms of a_0 and b_0 in the series developments (6).

1. $y' = xy + 3x^2 z, \qquad z' = (1 + x)y$
2. $y' = e^x y + z, \qquad z' = y + z$
3. $(1 - x)y' = z, \qquad z' = 2y - z$

4. Show that the system

$$xy' = 2y + z, \qquad xz' = 3y + 2z$$

has no solution expressible as power series of the form (6).

5. Show that the general solution of the system

$$xy' = 2y + z, \qquad xz' = 4y + 2z$$

may be obtained by power series of the form (6), although the point $x = 0$ is not an ordinary point of the system.

6. Show that the system of differential equations

$$xy' = (p_0 + p_1 x + \cdots)y + (q_0 + q_1 x + \cdots)z,$$
$$xz' = (r_0 + r_1 x + \cdots)y + (s_0 + s_1 x + \cdots)z$$

has solutions of the form $y = a_0 x^k + a_1 x^{k+1} + \cdots$, $z = b_0 x^k + b_1 x^{k+1} + \cdots$. Obtain an equation (the indicial equation) determining admissible values of the exponent k. In analogy to what was done for the single second- and nth-order differential equation, the point $x = 0$ for this system of differential equations is called a regular singular point.

Determine the roots of the indicial equation for the systems in Exercises 7, 8, and 9.

7. $xy' = 2y + z$, $xz' = 3y + 2z$
8. $xy' = 2y + z$, $xz' = 4y + 2z$
9. $xy' = y \sin x + z \cos x$, $xz' = x^2 y + e^x z$

5-8 Taylor series solutions for systems of nonlinear differential equations. To illustrate the use of power series for the solution of nonlinear systems of differential equations, let us briefly consider the system

$$y' = f(x, y, z), \qquad z' = g(x, y, z), \tag{1}$$

where f and g are given functions of the independent variable x and the dependent variables y and z.

In analogy to what we did for the equation $dy/dx = f(x, y)$ we assume first that the initial conditions are of the form

$$y(0) = 0, \qquad z(0) = 0. \tag{2}$$

Problems with more general initial conditions may be reduced to the present form.

We assume that f and g are of such nature that series solutions of (1) and (2) of the form

$$y = a_1 x + a_2 x^2 + \cdots = \sum_{j=1}^{\infty} a_j x^j,$$
$$z = b_1 x + b_2 x^2 + \cdots = \sum_{j=1}^{\infty} b_j x^j \tag{3}$$

are possible. In general, this means that all partial derivatives of f and g at the point $x = y = z = 0$ must exist.

The work of obtaining the coefficients in the solution series is much simplified if the functions f and g are expanded in the form

$$f(x, y, z) = A_{000} + A_{100}x + A_{010}y + A_{001}z + A_{200}x^2 + A_{020}y^2$$
$$+ A_{002}z^2 + A_{110}xy + A_{101}xz + A_{011}yz + \cdots$$

or, written more briefly,

$$f(x, y, z) = \sum_{k=0}^{\infty} \sum_{m=0}^{\infty} \sum_{n=0}^{\infty} A_{kmn}x^k y^m z^n, \tag{4}$$

and

$$g(x, y, z) = \sum_{k=0}^{\infty} \sum_{m=0}^{\infty} \sum_{n=0}^{\infty} B_{kmn}x^k y^m z^n. \tag{5}$$

We have the following formula:

$$A_{kmn} = \frac{1}{k!\,m!\,n!} \left[\frac{\partial^{k+m+n} f}{\partial x^k\, \partial y^m\, \partial z^n} \right]_{x=0,y=0,z=0} \tag{6}$$

and an analogous formula for B_{kmn}.

Introduction of (3), (4), and (5) into (1) gives the following relations for the determination of the solution coefficients a_j and b_j:

$$\sum_{j=1}^{\infty} ja_j x^{j-1} = \sum_{k=0}^{\infty} \sum_{m=0}^{\infty} \sum_{n=0}^{\infty} A_{kmn}x^k \left(\sum_{j=1}^{\infty} a_j x^j \right)^m \left(\sum_{j=1}^{\infty} b_j x^j \right)^n,$$
$$\sum_{j=1}^{\infty} jb_j x^{j-1} = \sum_{k=0}^{\infty} \sum_{m=0}^{\infty} \sum_{n=0}^{\infty} B_{kmn}x^k \left(\sum_{j=1}^{\infty} a_j x^j \right)^m \left(\sum_{j=1}^{\infty} b_j x^j \right)^n. \tag{7}$$

We must now carry out the indicated multiplications on the right and equate coefficients of corresponding powers of x on the left and on the right. By doing this, we shall be able to determine successively the coefficients $a_1, b_1; a_2, b_2; \ldots$

Convergence of the solution series obtained can be investigated similarly to what we did in connection with the equation $dy/dx = f(x, y)$. In particular, one can show that if the series (4) and (5) converge in the rectangular parallelepiped $|x| < a$, $|y| < b$, $|z| < c$, and if in this parallelepiped $|f| < M$, and $|g| < N$, then the series solutions (3) also possess intervals of convergence the lengths of which are bounded from below by a definite positive expression depending upon a, b, c, M, and N.

EXAMPLE 1. We take the system

$$y' = 1 + x^2 + yz^2, \qquad z' = 2 + xy^2 + z$$

with the initial conditions (2). If we insert the series (3) into the given system, we obtain

$$a_1 + 2a_2x + 3a_3x^2 + \cdots$$
$$= 1 + x^2 + (a_1x + a_2x^2 + \cdots)(b_1x + b_2x^2 + \cdots)^2$$
$$= 1 + x^2 + a_1b_1^2x^3 + (a_2b_1^2 + 2a_1b_1b_2)x^4 + \cdots,$$

$$b_1 + 2b_2x + 3b_3x^2 + \cdots$$
$$= 2 + x(a_1x + a_2x^2 + \cdots)^2 + (b_1x + b_2x^2 + \cdots)$$
$$= 2 + b_1x + b_2x^2 + (a_1^2 + b_3)x^3 + (2a_1a_2 + b_4)x^4 + \cdots$$

On equating the coefficients of like powers of x in the preceding two equations, we have

$$a_1 = 1, \quad b_1 = 2; \quad 2a_2 = 0, \quad 2b_2 = b_1;$$
$$3a_3 = 1, \quad 3b_3 = b_2; \quad 4a_4 = a_1b_1^2, \quad 4b_4 = a_1^2 + b_3;$$
$$5a_5 = a_2b_1^2 + 2a_1b_1b_2, \quad 5b_5 = 2a_1a_2 + b_4; \quad \ldots$$

From these, we find successively

$$a_1 = 1, \quad b_1 = 2; \quad a_2 = 0, \quad b_2 = 1; \quad a_3 = \tfrac{1}{3}, \quad b_3 = \tfrac{1}{3};$$
$$a_4 = 1, \quad b_4 = \tfrac{1}{3}; \quad a_5 = \tfrac{4}{5}, \quad b_5 = \tfrac{1}{15}; \quad \ldots$$

The first few terms of the solution series are seen to be

$$y = x + \tfrac{1}{3}x^3 + x^4 + \tfrac{4}{5}x^5 + \cdots,$$
$$z = 2x + x^2 + \tfrac{1}{3}x^3 + \tfrac{1}{3}x^4 + \tfrac{1}{15}x^5 + \cdots$$

If we wish to apply this same procedure in conjunction with the initial conditions

$$y(x_0) = y_0, \qquad z(x_0) = z_0, \tag{8}$$

where x_0, y_0, and z_0 are not necessarily zero, we modify the form of our series solutions (6) to

$$y - y_0 = \sum_{j=1}^{\infty} a_j(x - x_0)^j,$$

$$\tag{9}$$

$$z - z_0 = \sum_{j=1}^{\infty} b_j(x - x_0)^j$$

and we now assume that f and g are expanded in the form

$$f = \sum_{k=0}^{\infty} \sum_{m=0}^{\infty} \sum_{n=0}^{\infty} A_{kmn}(x - x_0)^k (y - y_0)^m (z - z_0)^n, \qquad (10)$$

$$g = \sum_{k=0}^{\infty} \sum_{m=0}^{\infty} \sum_{n=0}^{\infty} B_{kmn}(x - x_0)^k (y - y_0)^m (z - z_0)^n, \qquad (11)$$

where, of course, the coefficients a_j, b_j, A_{kmn}, and B_{kmn} are different from the corresponding coefficients in (3), (4), and (5).

The use of (9), (10), and (11) in conjunction with the initial conditions (8) makes possible a much simpler determination of the solution coefficients a_j and b_j than would be the case if we were to work with Eqs. (3), (4), and (5).

EXAMPLE 2.

$$y' = 1 + y + z^2, \qquad z' = 2 + x + y, \qquad y(1) = 1, \qquad z(1) = 2.$$

We first expand the two right members in series in powers of $x - 1$, $y - 1$, and $z - 2$, as follows:

$$1 + y + z^2 = 6 + (y - 1) + 4(z - 2) + (z - 2)^2,$$
$$2 + x + y = 4 + (x - 1) + (y - 1).$$

If we then insert the series

$$y - 1 = a_1(x - 1) + a_2(x - 1)^2 + \cdots,$$
$$z - 2 = b_1(x - 1) + b_2(x - 1)^2 + \cdots$$

into the given system, we obtain

$$a_1 + 2a_2(x - 1) + 3a_3(x - 1)^2 + \cdots$$
$$= 6 + [a_1(x - 1) + a_2(x - 1)^2 + \cdots] + 4[b_1(x - 1)$$
$$+ b_2(x - 1)^2 + \cdots] + [b_1(x - 1) + b_2(x - 1)^2 + \cdots]^2$$
$$= 6 + (a_1 + 4b_1)(x - 1) + (a_2 + 4b_2 + b_1^2)(x - 1)^2 + \cdots,$$
$$b_1 + 2b_2(x - 1) + 3b_3(x - 1)^2 + \cdots$$
$$= 4 + (x - 1) + [a_1(x - 1) + a_2(x - 1)^2 + \cdots]$$
$$= 4 + (a_1 + 1)(x - 1) + a_2(x - 1)^2 + \cdots.$$

On equating the coefficients of like powers of $x - 1$ in these two equations, we obtain

$$a_1 = 6, \quad b_1 = 4; \quad 2a_2 = a_1 + 4b_1 = 22, \quad 2b_2 = a_1 + 1 = 7;$$

$$3a_3 = a_2 + 4b_2 + b_1^2 = 41, \quad 3b_3 = a_2 = 11; \quad \cdots$$

and the first few terms of the solution series are

$$y - 1 = 6(x - 1) + 11(x - 1)^2 + \tfrac{41}{3}(x - 1)^3 + \cdots,$$

$$z - 2 = 4(x - 1) + \tfrac{7}{2}(x - 1)^2 + \tfrac{11}{3}(x - 1)^3 + \cdots.$$

EXERCISES

Find the first four nonvanishing terms in each of the two series developments of the solutions of each of the following three systems of differential equations with initial conditions $y(0) = 0$, $z(0) = 0$.

1. $y' = 1 + y + z^2$, $\quad z' = 2 + \tfrac{1}{2}x + y$
2. $y' = 2 + x + z$, $\quad z' = 1 + y^2$
3. $y' = xz - 1$, $\quad z' = 2 + x + yz$

4. Find the first four nonvanishing terms in the solutions series

$$y = a_0 + a_1(x - 1) + a_2(x - 1)^2 + \cdots,$$

$$z = b_0 + b_1(x - 1) + b_2(x - 1)^2 + \cdots$$

of the system

$$y' = 1 + z, \quad z' = y^2 + x + z$$

with the initial conditions $y(1) = 2$, $z(1) = 4$.

MISCELLANEOUS EXERCISES. CHAPTER 5

Obtain a system of two simultaneous differential equations for y and z with the solutions given in Exercises 1 through 3.

1. $y^2 + z^2 + c_1x + c_2 = 0$, $\quad y^3 + z^2 + c_1x^2 + c_2 = 0$
2. $y = A_1e^x + A_2e^{2x}$, $\quad z = A_1e^x - 2A_2e^{2x}$
3. $y = A_1e^{2x}$, $\quad z = (3A_1x + 2A_2)e^{2x}$

4, 5. Show that the given solutions in Exercises 2 and 3 are the general solutions.

Solve the following systems of differential equations:

6. $y_1' = y_1 + 2y_2$, $\quad y_2' = 2y_1 + 4y_2$

7. $dx/dt = y + z$, $dy/dt = z + x$, $dz/dt = x + y$

8. $y_1' = 4y_1 - y_2 + e^x$, $y_2' = 2y_1 + y_2$ (see Ex. 4 of Section 5–2)

9. $y_1' = 4y_2 - 2x$, $y_2' = y_1 + x$ (see Ex. 5 of Section 5–2)

10. $y' = \frac{1}{3}e^x - y - \frac{2}{3}z$, $z' = -x + \frac{4}{3}y + z$; $y(0) = 1$, $z(0) = 3$

11. $y' = ay + bz$, $z' = \lambda ay + \lambda bz$ (λ, a, b constants, $a^2 + b^2 \neq 0$)

12. $y_1' = 4y_1 - y_2 + e^x$, $y_2' = 2y_1 + y_2$; $y_{1,0} = 1$, $y_{2,0} = 0$

13. $y_1' = y_1$, $y_2' = 2y_1 + y_2$;
    (a) $y_{1,0} = 0$, $y_{2,0} = 1$;   (b) $y_{1,0} = 1$, $y_{2,0} = 0$,
    (c) $y_{1,0} = 1$, $y_{2,0} = 1$

14. Solve $y' = py - qz$, $z' = pz + qy$ for real-valued functions p, q, y, and z, by reducing the system to one equation for $y + iz$.

Determine the roots of the indicial equation for the systems in Exercises 15 and 16.

15. $xy' = y + z$, $xz' = y + 2z$

16. $xy' = y \cos x + ze^x$, $xz' = 2y + z \sin x$

For each of the following two systems of differential equations, determine a_1, a_2, a_3, b_1, b_2, and b_3 in terms of a_0 and b_0 in the series developments

$$y = a_0 + a_1 x + a_2 x^2 + \cdots, \qquad z = b_0 + b_1 x + b_2 x^2 + \cdots$$

17. $y' = xz$, $z' = x^2 y$ 18. $y' = y \sin x + z$, $z' = y + 2z$

Find the first four nonvanishing terms in each of the two series developments of the solutions of each of the following four systems of differential equations with initial conditions indicated. In Exercises 19 and 20 use series in powers of x, and in Exercises 21 and 22 use series in powers of $x - 1$.

19. $y' = 2 + x + z$, $z' = 1 + 2x + y^2$; $y(0) = z(0) = 0$

20. $y' = 2 + x + z^2$, $z' = 1 + 2x + yz$; $y(0) = z(0) = 0$

21. $y' = 1 + z$, $z' = y^2 + x + z$; $y(1) = 1$, $z(1) = 3$

22. $y' = x + z$, $z' = 1 + yz$; $y(1) = 2$, $z(1) = 1$

CHAPTER 6

APPROXIMATE SOLUTION OF FIRST-ORDER DIFFERENTIAL EQUATIONS AND PICARD'S THEOREM

6–1 Introduction. In the present chapter we shall begin by considering the problem of obtaining numerical values for the solution of a differential equation rather than an analytical expression for such a solution. A given analytical expression may usually be evaluated numerically in some manner, although not always easily. Sometimes it is preferable not to make use of an analytical solution but to proceed numerically right from the start; sometimes the numerical procedure is the only possible one.

To illustrate, the problem

$$\frac{dy}{dx} = \frac{y - x}{y + x}, \qquad y(0) = 1, \tag{1}$$

has the analytical solution

$$\tan^{-1}\left(\frac{x}{y}\right) = \tfrac{1}{2}\ln\,(x^2 + y^2). \tag{2}$$

If we wish y as a function of x, it would appear to be necessary to use some method of approximation to find numerical values of y for given numerical values of x.

As a second illustration, take the problem

$$\frac{dy}{dx} = 1 + xy^2, \qquad y(0) = 0. \tag{3}$$

We know from Section 2–12 that this problem has a power series solution

$$y = x + \tfrac{1}{4}x^4 + \tfrac{1}{14}x^7 + \cdots, \tag{4}$$

and from Section 2–13 that this series converges in an interval which is at least as large as the interval $-1.035 < x < 1.035$. In order to use this solution to obtain numerical values of y, we would like to know an answer to the following question. Given the *partial sums*

$$y_{(1)} = x, \qquad y_{(2)} = x + \tfrac{1}{4}x^4, \qquad y_{(3)} = x + \tfrac{1}{4}x^4 + \tfrac{1}{14}x^7, \quad \text{etc.,} \tag{5}$$

in what interval does a given partial sum represent the actual solution with an error of no more than, say, 1 percent or 5 percent? A practical answer to this question is often the following. For an acceptable approximation to a value $y(x_1)$, calculate successively $y_{(1)}(x_1)$, $y_{(2)}(x_1)$, $y_{(3)}(x_1)$, ..., and continue until three or four successive $y_{(k)}(x_1)$ agree with each other to a prescribed number of decimals.

Often numerical procedures other than the use of partial sums of power series prove convenient. Typical of such procedures for the case of ordinary integration are the trapezoidal rule and Simpson's rule.

There exist a substantial number of different procedures for the numerical solution of differential equations. We discuss in the following a few of the simpler of these procedures for the single first-order equation. Which procedure to use in practice depends on a variety of circumstances, such as accuracy required, computing time available, computing equipment available, and, at least until the present, preference of the computer. The rapidly progressing development of large-scale high-speed computing equipment is an indication of the importance of numerical procedures in the application of mathematics to the solution of practical problems. The proper use of such equipment presupposes a working knowledge of numerical methods.

One of the approximate methods of solution which we consider is an iteration method. This method can be developed so as to supply a rigorous proof of the existence and uniqueness of solutions of differential equations. We shall discuss this existence and uniqueness theorem, known as Picard's theorem, at the end of the present chapter. In this discussion we shall limit ourselves to the case of a single first-order differential equation.

EXERCISES

1. Show that the right and the left side of Eq. (2) differ by less than one unit in the second significant figure when

(a) $y(0.1) = 1.09$ (b) $y(0.2) = 1.17$ (c) $y(0.5) = 1.34$ (d) $y(1.0) = 1.50$

2. Given that a power series solution of Eq. (1) is $y = 1 + x - x^2 + \frac{4}{3}x^3 - \frac{5}{2}x^4 + \frac{16}{3}x^5 - \frac{221}{18}x^6 + \cdots$, calculate $y_{(k)}(x)$, $k = 1, 2, \ldots, 6$, for (a) $x = 0.1$, (b) $x = 0.2$, (c) $x = 0.5$, and compare the results with the corresponding values of $y(x)$ in Exercise 1.

3. Calculate $y_{(k)}(0.5)$ for $k = 1, 2, 3$, for the solution (4) of Eq. (3).

4. Show that the next nonvanishing term in Eq. (4) is $23x^{10}/1120$ and use this to calculate $y_{(k)}(0.5)$ for $k = 4$.

5. The differential equation problem

$$y' = 1 + y^2, \qquad y(0) = 0$$

has the solution $y = \tan x = x + \frac{1}{3}x^3 + \frac{1}{15}x^5 + \frac{11}{315}x^7 + \cdots$

(a) Compare the value of $\tan 0.1 = 0.10033$ with the values of $y_{(k)}(0.1)$, $k = 1, 2, 3$.

(b) Compare the value of $\tan 0.5 = 0.5453$ with the values of $y_{(k)}(0.5)$, $k = 1, 2, 3, 4$.

6. Determine the values of n for which $1 + x + x^2 + \cdots + x^{n-1}$ is within 1 percent of $(1 - x)^{-1}$ for (a) $0 < x < 1$, (b) $x = 0.1$, (c) $x = 0.5$, (d) $x = 0.9$.

6–2 Simple procedures for first-order equations. Given the differential equation and initial condition

$$y' = F(x, y), \qquad y(x_0) = y_0, \tag{1}$$

the problem is to determine values of y for values of x other than x_0. For any such value x_1 the corresponding $y_1 = y(x_1)$ satisfies the following relation:

$$y_1 - y_0 = \int_{x_0}^{x_1} F\big(x, y(x)\big)\, dx. \tag{2}$$

Since we do not know what $y(x)$ is, we cannot find y_1 by evaluating the integral in (2). We may, however, find approximate values of y_1 by approximating the integral in (2). The simplest such approximation $\tilde{y}_1$ of y_1 is obtained by neglecting the change of $F(x, y)$ in the interval (x_0, x_1). This gives

$$\tilde{y}_1 - y_0 = F(x_0, y_0)(x_1 - x_0'). \tag{3}$$

If we set h for $x_1 - x_0$ and write $F(x_0, y_0) = y_0'$, then

$$\tilde{y}_1 = y_0 + hy_0'. \tag{3'}$$

We see that $\tilde{y}_1$ may be considered a partial sum of the Taylor series $y_1 = y_0 + hy_0' + \frac{1}{2}h^2 y_0'' + \cdots$

A simple formula which would seem to be more accurate than (3) is

$$\tilde{y}_1 - y_0 = \tfrac{1}{2}[F(x_0, y_0) + F(x_1, \tilde{y}_1)](x_1 - x_0). \tag{4}$$

Equation (4) suffers from the fact that the unknown $\tilde{y}_1$ occurs on both sides, so that the task of finding $\tilde{y}_1$ depends on the solution of an algebraic or transcendental equation. However, since (4) is approximate anyway, one is tempted to simplify it by introducing on the right that value of $\tilde{y}_1$ which follows from the simpler formula (3). In this manner we obtain the further formula

$$\tilde{y}_1 - y_0 = \tfrac{1}{2}\{F(x_0, y_0) + F[x_1, y_0 + (x_1 - x_0)F(x_0, y_0)]\}(x_1 - x_0), \tag{5}$$

which can be written more simply as

$$\tilde{y}_1 = y_0 + \tfrac{1}{2}h[y_0' + F(x_0 + h, y_0 + hy_0')]. \tag{5'}$$

EXAMPLE 1. Find an approximate value for $y(0.5)$ when

$$y' = y, \qquad y(0) = 1. \tag{6}$$

In this simple example we know the exact solution, which is $y = e^x$. Accordingly,

$$y_1 = y(0.5) = 1.648 \ldots$$

We compare this result with what we obtain from the simple approximation formulas.

Equation (3') gives, with $y_0 = 1$, $h = \tfrac{1}{2}$, $y_0' = 1$,

$$\tilde{y}_1 = 1 + \tfrac{1}{2} = 1.5.$$

Equation (4) gives

$$\tilde{y}_1 = 1 + \tfrac{1}{2}(1 + \tilde{y}_1)\tfrac{1}{2}.$$

Since for the present problem this is a linear equation for $\tilde{y}_1$, we can solve it explicitly and get

$$\tilde{y}_1 = \tfrac{5}{3} = 1.666 \ldots$$

Equation (5') gives

$$\tilde{y}_1 = 1 + \tfrac{1}{4}[1 + (1 + \tfrac{1}{2})] = 1.625.$$

Note that while the use of Eq. (3) is associated with an error of about 10 percent, the use of both (4) and (5) reduces this error to less than 2 percent.

We have been careful up to now to distinguish, even in writing, between y_1 and approximations $\tilde{y}_1$ to it. So long as we are clear about what we are doing, we may in the writing omit the $\sim$ sign.

Since the formulas evidently hold in going from x_n to x_{n+1} as well as in going from x_0 to x_1, we repeat (3) and (5) once more in the following form:

$$y_{n+1} = y_n + hF(x_n, y_n), \tag{I}$$

$$y_{n+1} = y_n + \tfrac{1}{2}h\{F(x_n, y_n) + F[x_n + h, y_n + hF(x_n, y_n)]\}. \tag{II}$$

EXAMPLE 2. Use (I) and (II), with $h = \tfrac{1}{4}$, to find approximations for the value of $y(0.5)$ when $y' = y$ and $y(0) = 1$.

With $x_0 = 0$ and $h = \frac{1}{4}$, we have $y(0.5) = y_2$. From (I),

$$y_1 = 1 + \frac{1}{4} \cdot 1 = \frac{5}{4} = 1.25,$$

$$y_2 = \frac{5}{4} + \frac{1}{4} \cdot \frac{5}{4} = \frac{25}{16} = 1.5625.$$

From (II),

$$y_1 = 1 + \frac{1}{8}[1 + (1 + \frac{1}{4})] = 1 + \frac{9}{32} = 1.281 \ldots,$$

$$y_2 = \frac{41}{32} + \frac{1}{8}[\frac{41}{32} + (\frac{41}{32} + \frac{41}{4 \cdot 32})] = 1.641 \ldots,$$

which compares favorably with the exact value $1.648 \ldots$

EXERCISES

1. Given the initial value problem $y' = 1 + y^2$, $y(0) = 0$, find approximations $\bar{y}_1$ to the value $y_1 = y(\frac{1}{4}\pi) = 1$ by means of Eqs. (3') and (5').

2. Solve $y' = 1 + 2y/(1 + x)$, $y(0) = 0$, approximately, by the use of (I) and (II) for y_1, y_2, y_3, y_4, and y_5, with $h = 0.1$. Retain three decimals and compare with the exact solution.

3. Solve $y' = 1 + xy^2$, $y(0) = 0$, approximately for y_1, y_2, y_3, and y_4 with $h = \frac{1}{4}$, (a) by means of (I), (b) by means of (II).

4. Solve $y' = 1 + xy^2$, $y(0) = 0$ approximately for y_1, y_2, y_3, y_4, and y_5 where $h = \frac{1}{10}$, (a) by means of (I), (b) by means of (II). (c) Compare values of y_5 with values of y_2 in Exercise 3.

6-3 Taylor's theorem with remainder term. Basic to many formulas used for numerical solution of differential equations is Taylor's theorem with remainder. The theorem may be written in the following form:

$$y(x) = y(x_0) + \frac{y'(x_0)}{1!}(x - x_0) + \frac{y''(x_0)}{2!}(x - x_0)^2 + \cdots$$

$$+ \frac{y^{(m)}(x_0)}{m!}(x - x_0)^m + R_m(x, x_0), \quad (1)$$

where

$$R_m(x, x_0) = \frac{1}{m!} \int_{x_0}^{x} (x - \xi)^m y^{(m+1)}(\xi) \, d\xi. \quad (2)$$

Equation (1) is valid provided $y, y', \ldots, y^{(m)}$ are finite for $x = x_0$ and $y^{(m+1)}$ is such that the integral in (2) is finite.

Equation (1) is quite simply derived by successive integration by parts. We start with an integral I given by

$$I = \int_{x_0}^{x} f(\xi) \, d\xi. \quad (3)$$

A first integration by parts gives

$$I = (\xi + c_1)f(\xi)\Big|_{x_0}^{x} - \int_{x_0}^{x} (\xi + c_1)f'(\xi)\, d\xi. \tag{4}$$

The constant c_1 is at our disposal. We choose its value in such a way that the integrated portion of (4) does not involve $f(x)$, that is, such that $(\xi + c_1)_{\xi=x} = 0$. Setting $c_1 = -x$, Eq. (4) becomes

$$I = (x - x_0)f(x_0) + \int_{x_0}^{x} (x - \xi)f'(\xi)\, d\xi. \tag{5}$$

We now integrate once more by parts as follows:

$$I = (x - x_0)f(x_0) + \left[-\frac{(x - \xi)^2}{2} + c_2\right]f'(\xi)\Big|_{x_0}^{x}$$
$$- \int_{x_0}^{x}\left[-\frac{(x - \xi)^2}{2} + c_2\right]f''(\xi)\, d\xi. \tag{6}$$

We determine c_2 such that $f'(x)$ disappears in (6). This means that $c_2 = 0$ and

$$I = (x - x_0)f(x_0) + \tfrac{1}{2}(x - x_0)^2 f'(x_0) + \tfrac{1}{2}\int_{x_0}^{x} (x - \xi)^2 f''(\xi)\, d\xi. \tag{7}$$

Continuing in this manner, we obtain as a general formula of integration

$$\int_{x_0}^{x} f(\xi)\, d\xi = (x - x_0)f(x_0) + \tfrac{1}{2}(x - x_0)^2 f'(x_0) + \cdots$$
$$+ \frac{1}{m!}(x - x_0)^m f^{(m-1)}(x_0) + \frac{1}{m!}\int_{x_0}^{x} (x - \xi)^m f^{(m)}(\xi)\, d\xi. \tag{8}$$

All that remains in order to deduce Taylor's formula (1) from (8) is to identify the function $f(x)$ with the *derivative* y' of the function y for which Taylor's formula is wanted.

For what follows it is convenient to write (1) and (2) in alternative form by setting

$$x_0 = x_n, \qquad x = x_{n+1} = x_n + h, \qquad y^{(k)}(x_n) = y_n^{(k)}. \tag{9}$$

With this,

$$y_{n+1} = y_n + \frac{h}{1!}y_n' + \frac{h^2}{2!}y_n'' + \cdots + \frac{h^m}{m!}y_n^{(m)} + R_m(x_n, h) \tag{10}$$

and

$$R_m(x_n, h) = \frac{1}{m!}\int_{x_n}^{x_n+h} (x_n + h - \xi)^m y^{(m+1)}(\xi)\, d\xi. \tag{11}$$

An important concept in regard to Taylor's theorem is the order of magnitude of the remainder term $R_m(x_n, h)$. From the mean value theorem of the integral calculus follows

$$R_m(x_n, h) = \frac{y^{(m+1)}(x_n + \theta h)}{m!} \int_{x_n}^{x_n+h} (x_n + h - \xi)^m \, d\xi$$

$$= \frac{h^{m+1}}{(m+1)!} y^{(m+1)}(x_n + \theta h), \tag{12}$$

where θ is *some* number between 0 and 1. Note that in this form the remainder term has the same appearance as an additional series term except that the argument is not the definite quantity x_n but the unknown quantity $x_n + \theta h$.

For our present purposes it may be assumed that the function $y(x)$ is such that $|y^{(m+1)}|$ is less than some finite quantity M in the interval $x_n \le x \le x_{n+1}$. In terms of M we have then an *upper bound* for the remainder R_m in the form

$$|R_m(x_n, h)| \le \frac{h^{m+1}}{(m+1)!} M. \tag{13}$$

We express the dependence of R_m on the interval length h by saying that R_m is *of order of magnitude* h^{m+1}. A convenient shorthand way of writing this is

$$R_m(x_n, h) = O(h^{m+1}). \tag{14}$$

(In words: the remainder term R_m is "oh" h^{m+1}.)

For the purpose of estimating errors made in using numerical methods, the order of magnitude, so far as interval length h is concerned, is perhaps the most important. However, the actual magnitude of the denominator term, here equal to $(m + 1)!$, and information concerning the value of M often also play a role.

Exercises

1. From which equation in the text is it possible to conclude the relation

$$\int_{x_0}^{x} f(\xi) \, d\xi = \tfrac{1}{2}(x - x_0)[f(x) + f(x_0)] + \int_{x_0}^{x} [\tfrac{1}{2}(x + x_0) - \xi] f'(\xi) \, d\xi$$

and in what way?

2. Show that when $|f'(x)| \le M$ the largest possible value of the integral on the right of the formula of Exercise 1 is at most one-half the largest possible value of the corresponding integral in Eq. (5).

3. By suitable integration by parts derive the formula

$$\int_{x_0}^{x} f(\xi)\,d\xi = \tfrac{1}{2}(x - x_0)[f(x) + f(x_0)] + \tfrac{1}{2}\int_{x_0}^{x} [\xi^2 - (x + x_0)\xi + xx_0]f''(\xi)\,d\xi.$$

4. Show that the result of Exercise 3 may be used to obtain the formula

$$y_{n+1} = y_n + \tfrac{1}{2}(y'_{n+1} + y'_n)h + R(x_n, h),$$

and deduce the form of the remainder term R which corresponds to Eq. (12).

6–4 Use of three-term Taylor series formula. A simple and often quite accurate method of numerical solution of the problem

$$y' = F(x, y), \qquad y(x_0) = y_0 \tag{1}$$

may be based on the formula

$$y_{n+1} = y_n + hy'_n + \tfrac{1}{2}h^2 y''_n + \tfrac{1}{6}h^3 y'''(x_n + \theta h). \tag{2}$$

We assume that F is such that all the necessary derivatives exist, and that h and y''' are small enough to allow neglect of the remainder term in (2). We then have

$$y_{n+1} = y_n + hy'_n + \tfrac{1}{2}h^2 y''_n, \tag{3}$$

where

$$y'_n = F(x_n, y_n) \tag{4a}$$

and

$$y''_n = \left(\frac{dF}{dx}\right)_{x_n} = \left(\frac{\partial F}{\partial x} + \frac{\partial F}{\partial y}\frac{dy}{dx}\right)_{x_n} = \left(\frac{\partial F}{\partial x} + F\frac{\partial F}{\partial y}\right)_{x_n}. \tag{4b}$$

EXAMPLE. Given

$$y' = y, \qquad y(0) = 1,$$

calculate $y(\tfrac{1}{2})$.

For this particularly simple example, Eq. (3) becomes

$$y_{n+1} = (1 + h + \tfrac{1}{2}h^2)y_n.$$

Let us choose $h = \tfrac{1}{4}$. Then

$$y_1 = (1 + \tfrac{1}{4} + \tfrac{1}{32})y_0 = 1.28125,$$

$$y_2 = (1 + \tfrac{1}{4} + \tfrac{1}{32})y_1 = 1.641\ldots.$$

The magnitude of the remainder term in (2) is

$$R = \tfrac{1}{6}h^3 y''' = \tfrac{1}{6}h^3 y = \tfrac{1}{6\cdot64}y.$$

This means that in the interval (x_0, x_1), $R \approx 0.003$, and in the interval (x_1, x_2), $R \approx 0.004$. The sum of these remainders does in fact account for the difference between the calculated value 1.641 and the exact value $1.648 \ldots$ of $y(\frac{1}{2})$.

EXERCISES

1. In the formula $y_{n+1} = y_n + hy'_n + \frac{1}{2}h^2y''_n + \frac{1}{6}h^3y'''_n + \frac{1}{24}h^4y^{iv}(x_n + \theta h)$ express y'''_n in terms of F and its partial derivatives.

2. Given that $y' = 1 + x \cos y$, obtain upper bounds in the interval $-H \leq x \leq H$ in terms of H for (a) $y''(x)$, (b) $y'''(x)$.

3. Given $y' = 1 + x \cos y$ with $y(0) = 0$, use Eq. (2) and the result of Exercise 2(b) to show that $y(\frac{1}{10}) = 0.105$ with an error of magnitude 0.0004 at most.

6–5 Simpson's rule as a consequence of Taylor's theorem. A basic formula for numerical integration which is known as Simpson's rule can be written in the following form

$$\int_{x-h}^{x+h} f(\xi) \, d\xi \approx \frac{1}{3}h \, [f(x + h) + 4f(x) + f(x - h)]. \tag{1}$$

While in general the right side of (1) equals the left only approximately, Eq. (1) is exactly true whenever $f(x)$ is a cubic polynomial. The more nearly $f(\xi)$ can be represented by one and the same cubic polynomial in the interval $(x - h, x + h)$ the more nearly does (1) become an exact equality.

In what follows we show how an equation equivalent to (1), including a remainder term representing the exact difference between the left and the right side of (1), can be deduced from Taylor's theorem.

To establish contact with Taylor's theorem as stated in Eqs. (10) and (11) of Section 6–3, we write in Eq. (1)

$$f(\xi) = y'(\xi),$$

$$x = x_n, \qquad x + h = x_{n+1}, \qquad x - h = x_{n-1}, \qquad y(x) = y_n, \quad \text{etc.}$$

Therewith (1) assumes the form

$$y_{n+1} - y_{n-1} \approx \frac{1}{3}h[y'_{n+1} + 4y'_n + y'_{n-1}], \tag{2}$$

and this relation is exact whenever $y(x)$ is a quartic polynomial in the interval (x_{n-1}, x_{n+1}).

To *derive* (2), we write Taylor's theorem in the form

$$y_{n+1} = y_n + hy'_n + \tfrac{1}{2}h^2 y''_n + \tfrac{1}{6}h^3 y'''_n + \tfrac{1}{24}h^4 y_n^{(4)} + R_4(x_n, h), \quad (3)$$

where

$$R_4(x_n, h) = \tfrac{1}{24} \int_{x_n}^{x_n+h} (x_n + h - \xi)^4 y^{(5)}(\xi)\, d\xi. \quad (4)$$

Since we wish to obtain the difference $y_{n+1} - y_{n-1}$ we need an expression corresponding to (3) for the quantity $y_{n-1} = y(x_{n-1})$ in terms of y_n. From the derivation of Taylor's theorem it is clear that we obtain y_{n-1} instead of y_{n+1} by simply changing h to $-h$ in (3). Accordingly,

$$y_{n-1} = y_n - hy'_n + \tfrac{1}{2}h^2 y''_n - \tfrac{1}{6}h^3 y'''_n + \tfrac{1}{24}h^4 y_n^{(4)} + R_4(x_n, -h). \quad (5)$$

Subtraction of (5) from (3) gives

$$y_{n+1} - y_{n-1} = 2hy'_n + \tfrac{1}{3}h^3 y'''_n + R, \quad (6)$$

where for brevity we have written $R = R_4(x_n, h) - R_4(x_n, -h)$.

To eliminate y'''_n from (6), we apply Taylor's theorem to the function y' instead of to y, as follows:

$$y'_{n+1} = y'_n + hy''_n + \tfrac{1}{2}h^2 y'''_n + \tfrac{1}{6}h^3 y_n^{(4)}$$

$$+ \tfrac{1}{6} \int_{x_n}^{x_n+h} (x_n + h - \xi)^3 y^{(5)}(\xi)\, d\xi, \quad (7)$$

and

$$y'_{n-1} = y'_n - hy''_n + \tfrac{1}{2}h^2 y'''_n - \tfrac{1}{6}h^3 y_n^{(4)}$$

$$+ \tfrac{1}{6} \int_{x_n}^{x_n-h} (x_n - h - \xi)^3 y^{(5)}(\xi)\, d\xi. \quad (8)$$

Addition of (7) and (8) gives

$$y'_{n+1} + y'_{n-1} = 2y'_n + h^2 y'''_n + Q, \quad (9)$$

where Q is a temporary abbreviation for the sum of the two integrals in (7) and (8). We now solve (9) for y'''_n and introduce the result into (6). This gives

$$y_{n+1} - y_{n-1} = 2hy'_n + \tfrac{1}{3}h[y'_{n+1} + y'_{n-1} - 2y'_n] + R - \tfrac{1}{3}hQ. \quad (10)$$

A slight rearrangement of (10) leads to *Simpson's formula with remainder term*,

$$y_{n+1} - y_{n-1} = \tfrac{1}{3}h[y'_{n+1} + 4y'_n + y'_{n-1}] + R_S. \quad (11)$$

The remainder term R_S is given by

$$R_S = \int_{x_n}^{x_n+h} \left[\frac{(x_n + h - \xi)^4}{24} - \frac{h(x_n + h - \xi)^3}{18} \right] y^{(5)}(\xi) \, d\xi$$

$$- \int_{x_n}^{x_n-h} \left[\frac{(x_n - h - \xi)^4}{24} + \frac{h(x_n - h - \xi)^3}{18} \right] y^{(5)}(\xi) \, d\xi. \quad (12)$$

To apply the mean value theorem of integral calculus to the formula for R_S, we write this formula as follows:

$$R_S = \int_{x_n-h}^{x_n+h} P(x_n - \xi, h) y^{(5)}(\xi) \, d\xi, \quad (13)$$

where

$$P(x_n - \xi, h)$$

$$= \begin{cases} \dfrac{(x_n - \xi + h)^4}{24} - \dfrac{h(x_n - \xi + h)^3}{18}, & x_n \leq \xi \leq x_n + h, \\[2mm] \dfrac{(x_n - \xi - h)^4}{24} + \dfrac{h(x_n - \xi - h)^3}{18}, & x_n - h \leq \xi \leq x_n. \end{cases} \quad (14)$$

Since $P(x_n - \xi, h)$ is continuous and does not change signs in the whole interval $x_n - h \leq \xi \leq x_n + h$, we conclude from (13) that

$$R_S = y^{(5)}(x_n + \theta h) \int_{x_n-h}^{x_n+h} P(x_n - \xi, h) \, d\xi, \quad (15)$$

where θ is *some* number between -1 and 1.

Evaluation of the integral in (15) furnishes the following simple expression for the remainder term R_S:

$$R_S = -\tfrac{1}{90}h^5 y^{(5)}(x_n + \theta h). \quad (16)$$

We note that the remainder term is zero for all quartic polynomials $y(x)$, since for these $y^{(5)}(x) = 0$, identically. This proves the fact stated previously that the form (2) of Simpson's rule is an exact relation for all quartic polynomials.

There are three characteristics of Simpson's formula (11) which are significant in the applications to solving differential equations:

(1) The formula involves values of the function y and its derivative at *three* successive points. This means that in order to compute y_{n+1} we must know values of y and y' at *two* preceding stages.

(2) Computation of y_{n+1} involves knowledge of y'_{n+1}.

(3) The remainder term is $O(h^5)$ with a numerical factor $\tfrac{1}{90}$.

6–6 Application of Simpson's formula. We illustrate use of the formula

$$y_{n+1} = y_{n-1} + \tfrac{1}{3}h[y'_{n+1} + 4y'_n + y'_{n-1}] \tag{1}$$

for the solution of the problem

$$y' = F(x, y), \qquad y(x_0) = y_0, \tag{2}$$

by means of an example.

We ask for the value of $y(\tfrac{1}{4})$ when $y(x)$ is the solution of

$$y' = y^3, \qquad y(0) = 1. \tag{3}$$

For this particular problem it is, of course, easiest to obtain the solution in analytical form. By separation of variables,

$$y(x) = \frac{1}{\sqrt{1 - 2x}} \tag{4}$$

and therewith $y(\tfrac{1}{4}) = \sqrt{2} = 1.41 \ldots$

To show the use of Simpson's formula (1), we take $h = \tfrac{1}{8}$, and then

$$y(\tfrac{1}{4}) = y_2 = y_0 + \tfrac{1}{24}[y'_2 + 4y'_1 + y'_0]. \tag{5}$$

We have $y_0 = 1$ and $y'_n = y_n^3$, and this reduces our expression for y_2 to the following:

$$y_2 = 1 + \tfrac{1}{24}[y_2^3 + 4y_1^3 + 1]. \tag{6}$$

We now encounter two difficulties:

(1) We must find a value of y_1.

(2) Even after that, the wanted value of y_2 occurs on both sides of the equation.

The first difficulty occurs only once; that is, once we have calculated y_2, we can find y_3, y_4, etc., based on the known values of y_2, y_1, and y_0. The second difficulty arises at every stage of the computation.

Usually it is possible to find the *additional starting value* y_1 from a power series. Since the formula for y_2 involves an error which is of order h^5, it is reasonable to calculate y_1 with an error which is $O(h^5)$. Accordingly, we take

$$y_1 = y_0 + hy'_0 + \tfrac{1}{2}h^2y''_0 + \tfrac{1}{6}h^3y'''_0 + \tfrac{1}{24}h^4y_0^{iv}$$
$$= 1 + \tfrac{1}{8} + \tfrac{3}{128} + \tfrac{15}{48 \cdot 64} + \tfrac{105}{24 \cdot 64 \cdot 64}$$
$$= 1 + 0.125 + 0.0234 + 0.0049 + 0.0011 = 1.154.$$

With this value of y_1 we have further

$$y_2 = 1.297 + 0.042y_2^3. \tag{7}$$

The smallness of the factor in front of y_2^3 makes it appear as if this term would be less important than the first term on the right of the equation. Accordingly, a rough approximation would seem to be $y_2 \approx 1.297$ or, since y_2 will certainly be somewhat larger than this,

$$y_2 \approx 1.3.$$

Suppose we introduce this value of y_2 on the right side of Eq. (7). This makes the right side equal to $1.297 + 0.042(1.3)^3 = 1.297 + 0.092 = 1.389$, which shows that the original guess was not accurate enough. However, if we try 1.39 on the right of the equation, then we have $1.297 + 0.042(1.39)^3 = 1.297 + 0.113 = 1.410$. Repeating this process once more, we find that to three significant figures

$$y_2 = 1.41.$$

EXERCISES

1. Use Simpson's formula to obtain a value of $y(\frac{3}{8})$ for the problem stated in Eq. (3), using again $h = \frac{1}{8}$.

2. Consider the possibility of obtaining by means of Simpson's formula a value of $y(\frac{1}{2})$ for the problem of Eq. (3).

6–7 Equation solving by iteration. In applying Simpson's formula to the solution of $y' = y^3$ we were led to the algebraic equation $y = 1.297 + 0.042y^3$, and we solved this equation by a process of successive substitutions, or *iterations*. We now consider the application of this process to more general equations of the form

$$x = f(x). \tag{1}$$

We start with a value x_0 which we think is an approximation to the solution x of (1) and introduce this value x_0 on the right. If x_0 is a solution of (1), then $f(x_0) = x_0$. If x_0 is not a solution, then $f(x_0)$ will equal some value $x_1 \neq x_0$,

$$x_1 = f(x_0). \tag{2}$$

We now take x_1 and use it to calculate x_2, as follows:

$$x_2 = f(x_1). \tag{3}$$

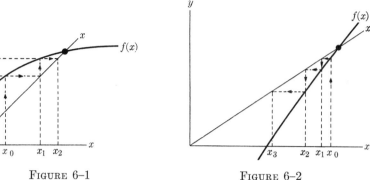

FIGURE 6-1   FIGURE 6-2

Repeating this process, we write

$$x_n = f(x_{n-1}), \tag{4}$$

and we continue until x_n differs from x_{n-1} by less than a specified percentage. When and if this stage has been reached, we may ordinarily consider x_n as an approximation to a solution x of the given equation (1).

It is simple and instructive to describe the above process of iteration graphically. We draw the curve $y = x$ and the curve $y = f(x)$. A point of intersection of the two curves is a solution of the given equation (1). Suppose we have an approximation x_0 to the solution. To find $x_1 = f(x_0)$ we locate x_1 on the line $y = x$ by a parallel to the x-axis through the point $(x_0, f(x_0))$. Having x_1, we find $x_2 = f(x_1)$ in the same manner. It is apparent that for a function $f(x)$ as sketched in Fig. 6-1 the process converges to a solution of $x = f(x)$.

The fact that the same process may also *fail* to converge to a solution is illustrated just as readily by Fig. 6-2.

It appears that a condition for convergence of the iterative process may be the condition that the slope $f'(x)$ of the function $f(x)$ be less than the slope 1 of the function x, in the range in which the iterative process is carried out.

We shall show that if $f'(x)$ is less than one in absolute value in a suitable interval, then indeed the iterative process (4) converges to a solution of Eq. (1).

We begin our convergence proof by considering the difference of two successive iterations

$$x_{n+1} - x_n = f(x_n) - f(x_{n-1}). \tag{5}$$

By the mean value theorem of the differential calculus this may be replaced by

$$x_{n+1} - x_n = f'(\xi_n)(x_n - x_{n-1}), \tag{6}$$

where ξ_n is somewhere in the interval (x_n, x_{n-1}).

We conclude by induction that then also

$$x_{n+1} - x_n = f'(\xi_n)f'(\xi_{n-1}) \ldots f'(\xi_1)(x_1 - x_0). \tag{7}$$

We now assume that

$$|f'(x)| \leq M < 1. \tag{8}$$

According to (7), we then have the inequality

$$|x_{n+1} - x_n| \leq M^n|x_1 - x_0|. \tag{9}$$

Since $M < 1$, this means that

$$\lim_{n \to \infty} (x_{n+1} - x_n) = 0. \tag{10}$$

Of course, Eq. (10) by itself does not guarantee the existence of a limiting value $x = \lim_{n \to \infty} x_n$. However, the quantitative statement (9), which we used to conclude (10), may also be used to obtain the much stronger result of the existence of a limiting value x of the sequence x_n. To see this, we write

$$x_n = (x_n - x_{n-1}) + (x_{n-1} - x_{n-2}) + \cdots + (x_1 - x_0) + x_0. \tag{11}$$

In view of (9) and the fact that $M < 1$, the series on the right side of (11) is the partial sum of an absolutely convergent series, and this means that we have the existence of a limiting value

$$x = \lim_{n \to \infty} x_n, \tag{12}$$

which solves the given equation (1).

EXERCISES

1. Starting with $x_0 = 1$, solve by iteration the equation $x = 1 + \frac{1}{4}x^{-1}$, and compare the result with an exact solution.

2. Solve $x = 1 - \frac{1}{4}x^2$, for some starting value in the interval $(-2, 2)$.

3. Starting with $x_0 = 2$, solve by iteration $x = 2x^{1/2}$.

4. Show explicitly that an iterative solution of $x = 1 + \alpha x$, with $x_0 = 1$, converges when $\alpha < 1$ but diverges when $1 \leq \alpha$.

5. Given the quadratic equation $x^2 - 4x + 3 = 0$, with solutions $x = 1$ and $x = 3$, show that if this equation is written as $x = 4 - 3/x$, the iterative process of this section, with starting value either 4 or $\frac{1}{2}$, leads to the solution $x = 3$.

6-8 Iterative solution of differential equations.   Picard's method. The method of iteration, as described for the algebraic equation $x = f(x)$, may also be used to obtain solutions of differential equations. We show this for the problem

$$y' = f(x, y), \qquad y(x_0) = y_0, \tag{1}$$

which we write in the equivalent "integral equation" form

$$y(x) = y_0 + \int_{x_0}^{x} f\big(t, y(t)\big)\, dt. \tag{2}$$

A crude approximation is $y(x) = y_0$, identically. We substitute this approximation for y on the right side of (2) in order to obtain a new (and presumably better) approximation y_1 as follows:

$$y_1(x) = y_0 + \int_{x_0}^{x} f(t, y_0)\, dt. \tag{3}$$

Proceeding in this manner, we have in the nth stage of the process of iteration

$$y_n(x) = y_0 + \int_{x_0}^{x} f\big(t, y_{n-1}(t)\big)\, dt. \tag{4}$$

We illustrate this procedure, which is often called Picard's method, by a number of examples.

EXAMPLE 1. As a particularly simple illustration, we take the problem

$$y' = y, \qquad y(0) = 1$$

or

$$y(x) = 1 + \int_{0}^{x} y(t)\, dt.$$

With $y_0 = 1$, we have

$$y_1(x) = 1 + \int_{0}^{x} dt = 1 + x.$$

Next

$$y_2(x) = 1 + \int_{0}^{x} (1 + t)\, dt = 1 + x + \tfrac{1}{2}x^2,$$

and

$$y_3(x) = 1 + \int_{0}^{x} (1 + t + \tfrac{1}{2}t^2)\, dt = 1 + x + \tfrac{1}{2}x^2 + \tfrac{1}{6}x^3.$$

Continuing in this fashion, we obtain

$$y_n(x) = 1 + \frac{x}{1!} + \frac{x^2}{2!} + \cdots + \frac{x^n}{n!},$$

which is the nth partial sum of the Taylor series for e^x.

Since the exact solution of the given problem is $y = e^x$, we see clearly how for this example the iteration process leads to successively better approximations to the true solution.

EXAMPLE 2. The problem

$$y' = y^2, \qquad y(0) = 1$$

has the exact solution

$$y = \frac{1}{1 - x} = 1 + x + x^2 + \cdots, \qquad |x| < 1.$$

An iterative solution of the equivalent integral equation

$$y(x) = 1 + \int_0^x [y(t)]^2 \, dt,$$

with $y_0 = 1$, gives

$$y_1 = 1 + \int_0^x dt = 1 + x,$$

$$y_2 = 1 + \int_0^x (1 + t)^2 \, dt = 1 + x + x^2 + \tfrac{1}{3}x^3,$$

$$y_3 = 1 + \int_0^x (1 + t + t^2 + \tfrac{1}{3}t^3)^2 \, dt$$

$$= 1 + x + x^2 + x^3 + \tfrac{2}{3}x^4 + \tfrac{2}{15}x^5 + \tfrac{1}{9}x^6.$$

It appears from the evidence at this stage that $y_n(x)$ agrees with the power-series expansion of the exact solution up to the term x^n. That this is in fact generally true can be shown explicitly. It is also found that so long as $|x|$ is smaller than unity, the numerical value of $y_n(x)$ will come closer and closer to the numerical value of the exact solution $y(x)$ as n becomes larger and larger.

EXAMPLE 3. We now consider a simple example which is designed to illustrate certain practically infrequent, but theoretically important occurrences.

The example is

$$y' = \sqrt{\tfrac{1}{4}x^2 + y} - \tfrac{1}{2}x, \qquad y(0) = 0,$$

in the range $x \geq 0$. We may start the process of iteration with $y_0 = 0$. Then

$$y_1' = \sqrt{\tfrac{1}{4}x^2 + 0} - \tfrac{1}{2}x = 0, \qquad y_1(0) = 0,$$

and therewith $y_1 = 0$. We see that this result repeats itself, so that every $y_n = 0$. We should, of course, not be surprised about this, since $y(x) = 0$ is an exact solution of the given problem.

However, the solution $y(x) = 0$ is not *unique*. It is readily verified that

$$y = -\tfrac{1}{4}x^2$$

is also a solution of the given problem.

We are tempted to assume that we may "reach" the solution $-\frac{1}{4}x^2$ by the iteration process, provided we began with a more suitable function $y_0(x)$. To show that this is not likely to be true, consider the starting function

$$y_0(x) = -\tfrac{1}{4}k_0 x^2$$

with $0 \leq k_0 \leq 1$. We know that when $k_0 = 0$ then $y_n(x) = y(x) = 0$. We can further easily see that when $k_0 = 1$ then $y_n(x) = y(x) = -\frac{1}{4}x^2$. But what about intermediate values of k_0? We introduce y_0 on the right side of the differential equation and have

$$y_1' = -\tfrac{1}{2}(1 - \sqrt{1 - k_0})x, \qquad y_0(0) = 0.$$

From this

$$y_1(x) = -\tfrac{1}{4}k_1 x^2,$$

where

$$k_1 = 1 - \sqrt{1 - k_0}.$$

It is readily seen that the value of k_1 also lies between zero and one.

Continuing in this manner, we obtain

$$y_n(x) = -\tfrac{1}{4}k_n x^2,$$

where

$$k_n = 1 - \sqrt{1 - k_{n-1}}, \qquad 0 < k_n < 1.$$

The question now arises whether the quantities k_n defined in this manner tend to a limit as n increases, and if so, what this limit is. Let us write the recurrence relation for k_n in the form

$$1 - k_n = (1 - k_{n-1})^{1/2}.$$

From this

$$1 - k_n = (1 - k_{n-2})^{\frac{1}{2}\cdot\frac{1}{2}}.$$

Continuing in this manner, we may express k_n in terms of k_0, as follows:

$$1 - k_n = (1 - k_0)^{1/2^n}.$$

No matter how near k_0 is to 1, so long as it is actually less than 1, the limit on the right side is 1 as n approaches ∞. Thus

$$\lim_{n \to \infty} k_n = 0, \qquad 0 \leq k_0 < 1.$$

In terms of the iteration procedure for our given differential equation, this means that with the starting function $-\frac{1}{4}k_0 x^2$ we shall always approach the solution function $y(x) = 0$, and never the other solution function $-\frac{1}{4}x^2$, so long as k_0 is actually less than 1.

All three of the preceding examples *illustrate* the convergence of the iteration process to *a* solution function. We do not yet know what conditions must be imposed on the form of the differential equation to be *assured* of such convergence.

Further, we do not yet know under what additional conditions convergence toward a *unique* solution is assured.

EXERCISES

1. For the differential equation problem $y' = x + y^2$, $y(0) = 0$, define $y_0(x) = 0$, and $y_n(x) = \int_0^x \{t + [y_{n-1}(t)]^2\} \, dt$ for $n = 1, 2, 3, \ldots$. Determine $y_1(x)$, $y_2(x)$, and $y_3(x)$.

2. The differential equation problem $y' = 2x(1 + y)$, $y(0) = 0$, has the explicit solution $y = e^{x^2} - 1$. Show that Picard's method of successive approximations with $y_0(x) = 0$ gives $y_n(x) = x^2 + x^4/2! + x^6/3! + \cdots + x^{2n}/n!$.

3. The differential equation problem $y' = 2x(1 + y)$, $y(1) = 2$, has the explicit solution $y = 3e^{x^2-1} - 1$. Starting with $y_0(x) = 2$, determine explicitly $y_1(x)$ and $y_2(x)$.

4. For the differential equation problem $y' = 1 + xy^2$, $y(0) = 0$, choose $y_0(x) = 0$ and determine $y_1(x)$, $y_2(x)$, and $y_3(x)$ by Picard's method. Compare the result $y_3(x)$ with the partial sum $y_{(4)}(x)$ of the power-series solution in Exercise 4 of Section 6–1.

5. For the differential equation problem $y' = x + y^2$, $y(0) = 1$, choose (a) $y_0(x) = 1$, (b) $y_0(x) = 1 + x$, and in each case determine $y_1(x)$ and $y_2(x)$ by Picard's method.

6. For the differential equation problem $y' = y^2$, $y(0) = 1$, choose $y_0(x) = 1 + x^2$ and determine $y_1(x)$ and $y_2(x)$ by Picard's method. Compare the result with the result of Example 2.

6–9 Existence proof by Picard's method. A special case. We now consider the iterative sequence

$$y_n(x) = y_0 + \int_{x_0}^x f[t, y_{n-1}(t)] \, dt, \qquad n = 1, 2, \ldots, \qquad (1)$$

with $y_0(t) = y_0$, for the differential equation problem

$$y' = f(x, y), \qquad y(x_0) = y_0, \qquad (2)$$

with a view toward using it for a proof of the existence of a solution of (2).

We must show that the sequence of functions $y_n(x)$ converges to a limiting function $y(x)$ which is a solution of (2), or of the equivalent integral equation

$$y(x) = y_0 + \int_{x_0}^x f[t, y(t)] \, dt. \qquad (3)$$

To prove the existence of a limiting function

$$y(x) = \lim_{n \to \infty} y_n(x), \tag{4}$$

we make use of the fact that y_n may be written as a sum of successive differences:

$$y_n = y_0 + \sum_{j=0}^{n-1} (y_{j+1} - y_j). \tag{5}$$

This means that convergence of the sequence y_n is equivalent to convergence of the infinite series $\sum (y_{j+1} - y_j)$. We shall see that under suitable conditions on the given function $f(x, y)$ we can obtain bounds on the successive differences which occur on the right of Eq. (5) of such a nature that convergence of the infinite series is assured.

By Eq. (1) we have that the successive differences $y_{j+1} - y_j$ satisfy the following relations:

$$y_{j+1}(x) - y_j(x) = \int_{x_0}^{x} \{f[t, y_j(t)] - f[t, y_{j-1}(t)]\} \, dt. \tag{6}$$

Equation (6) holds for all integers beginning with $j = 1$. For $j = 0$ we have as a relation taking its place

$$y_1(x) - y_0 = \int_{x_0}^{x} f(t, y_0) \, dt. \tag{7}$$

To make sure that the integrals in (6) and (7) exist we make the assumption

$$|f(t, z)| \leq M, \tag{8a}$$

where M is a positive constant.

Furthermore, in order to simplify the treatment of (6), we make the additional assumption

$$|f(t, z_2) - f(t, z_1)| \leq M|z_2 - z_1|, \tag{8b}$$

which is known as a *Lipschitz condition*.

For the present we require (8) to hold for all real values of t and z. We shall later see that an important refinement of the proof is possible in which the inequalities (8) need to be satisfied in certain finite t- and z-intervals only.

We are now ready to consider the successive differences (7) and (6). For the first of these, we have

$$|y_1(x) - y_0| \leq \left| \int_{x_0}^{x} |f(t, y_0)| \, dt \right| \leq \left| \int_{x_0}^{x} M \, dt \right| = M|x - x_0|. \tag{9a}$$

Next, from (6) and (8b)

$$|y_2(x) - y_1(x)| \leq \left| \int_{x_0}^x |f(t, y_1(t)) - f(t, y_0)| \, dt \right|$$

$$\leq \left| \int_{x_0}^x M|y_1(t) - y_0| \, dt \right|.$$

By (9a) this becomes

$$|y_2(x) - y_1(x)| \leq \left| \int_{x_0}^x M \cdot M(t - x_0) \, dt \right| = M^2 \frac{|x - x_0|^2}{2}. \quad (9b)$$

We may now proceed by mathematical induction. The form of (9a) and (9b) suggests that we shall have

$$|y_j(x) - y_{j-1}(x)| \leq M^j \frac{|x - x_0|^j}{j!}. \quad (9c)$$

We shall have established the validity of this inequality if we can show that (9c) implies the corresponding relation with j replaced by $j + 1$. For this purpose, we again make use of (6) and (8b). We write

$$|y_{j+1}(x) - y_j(x)| \leq \left| \int_{x_0}^x |f(t, y_j(t)) - f(t, y_{j-1}(t))| \, dt \right|$$

$$\leq \left| \int_{x_0}^x M|y_j(t) - y_{j-1}(t)| \, dt \right|$$

$$\leq \left| \int_{x_0}^x M \cdot M^j \frac{(t - x_0)^j}{j!} \, dt \right|$$

$$= M^{j+1} \frac{|x - x_0|^{j+1}}{(j + 1)!}. \quad (9d)$$

Relation (9d) proves the validity of (9c) for all values of j.

In view of (9d), the absolute values of terms in the series (5) are smaller than the corresponding terms in the Taylor series for the function

$$e^{M|x-x_0|}.$$

Since the Taylor series for this function converges for all values of $(x - x_0)$, the functions $y_n(x)$ converge toward a function $y(x)$ for all values of x, uniformly in any finite interval.

It is now plausible, but must be proved, that the limit function $y(x)$ which we have obtained does in fact solve the integral equation (3). To see what is involved in this proof, we consider the limit, as n goes to infinity, on both sides of (1).

$$y(x) = y_0 + \lim_{n \to \infty} \int_{x_0}^x f(t, y_{n-1}(t)) \, dt. \quad (10)$$

What we must know now are conditions sufficient to make the following interchanges of limiting operations valid:

$$\lim_{n \to \infty} \int_{x_0}^{x} f(t, y_n(t)) \, dt = \int_{x_0}^{x} \lim_{n \to \infty} f(t, y_n(t)) \, dt$$

$$= \int_{x_0}^{x} f(t, \lim_{n \to \infty} y_n(t)) \, dt. \tag{11}$$

In advanced texts on the calculus it is shown that these interchanges are valid provided (i) that $f(t, z)$ is a continuous function of both t and z in the range of values considered, and (ii) that the convergence of $y_n(t)$ to $y(t)$ is uniform over the interval in question.

We may state the result which we have obtained as a theorem.

THEOREM. The iterative sequence (1) converges towards a solution of the differential equation problem (2) for all values of x, provided the function $f(x, y)$ is continuous and bounded and in addition satisfies the Lipschitz condition (8b) for all values of its arguments.

EXERCISES

1. Given that $f(x, y)$ satisfies the condition $|\partial f / \partial y| \leq M$ for all values of x and y, show that the Lipschitz condition (8b) is also satisfied, with the same constant M.

2. Determine which of the following functions $f(x, y)$ satisfy the two conditions $|f(x, y)| \leq M$, $|\partial f / \partial y| \leq M$, for *all* values of x and y.

(a) $\sin y$ (b) e^y,   (c) $\sin xy$

(d) $(x^2 + y^2)^{-1}$ (e) e^{xy},   (f) y

(g) x/y (h) $\tanh^{-1}(x + y)$ (i) $y^{2/3}$

6–10 Uniqueness by Picard's method. To see whether or not the initial value problem (2) of the preceding section has a unique solution, we consider the possibility of two distinct solutions, y and $\tilde{y}$. In view of Eq. (3) of the preceding section, the difference $y(x) - \tilde{y}(x)$ satisfies the relation

$$y(x) - \tilde{y}(x) = \int_{x_0}^{x} [f(t, y(t)) - f(t, \tilde{y}(t))] \, dt. \tag{1}$$

We shall show that the same conditions which assure convergence of the iterative process, namely,

$$|f(t, z)| \leq M, \tag{2}$$

$$|f(t, z_2) - f(t, z_1)| < M|z_2 - z_1|, \tag{3}$$

are sufficient to prove that $y(x) - \tilde{y}(x) = 0$.

We begin by using (1) and (2) to prove

$$|y(x) - \tilde{y}(x)| \leq 2M|x - x_0|. \tag{4}$$

We next use (1) and (3) to obtain

$$|y(x) - \tilde{y}(x)| \leq \left| \int_{x_0}^{x} M|y(t) - \tilde{y}(t)|\, dt \right|. \tag{5}$$

Combination of (4) and (5) gives us

$$|y(x) - \tilde{y}(x)| \leq \left| \int_{x_0}^{x} M \cdot 2M(t - x_0)\, dt \right| = 2M^2 \frac{|x - x_0|^2}{2!}. \tag{6}$$

Equation (6) may in turn be introduced on the right side of Eq. (5). In this way we obtain

$$|y(x) - \tilde{y}(x)| \leq 2M^3 \frac{|x - x_0|^3}{3!}. \tag{7}$$

Continuing in this manner, we obtain the successively stronger inequalities

$$|y(x) - \tilde{y}(x)| \leq 2\frac{M^n|x - x_0|^n}{n!}, \qquad n = 1, 2, 3, \ldots \tag{8}$$

Since for every finite value of x the right side of (8) tends to zero as n tends to infinity, we have

$$y(x) - \tilde{y}(x) = 0$$

for all finite values of x. In other words, we have proved uniqueness of the solution everywhere.

6–11 Existence and uniqueness by Picard's method. The general case. The existence proof for the special case of Section 6–9 depended on the fact that we could obtain the inequality

$$|y_{j+1}(x) - y_j(x)| \leq M^{j+1} \frac{(x - x_0)^{j+1}}{(j + 1)!} \tag{1}$$

for all values of x, thereby establishing existence everywhere. This result held for the class of continuous functions $f(x, y)$ which satisfy the boundedness and Lipschitz conditions (8) of Section 6–9 for all values of x.

We now wish to see for what wider class of functions $f(x, y)$ we can establish (1) for some limited range

$$|x - x_0| \leq a. \tag{2}$$

To this end we consider again the relations

$$y_{j+1}(x) - y_j(x) = \int_{x_0}^{x} \{f[t, y_j(t)] - f[t, y_{j-1}(t)]\} \, dt, \qquad j = 1, 2, \ldots$$
(3)

Since we do not wish to require boundedness and a Lipschitz condition for all values of y but merely in a suitable neighborhood of y_0 we are led to consider first the possibility of obtaining bounds not for $y_{j+1} - y_j$ but for $y_j - y_0$, which is given by

$$y_j(x) - y_0 = \int_{x_0}^{x} f[t, y_{j-1}(t)] \, dt.$$
(4)

So long as $|f| \leq M$ for $|t - x_0| \leq a$ and $y = y_0$, we have from (4)

$$|y_1(x) - y_0| \leq M|x - x_0| \leq Ma.$$
(5)

If we now require, in view of (5), that

$$|f(t, z)| \leq M$$
(6)

for

$$|t - x_0| \leq a \qquad \text{and} \qquad |z - y_0| \leq Ma,$$
(7)

then we conclude next from

$$y_2(x) - y_0 = \int_{x_0}^{x} f[t, y_1(t)] \, dt$$

that

$$|y_2(x) - y_0| \leq Ma$$
(8)

and then, by induction, that

$$|y_j(x) - y_0| \leq Ma$$
(9)

for $|x - x_0| \leq a$, and all j.

Having the bound (9) for y_j, we formulate our Lipschitz condition for (3) in the following manner:

$$|f(t, z_2) - f(t, z_1)| \leq M|z_2 - z_1|$$
(10)

in the range (7). This allows us to write

$$|y_{j+1}(x) - y_j(x)| \leq \left| \int_{x_0}^{x} M|y_j(t) - y_{j-1}(t)| \, dt \right|.$$
(11)

We know from (5) that $|y_1(x) - y_0| \leq M|x - x_0|$. If we introduce this result into (11) with $j = 1$, we see that

$$|y_2(x) - y_1(x)| \leq \left| \int_{x_0}^{x} M^2|t - x_0| \, dt \right| = \tfrac{1}{2}M^2|x - x_0|^2.$$
(12)

Continuing in this manner, we arrive at the fundamental estimate (1), valid in the interval $|x - x_0| \leq a$.

Having established the inequality (1), the remainder of the existence proof and also the uniqueness proof proceed exactly as in Sections 6–9 and 6–10.

We summarize our result in the following form:

THEOREM. The iterative sequence

$$y_n(x) = y_0 + \int_{x_0}^{x} f[t, y_{n-1}(t)] \, dt \tag{13}$$

converges toward a unique solution of the differential equation problem

$$y' = f(x, y), \qquad y(x_0) = y_0, \tag{14}$$

for all values of x in the range $|x - x_0| \leq a$, provided the function $f(x, z)$ is continuous and satisfies the two conditions

$$|f(x, z)| \leq M, \qquad |f(x, z_2) - f(x, z_1)| \leq M|z_2 - z_1| \tag{15}$$

for

$$|x - x_0| \leq a \qquad \text{and} \qquad |z - y_0| \leq Ma. \tag{16}$$

For practical applications it is useful to know that the Lipschitz condition $|f(x, z_2) - f(x, z_1)| \leq M|z_2 - z_1|$ in the region defined by Eq. (16) is a less stringent condition than the condition $|\partial f(x, z)/\partial z| \leq M$ in this region, in the sense that satisfaction of the partial derivative condition implies satisfaction of the Lipschitz condition. The existence and uniqueness theorem with the Lipschitz condition replaced by the partial derivative condition, which we have stated in Chapter 2, is therefore a corollary to the theorem as worded above.

EXAMPLE. To indicate the scope of Picard's existence theorem, consider the following simple example:

$$y' = e^y, \qquad y(0) = 0.$$

We are interested in finding the largest interval $|x| \leq a$ in which the theorem guarantees existence of a unique solution.

The boundedness condition on f assumes the form

$$e^z \leq M \qquad \text{for} \qquad |z| \leq Ma,$$

and by the mean value theorem this also ensures satisfaction of the Lipschitz condition.

The inequality $e^z \leq M$ will be satisfied for all values of z such that $|z| \leq Ma$, provided it is satisfied if $z = Ma$. Accordingly, we must have

$$e^{Ma} \leq M \qquad \text{or} \qquad a \leq \frac{\ln M}{M}.$$

Since a is positive, M lies in the range $1 \leq M < \infty$. In this range the largest value of a is obtained if

$$M = e = 2.718\ldots$$

and Picard's theorem assures existence of a unique solution in the interval $|x| \leq a$, where

$$a = e^{-1} = 0.368.$$

The actual interval in which a unique solution exists is considerably larger. Since, by separation of variables,

$$y = \ln \frac{1}{1-x},$$

we know that a unique solution exists in the interval $-\infty < x < 1$.

We conclude these considerations with the following observation. The proof of Picard's theorem as given requires satisfaction of a Lipschitz condition both for existence and for uniqueness. In actual fact it is possible, however, to prove existence by more advanced methods without requiring a Lipschitz condition. On the other hand, in order to prove uniqueness a Lipschitz condition or something very similar is required.

EXERCISES

For each of the following two problems, show that Picard's theorem ensures existence of a unique solution in the interval $|x| \leq \frac{1}{2}$.

1. $y' = x + y^2$, $\quad y(0) = 0$ $\qquad$ 2. $y' = 1 + xy^2$, $\quad y(0) = 0$

3. Show that for the problem $y' = y$, $y(0) = 1$, the constant a in Picard's theorem must be smaller than unity.

MISCELLANEOUS EXERCISES.   CHAPTER 6

1. Given that a power-series solution of the differential equation problem

$$y' = 1 + x \cos y, \qquad y(0) = 0$$

is $y = x + \frac{1}{2}x^2 - \frac{1}{8}x^4 - \frac{1}{10}x^5 + \cdots$. Calculate $y_{(k)}(x)$, $k = 1, 2, 3, 4$ for (a) $x = 0.1$, (b) $x = 0.5$.

2. The differential equation problem

$$y' - xy = 0, \qquad y(0) = 1$$

has the explicit solution

$$y = e^{x^2/2} = 1 + \frac{1}{2}x^2 + \frac{1}{2!}\left(\frac{x^2}{2}\right)^2 + \cdots + \frac{1}{n!}\left(\frac{x^2}{2}\right)^n + \cdots$$

Show that Picard's method of successive approximations, with $y_0(x) = 1$, gives

$$y_n(x) = 1 + \frac{1}{2}x^2 + \frac{1}{2!}\left(\frac{x^2}{2}\right)^2 + \cdots + \frac{1}{n!}\left(\frac{x^2}{2}\right)^n.$$

3. Calculate approximations $\tilde{y}_1$ to $y(h)$ for the initial value problem

$$y' = 1 + x\cos y, \qquad y(0) = 0$$

by means of Eqs. (3') and (5') of Section 6–2.

4. Use the appropriate result in Section 6–3 to show that the magnitude of the remainder term R_m in the Taylor formula $y_{n+1} = y_n + hy_n' + \cdots + (h^m/m!)y_n^{(m)} + R_m$ for the function $y = \sin x$ is limited by the relation $|R_m| \le h^{m+1}/(m+1)!$

5. By reference to relevant results in Section 6–5 obtain the approximation $\int_0^\pi \sin x \, dx = 2\pi/3$ and show that this differs from the correct result by no more than $(\pi/2)^5/90$.

6. Given the problem $y' = 1 + xy^2$, $y(0) = 0$ with the power-series solution $y = x + \frac{1}{4}x^4 + \cdots$. Show that a consistent application of the idea of Section 6–6 leads to the approximation formulas $y_1 = h + \frac{1}{4}h^4$ and $y_2 = 2h + \frac{4}{3}h^4 + \frac{2}{3}h^2 y_2^2$. When $h = 0.5$ the above formula for y_2 reduces to the form $y_2 = 1.083 + 0.166y_2^2$. Determine y_2 by iteration, starting with $y_{2,0} = 1.25$.

In Exercises 7, 8, and 9 use Picard's method of successive approximations, with the indicated starting value for $y_0(x)$, to determine the approximating functions indicated.

7. $y' = 2 + xy^2$, $y(0) = 1$. Start with $y_0(x) = 1$. Determine $y_1(x)$ and $y_2(x)$.

8. $y' = y$, $y(0) = 1$. Start with $y_0(x) = 0$. Determine $y_1(x), \ldots, y_4(x)$ and compare these approximations with those found in Example 1 of Section 6–8.

9. $y' = \cos y$, $y(0) = 0$. Start with $y_0(x) = x$. Determine $y_1(x)$ and $y_2(x)$. Also obtain an explicit solution $y = y(x)$ and show that it is a continuous function for $-\infty < x < \infty$, with values in the interval $-\frac{1}{2}\pi < y < \frac{1}{2}\pi$.

10. Show that Picard's theorem assures existence and uniqueness of the solution of $y' = \sec y$, $y(0) = 0$ in the interval $|x| < \pi/4\sqrt{2}$ by showing that $|\sec y| < \sqrt{2}$ and $|\tan y \sec y| < \sqrt{2}$ for $|y| < \frac{1}{4}\pi$. In what interval is the explicit solution $y = y(x)$ defined?

CHAPTER 7

FINITE DIFFERENCE EQUATIONS

7-1 Introduction. Consideration of numerical procedures for solving differential equations leads to a subject which somewhat parallels the subject of differential equations, namely, the subject of *finite difference equations*. We shall consider in the present chapter some simple interesting aspects of the field of finite difference equations.

To solve the differential equation $dy/dx = F(x, y)$ approximately, we may replace this equation by

$$y_{n+1} - y_n = hF(x_n, y_n), \tag{1}$$

where

$$x_n = x_{n-1} + h = x_0 + nh \tag{2}$$

and

$$y_n = y(x_n) = y(x_0 + nh). \tag{3}$$

The quantities $x_n - x_{n-1} = h$ and $y_n - y_{n-1}$ are *finite differences* of the independent variable and of the dependent variable.

A more accurate approximation to the differential equation and its solution, for the same interval length h, is obtained by taking instead of (1) the relation

$$y_{n+1} - y_{n-1} = \tfrac{1}{3}h[F(x_{n+1}, y_{n+1}) + 4F(x_n, y_n) + F(x_{n-1}, y_{n-1})], \tag{4}$$

which follows from the integral formula

$$y_{n+1} - y_{n-1} = \int_{x_{n-1}}^{x_{n+1}} F(x, y)\, dx$$

if we apply Simpson's rule to it.

Equations of the form (1) and (4) which contain finite differences, rather than infinitesimal differences in derivative form, are often called *finite difference equations*.

In our earlier work, equations of this form were solved step by step, with or without using iterative procedures. In many instances to do so will be the only practical means of solution. However, we shall see that there are important classes of finite difference equations which can be solved explicitly, just as important classes of differential equations can be solved explicitly.

Problems of numerical solution of differential equations are not the only sources of finite difference equations. All kinds of recurrence relations can be interpreted as finite difference equations. The formulation of physical and chemical problems for systems with many similar components generally leads to finite difference equations.

EXAMPLE 1. The linear differential equation

$$y' = \alpha(x)y + \beta(x) \tag{5}$$

can be approximated by the finite difference equation

$$y_{n+1} - y_n = (\alpha_n y_n + \beta_n)h. \tag{6}$$

An alternate form of (6) is

$$y_{n+1} + a_n y_n = b_n, \tag{7}$$

where

$$a_n = -(1 + h\alpha_n), \qquad b_n = h\beta_n. \tag{8}$$

The more accurate formula (4) approximates (5) by

$$y_{n+1} - y_{n-1} = \tfrac{1}{3}h[\alpha_{n+1}y_{n+1} + \beta_{n+1} + 4\alpha_n y_n$$
$$+ 4\beta_n + \alpha_{n-1}y_{n-1} + \beta_{n-1}] \tag{9}$$

or

$$a_{n+1}y_{n+1} + a_n y_n + a_{n-1}y_{n-1} = b_{n+1}, \tag{10}$$

where

$$a_{n+1} = 1 - \tfrac{1}{3}h\alpha_{n+1}, \quad a_n = -\tfrac{4}{3}h\alpha_n, \quad a_{n-1} = -1 - \tfrac{1}{3}h\alpha_{n-1},$$
$$b_{n+1} = \tfrac{1}{3}h[\beta_{n+1} + 4\beta_n + \beta_{n-1}]. \tag{11}$$

EXAMPLE 2. Obtain a finite difference equation for the general term in the sequence 0, 1, 1, 2, 3, 5, 8, 13, . . . , each term of which is the sum of the two preceding terms.

Let y_n be the general term of the sequence. Since each term in it is the sum of the two preceding terms, we have the recurrence relation

$$y_n = y_{n-1} + y_{n-2}, \tag{12}$$

together with the *initial conditions*

$$y_1 = 0, \qquad y_2 = 1. \tag{13}$$

The numbers representing the solution of the finite difference equation (12) are known as the numbers of Fibonacci.

EXERCISES

1. Given that in first approximation

$$y'_n = (y_{n+1} - y_n)/h,$$

show that a corresponding approximation for second derivatives is

$$y''_n = (y_{n+2} - 2y_{n+1} + y_n)/h^2.$$

2. An alternate form of an approximation for y'_n is

$$y'_n = [y(x_n + \tfrac{1}{2}h) - y(x_n - \tfrac{1}{2}h)]/h.$$

Use this formula to deduce the following symmetrical approximation formula for y''_n:

$$y''_n = (y_{n+1} - 2y_n + y_{n-1})/h^2.$$

3. A sum of money A_0 is invested at p percent interest per year. Assuming that the interest at the end of every year is added to the capital, obtain a difference equation for the capital A_n at the end of n years.

Given the linear differential equations

4. $y'' - y = 0$,   5. $y'' - (1 + x)y = 0$,   6. $y'' - xy' + 2y = 0$,

obtain difference equations for the determination of the coefficients a_n in the series $y = \sum a_n x^n$.

7–2 Solution of first-order difference equations.   A finite difference equation is called of first order if no more than two successive functional values, y_n and y_{n+1}, are contained in it. The most general form of such an equation is

$$F(y_{n+1}, y_n, n) = 0, \tag{1}$$

and just as in the case of first-order differential equations, it is not possible to solve this most general case explicitly.

An important special class of first-order difference equations which can be solved explicitly is the *linear first-order difference equation*. We may write this equation in the form

$$y_{n+1} = a_n y_n + b_n. \tag{2}$$

To solve (2) in a direct manner, we introduce on the right side of it the equivalent relation

$$y_n = a_{n-1} y_{n-1} + b_{n-1}.$$

This gives us

$$y_{n+1} = a_n(a_{n-1} y_{n-1} + b_{n-1}) + b_n.$$

On the right side of this we write

$$y_{n-1} = a_{n-2}y_{n-2} + b_{n-2},$$

and this gives us in turn

$$y_{n+1} = a_n[a_{n-1}(a_{n-2}y_{n-2} + b_{n-2}) + b_{n-1}] + b_n.$$

Continuing in this manner, we arrive at the following explicit expression for y_{n+1} in terms of y_0 and in terms of the coefficients a_k and b_k:

$$y_{n+1} = (a_n a_{n-1} \ldots a_1 a_0)y_0 + (a_n a_{n-1} \ldots a_1)b_0 + \cdots$$
$$+ a_n a_{n-1} b_{n-2} + a_n b_{n-1} + b_n. \quad (3)$$

If we set as an abbreviation

$$a_j a_{j-1} \ldots a_1 a_0 = \prod_{k=0}^{j} a_k, \quad (4)$$

then (3) may be written more compactly as follows:

$$y_{n+1} = \left[y_0 + \sum_{j=0}^{n} \frac{b_j}{\prod_{k=0}^{j} a_k} \right] \prod_{k=0}^{n} a_k. \quad (3')$$

The solution (3) contains *one arbitrary constant*, y_0. This parallels a corresponding result for differential equations.

The formulas (3) and (3') are based on the assumption that the difference equation (2) holds for all values of $n = 0, 1, 2, \ldots$, with y_0 given. If instead of this we have (1) only for values of n starting with some other value m, with y_m given, then the solution takes the alternative form

$$y_{n+1} = \left[y_m + \sum_{j=m}^{n} \frac{b_j}{\prod_{k=m}^{j} a_k} \right] \prod_{k=m}^{n} a_k, \quad n = m, m+1, \ldots \quad (3'')$$

As a first illustration of the use of the general formula (3''), consider the recurrence relation

$$(2n)^2 \beta_{2n} + \beta_{2n-2} = \frac{(-1)^{n+1} n}{(n!)^2 2^{2n-2}}, \quad n = 2, 3, \ldots, \quad (5)$$

with $\beta_2 = \frac{1}{4}$. We met this formula in Eq. (11) of Section 3–16 in connection with the Bessel function of the second kind. In order to reduce (5) to a difference equation of the form (2) we set

$$y_n = \beta_{2n-2}. \quad (6)$$

The relation (5), with the initial condition $\beta_2 = \frac{1}{4}$, then becomes

$$y_{n+1} = -\frac{y_n}{(2n)^2} + \frac{(-1)^{n+1}}{(n!)^2 2^{2n} n}, \qquad n = 2, 3, \ldots, \tag{7}$$

$$y_2 = \frac{1}{4}. \tag{8}$$

The solution formula (3''), with $m = 2$ and

$$a_n = -\frac{1}{(2n)^2}, \qquad b_n = \frac{(-1)^{n+1}}{(n!)^2 2^{2n} n},$$

becomes

$$y_{n+1} = \left[y_2 + \sum_{j=2}^{n} \frac{(-1)^{j+1}}{(j!)^2 2^{2j} j} \frac{2^{2j-2}(j!)^2}{(-1)^{j-1}} \right] \frac{(-1)^{n-1}}{2^{2n-2}(n!)^2}$$

$$= \left[y_2 + \sum_{j=2}^{n} \frac{2^{-2}}{j} \right] \frac{(-1)^{n-1} 2^2}{2^{2n}(n!)^2}. \tag{9}$$

On inserting the value $y_2 = \frac{1}{4}$ from (8) and simplifying further, we obtain the expression

$$y_{n+1} = \frac{(-1)^{n-1}}{2^{2n}(n!)^2} \sum_{j=1}^{n} \frac{1}{j}, \qquad n = 2, 3, \ldots \tag{9'}$$

If we return to the original β's by use of (6), we have the solution

$$\beta_{2n} = \frac{(-1)^{n-1}}{2^{2n}(n!)^2} \sum_{j=1}^{n} \frac{1}{j}, \qquad n = 1, 2, \ldots, \tag{10}$$

which agrees with Eq. (12d) of Section 3–16.

Two important special cases of the linear first-order difference equation are the following:

1. *First-order homogeneous equation with constant coefficient.* When

$$y_{n+1} = a y_n, \tag{11}$$

the solution (3) becomes $y_{n+1} = a^{n+1} y_0$. We may write this result in the form

$$y_n = c a^n, \tag{12}$$

where c is an arbitrary constant.

2. *Nonhomogeneous equation with constant coefficient.* When

$$y_{n+1} = a y_n + b_n, \tag{13}$$

then (3) may be written in the form

$$y_n = \left[c + \sum_{j=0}^{n-1} \frac{b_j}{a^{j+1}} \right] r^n, \qquad n = 1, 2, \ldots \qquad (14)$$

For future reference we restate the result (14) for the following special case of Eq. (13):

$$\Delta y_n \equiv y_{n+1} - y_n = b_n. \qquad (15)$$

Setting $a = 1$ in (14) reduces this solution to the form

$$y_n = c + \sum_{j=0}^{n-1} b_j. \qquad (16)$$

Solution of a nonlinear equation. To illustrate the possibility of solving a nonlinear equation, consider the relation

$$y_{n+1} = a y_n^2, \qquad a \neq 0. \qquad (17)$$

By successive substitution we obtain

$$y_{n+1} = a a^2 y_{n-1}^4 = a a^2 a^4 y_{n-2}^8 = \ldots,$$

and this means that in terms of an arbitrary constant y_0,

$$y_{n+1} = a^{1+2+2^2+\cdots+2^n} y_0^{2^{n+1}}, \qquad n = 0, 1, 2, \ldots$$

If we further write

$$1 + 2 + 2^2 + \cdots + 2^{n-1} = \frac{2^n - 1}{2 - 1} = 2^n - 1, \qquad a y_0 = c,$$

then the solution of (17) assumes the form

$$y_n = \frac{c^{2^n}}{a}, \qquad n = 0, 1, 2, \ldots \qquad (18)$$

where c is an arbitrary constant.

EXERCISES

Solve the difference equations in Exercises 1 through 6.

1. $y_{n+1} - 2y_n = 0$ 2. $y_{n+1} = n y_n, \quad n = 1, 2, 3, \ldots$
3. $y_{n+1} = n^{-1} y_n, \quad n = 1, 2, 3, \ldots$ 4. $y_{n+1} = a y_n + b$
5. $y_{n+1} = a y_n + bn$ 6. $y_{n+1} = \sqrt{y_n}$

Obtain a first-order finite difference equation which is satisfied by y_n, c being an arbitrary constant, for Exercises 7 through 9.

7. $y_n = n + ce^n$　　　　8. $y_n = cn + c^2$　　　　9. $y_n = c2^n + n/c$

10. Show that the solution of the homogeneous equation $y_{n+1} = a_n y_n$ is

$$y_n = c \prod_{k=0}^{n-1} a_k.$$

11. Given that u_n is the solution of the homogeneous equation $u_{n+1} = a_n u_n$, obtain the solution of the nonhomogeneous equation $y_{n+1} = a_n y_n + b_n$ by the method of variation of parameters, setting $y_n = C_n u_n$. Observe that C_n is a solution of a first-order difference equation with constant coefficient.

12. Show that the difference equation satisfied by the function y_n of Exercise 8 also has a solution of the form $y_n = An^2 + Bn + C$, and determine the values of A, B, and C.

7–3 The homogeneous linear second-order difference equation with constant coefficients.

We consider the second-order equation

$$y_{n+2} + 2ay_{n+1} + by_n = 0, \tag{1}$$

where a and b are given constants. We note that Eq. (1) is similar in appearance to the differential equation $y'' + 2ay' + by = 0$. We shall find that this similarity carries over to the solutions of these equations as well.

Knowing that the first-order equation with constant coefficient, $y_{n+1} = ay_n$, has the solution $y_n = ca^n$, we consider the possibility of a similar solution for the corresponding second-order equation (1). To this end we set tentatively

$$y_n = c\beta^n, \tag{2}$$

where c is an arbitrary constant and β a quantity to be determined. From (2),

$$y_{n+1} = c\beta^{n+1}, \qquad y_{n+2} = c\beta^{n+2}. \tag{3}$$

Introduction of (2) and (3) into (1) leads to the relation

$$(\beta^2 + 2a\beta + b)c\beta^n = 0. \tag{4}$$

Since $c\beta^n \neq 0$, Eq. (2) is a solution of (1) provided β is a solution of the quadratic

$$\beta^2 + 2a\beta + b = 0. \tag{5}$$

In analogy to the corresponding result for differential equations, this equation may be called the *auxiliary equation*.

Let β_1 and β_2 be the two roots of the auxiliary equation (5). Both $c\beta_1^n$ and $c\beta_2^n$ will satisfy the given difference equation. Since this equation is linear, any superposition of the two solutions will also be a solution. Accordingly, the homogeneous second-order difference equation (1) has solutions of the form

$$y_n = c_1\beta_1^n + c_2\beta_2^n, \tag{6}$$

where c_1 and c_2 are arbitrary constants and β_1 and β_2 are solutions of the auxiliary equation (5).

A general solution of the second-order linear difference equation may be defined as a solution which can assume arbitrarily prescribed initial values y_0 and y_1, through proper choice of the constants c_1 and c_2. With this definition, Eq. (6) is readily seen to be the general solution of (1), provided $\beta_1 \neq \beta_2$.

Complex roots of the auxiliary equation. We assume that the coefficients a and b in (1) are real. Then when β_1 is complex, β_2 is its conjugate:

$$\beta_1 = \alpha + i\gamma, \qquad \beta_2 = \alpha - i\gamma. \tag{7}$$

To obtain a real expression for the solution $c_1\beta_1^n + c_2\beta_2^n$, we write

$$\alpha \pm i\gamma = \rho e^{\pm i\phi}, \qquad (\alpha \pm i\gamma)^n = \rho^n e^{\pm in\phi}, \tag{8}$$

where

$$\rho^2 = \alpha^2 + \gamma^2 \qquad \text{and} \qquad \tan\phi = \gamma/\alpha. \tag{9}$$

Therewith,

$$y_n = (c_1 e^{in\phi} + c_2 e^{-in\phi})\rho^n.$$

By further writing

$$c_1 + c_2 = C_1, \qquad i(c_1 - c_2) = C_2,$$

where C_1 and C_2 are new, real constants, this solution assumes the real form

$$y_n = (C_1 \cos n\phi + C_2 \sin n\phi)\rho^n. \tag{10}$$

It is instructive to see in which way the quantities ρ and ϕ enter into the coefficients of the difference equation of which (10) is the solution. To this end we write the auxiliary equation (5) in the form

$$(\beta - \rho e^{i\phi})(\beta - \rho e^{-i\phi}) = 0, \tag{11a}$$

or

$$\beta^2 - 2\rho \cos\phi\,\beta + \rho^2 = 0. \tag{11b}$$

This shows that (10) is the general solution of the difference equation

$$y_{n+2} - 2\rho \cos \phi \, y_{n+1} + \rho^2 y_n = 0. \tag{12}$$

EXAMPLE 1. The difference equation

$$y_{n+2} - 5y_{n+1} + 6y_n = 0$$

has the auxiliary equation

$$\beta^2 - 5\beta + 6 = 0,$$

the solutions of which are $\beta_1 = 2$, $\beta_2 = 3$. Accordingly, the general solution of the given difference equation is

$$y_n = c_1 2^n + c_2 3^n.$$

EXAMPLE 2. The equation

$$y_{n+2} - \sqrt{2} y_{n+1} + y_n = 0$$

is a special case of Eq. (12). In view of (10), its general solution is

$$y_n = C_1 \cos \tfrac{1}{4} n\pi + C_2 \sin \tfrac{1}{4} n\pi.$$

Auxiliary equation with double roots. When $\beta_1 = \beta_2 \neq 0$, the solution (6) no longer has two independent arbitrary constants, and it ceases to be the general solution. In its stead the general solution assumes the form

$$y_n = (c_1 + c_2 n)\beta_1^n. \tag{13}$$

There are various ways of deriving this result, the correctness of which is readily verified. We outline one method of derivation. When $\beta_1 = \beta_2$, the difference equation may be written as

$$y_{n+2} - 2\beta_1 y_{n+1} + \beta_1^2 y_n = 0. \tag{14}$$

Equivalently,

$$(y_{n+2} - \beta_1 y_{n+1}) - \beta_1(y_{n+1} - \beta_1 y_n) = 0. \tag{15}$$

We set

$$y_{n+1} - \beta_1 y_n = z_n, \tag{16}$$

and have

$$z_{n+1} - \beta_1 z_n = 0. \tag{17}$$

We now solve first the homogeneous first-order equation (17) and then, having z_n, the nonhomogeneous first-order equation (16). In this way we arrive at the general solution (13) of Eq. (14).

EXERCISES

Solve the difference equations in Exercises 1 through 4.

1. $y_{n+2} - \frac{5}{2}y_{n+1} + y_n = 0$ 2. $y_{n+2} - y_{n+1} - 2y_n = 0$

3. $y_{n+2} - y_{n+1} + y_n = 0$ 4. $y_{n+2} - 2y_{n+1} + 2y_n = 0$

5. Determine the nth Fibonacci number, as defined in Example 2 of Section 7-1.

6. Show that the general solution of $y_{n+1} - 2y_n \cosh \mu + y_{n-1} = 0$ can be written in the form $y_n = c_1 e^{\mu n} + c_2 e^{-\mu n}$.

7. Obtain a second-order linear difference equation with constant coefficients which has the solutions

(a) $y_n = c_1 2^n + c_2 3^n$, (b) $y_n = (c_1 + c_2 n)2^n$, (c) $y_n = c_1 \cos \alpha n + c_2 \sin \alpha n$,

where c_1 and c_2 are arbitrary constants.

8. Obtain a second-order linear difference equation with variable coefficients which has the solutions

(a) $y_n = c_1 n + c_2 n^2$,   (b) $y_n = c_1 f(n) + c_2 g(n)$,

c_1 and c_2 being arbitrary constants.

9. Show that the solution (13) of Eq. (14) is in fact the general solution by showing that through proper choice of the constants c_1 and c_2 the solution may assume arbitrarily prescribed initial values y_0 and y_1.

7-4 Systems of homogeneous linear difference equations with constant coefficients. The method of solution for one second-order equation of the form $y_{n+2} + 2ay_{n+1} + by_n = 0$ is readily generalized to apply to the corresponding kth-order equation and to systems of simultaneous first-order equations.

To illustrate, the system

$$y_{n+1} = ay_n + bz_n, \qquad z_{n+1} = py_n + qz_n, \tag{1}$$

can be solved by tentatively assuming

$$y_n = A\beta^n, \qquad z_n = B\beta^n. \tag{2}$$

Substitution of (2) into (1) results in the following equations for the coefficients A and B:

$$(a - \beta)A + bB = 0, \qquad pA + (q - \beta)B = 0. \tag{3}$$

Since we do not wish to have both A and B equal to zero, we require that β satisfy the determinantal equation

$$
\begin{vmatrix} a - \beta & b \\ p & q - \beta \end{vmatrix} = 0. \tag{4}
$$

Equation (4), the auxiliary equation, is a quadratic for β, with solutions β_1 and β_2. So long as $\beta_1 \neq \beta_2$, which is what we shall assume here, we have obtained two distinct pairs of solutions in this manner. Because of the superposition principle for linear systems, we have further that

$$
y_n = A_1\beta_1^n + A_2\beta_2^n, \qquad z_n = B_1\beta_1^n + B_2\beta_2^n \tag{5}
$$

are also solutions of (1), provided that A_1, B_1, and β_1 and A_2, B_2, and β_2 are related through (3). It can be shown that so long as $\beta_1 \neq \beta_2$ Eqs. (5) represent the general solution of the system (1).

EXAMPLE 1. The system

$$
y_{n+1} = y_n + 3z_n, \qquad z_{n+1} = 2y_n - z_n
$$

has solutions of the form (2), provided

$$
(1 - \beta)A + 3B = 0, \qquad 2A - (1 + \beta)B = 0.
$$

The auxiliary equation is

$$
(1 - \beta)(1 + \beta) + 6 = 0.
$$

From this,

$$
\beta_1 = \sqrt{7}, \qquad \beta_2 = -\sqrt{7}
$$

and

$$
B_1 = \tfrac{1}{3}(\sqrt{7} - 1)A_1, \qquad B_2 = -\tfrac{1}{3}(\sqrt{7} + 1)A_2.
$$

The solution of the given system is then

$$
y_n = A_1(\sqrt{7})^n + A_2(-\sqrt{7})^n,
$$
$$
3z_n = (\sqrt{7} - 1)A_1(\sqrt{7})^n - (\sqrt{7} + 1)A_2(-\sqrt{7})^n.
$$

EXAMPLE 2. Obtain a fourth-order linear difference equation with constant coefficients which has the general solution

$$
y_n = c_1 + c_2 2^n + c_3 3^n + c_4 4^n.
$$

The auxiliary equation leading to this solution will be

$$(\beta - 1)(\beta - 2)(\beta - 3)(\beta - 4) = 0$$

or

$$\beta^4 - 10\beta^3 + 35\beta^2 - 50\beta + 24 = 0.$$

Accordingly, the desired difference equation is

$$y_{n+4} - 10y_{n+3} + 35y_{n+2} - 50y_{n+1} + 24y_n = 0.$$

EXERCISES

1. Show that the kth-order difference equation

$$y_{n+k} + a_1 y_{n+k-1} + \cdots + a_{k-1} y_{n+1} + a_k y_n = 0$$

has solutions of the form $y_n = c\beta^n$, where β is a solution of the auxiliary equation

$$\beta^k + a_1 \beta^{k-1} + \cdots + a_{k-1}\beta + a_k = 0.$$

2. Solve $y_{n+3} - y_{n+2} + y_{n+1} - y_n = 0.$

3. Solve $y_{n+3} - 3y_{n+2} - 4y_{n+1} + 12y_n = 0.$

4. Obtain a third-order difference equation with constant coefficients which has the solution $y_n = (c_1 + c_2 n + c_3 n^2)(-1)^n.$

5. Solve $y_{n+1} = y_n - 4z_n, \quad z_{n+1} = 2y_n - z_n.$

6. Solve $y_{n+1} = y_n, \quad z_{n+1} = 3y_n + 2z_n.$

7. Solve $y_{n+1} = y_n + 2z_n, \quad z_{n+1} = 2y_n - z_n.$

8. Show that the expressions $y_n = c_1 f_n + c_2 g_n, z_n = c_1 h_n + c_2 k_n$, where c_1 and c_2 are arbitrary constants and $f_n, g_n, h_n,$ and k_n given functions of n, are solutions of the following system of first-order simultaneous linear difference equations:

$$\begin{vmatrix} f_n & g_n \\ h_n & k_n \end{vmatrix} y_{n+1} = \begin{vmatrix} y_n & g_n \\ z_n & k_n \end{vmatrix} f_{n+1} + \begin{vmatrix} f_n & y_n \\ g_n & z_n \end{vmatrix} g_{n+1},$$

$$\begin{vmatrix} f_n & g_n \\ h_n & k_n \end{vmatrix} z_{n+1} = \begin{vmatrix} y_n & g_n \\ z_n & k_n \end{vmatrix} h_{n+1} + \begin{vmatrix} f_n & y_n \\ g_n & z_n \end{vmatrix} k_{n+1}.$$

7-5 Particular solutions of nonhomogeneous linear difference equations. Let us consider the nonhomogeneous equation

$$y_{n+2} + 2ay_{n+1} + by_n = f_n, \tag{1}$$

where a and b are constants and f_n is a given function of n. Equation (1) is satisfied by setting

$$y_n = y_{n,H} + y_{n,P}, \tag{2}$$

where $y_{n,H}$ is the general solution of the associated homogeneous equation and $y_{n,P}$ is any particular solution of the complete equation.

We know that the general solution of the homogeneous equation is of the form

$$y_{n,H} = c_1 u_n + c_2 v_n, \tag{3}$$

and we know how to obtain u_n and v_n for the second-order equation with constant coefficients.

The method of undetermined coefficients. Just as in the analogous case of differential equations, it is possible to use a method of undetermined coefficients for certain forms of the right side of (1). The most important cases for which this is possible are given when f_n is a linear combination of terms of the form q^n, where q is any constant, and n^p, where p is any positive integer.

The following example will illustrate this procedure. The equation

$$y_{n+2} - 5y_{n+1} + 6y_n = q^n + n$$

has as general solution of the associated homogeneous equation

$$y_{n,H} = c_1 2^n + c_2 3^n.$$

For a particular solution, we set

$$y_{n,P} = Aq^n + Bn + C,$$

where A, B, and C are constant coefficients which must be determined. Substitution of $y_{n,P}$ in the given difference equation leads to the following relation:

$$Aq^n[q^2 - 5q + 6] + B[(n + 2) - 5(n + 1) + 6n]$$
$$+ C[1 - 5 + 6] = q^n + n.$$

In order that this be satisfied for all integers n, we must have

$$A[q^2 - 5q + 6] = 1, \qquad B[1 - 5 + 6] = 1,$$
$$B[2 - 5] + C[1 - 5 + 6] = 0.$$

From these equations we have for a particular solution, *so long as* $q \neq 2$ *and* $q \neq 3$,

$$y_{n,P} = \frac{q^n}{q^2 - 5q + 6} + \frac{n}{2} + \frac{3}{4}.$$

It is clear that when q has one of the values 2 or 3, then Aq^n cannot be a particular solution, since it is already a solution of the associated homogeneous equation. It is possible to extend the method of undetermined coefficients to apply in this case also, but we shall not discuss here how this is done.

The method of variation of parameters. We shall now show that, just as in the corresponding case of differential equations, we can *always* find a particular solution of (1) by the *method of variation of parameters.* For this purpose we assume an expression for $y_{n,P}$ in the form

$$y_{n,P} = C_{1,n}u_n + C_{2,n}v_n. \tag{4}$$

We attempt to determine the coefficient functions $C_{1,n}$ and $C_{2,n}$ in terms of the function f_n in (1).

From (4) follows

$$y_{n+1,P} = C_{1,n+1}u_{n+1} + C_{2,n+1}v_{n+1}. \tag{5a}$$

The first step toward the solution consists in writing this expression in the form

$$y_{n+1,P} = C_{1,n}u_{n+1} + C_{2,n}v_{n+1} \\ + (C_{1,n+1} - C_{1,n})u_{n+1} + (C_{2,n+1} - C_{2,n})v_{n+1}. \tag{5b}$$

We now arbitrarily prescribe the relation

$$(C_{1,n+1} - C_{1,n})u_{n+1} + (C_{2,n+1} - C_{2,n})v_{n+1} = 0. \tag{6}$$

This leaves us an abbreviated expression for $y_{n+1,P}$, namely,

$$y_{n+1,P} = C_{1,n}u_{n+1} + C_{2,n}v_{n+1}. \tag{5c}$$

From (5c),

$$y_{n+2,P} = C_{1,n+1}u_{n+2} + C_{2,n+1}v_{n+2}. \tag{7a}$$

The next step consists in writing (7a) in the form

$$y_{n+2,P} = C_{1,n}u_{n+2} + C_{2,n}v_{n+2} + (C_{1,n+1} - C_{1,n})u_{n+2} \\ + (C_{2,n+1} - C_{2,n})v_{n+2}. \tag{7b}$$

We now introduce $y_{n,P}$ from (4), $y_{n+1,P}$ from (5c), and $y_{n+2,P}$ from (7b) into Eq. (1). In this manner we obtain

$$C_{1,n}(u_{n+2} + 2au_{n+1} + bu_n) + C_{2,n}(v_{n+2} + 2av_{n+2} + bv_n) \\ + (C_{1,n+1} - C_{1,n})u_{n+2} + (C_{2,n+1} - C_{2,n})v_{n+2} = f_n. \tag{8a}$$

Since u_n and v_n are solutions of the homogeneous equation associated with (1), Eq. (8a) reduces to

$$(C_{1,n+1} - C_{1,n})u_{n+2} + (C_{2,n+1} - C_{2,n})v_{n+2} = f_n. \tag{8b}$$

Equations (6) and (8b) are two linear algebraic equations for $C_{1,n+1} - C_{1,n}$ and $C_{2,n+1} - C_{2,n}$. These are solved in the form

$$C_{1,n+1} - C_{1,n} = \frac{-v_{n+1}f_n}{\begin{vmatrix} u_{n+1} & v_{n+1} \\ u_{n+2} & v_{n+2} \end{vmatrix}}, \tag{9a}$$

$$C_{2,n+1} - C_{2,n} = \frac{+u_{n+1}f_n}{\begin{vmatrix} u_{n+1} & v_{n+1} \\ u_{n+2} & v_{n+2} \end{vmatrix}}. \tag{9b}$$

Since we know how to solve the first-order equations (9) for $C_{1,n}$ and $C_{2,n}$, we know then also how to obtain the particular solution (5a) of the second-order difference equation (1).

We note further that at no stage of the derivation have we made use of the fact that the coefficients $2a$ and b are independent of n. Consequently the solution (5a) with $C_{1,n}$ and $C_{2,n}$ determined by (9) is valid for *any* second-order linear difference equation, provided the solutions u_n and v_n in $y_{n,H}$ are such that the determinant in (9) does not vanish.

To illustrate the method of variation of parameters, consider the equation

$$y_{n+2} + 2ay_{n+1} + by_n = q^n, \qquad b \neq 0,$$

where again q is a constant. We shall assume that $a^2 - b \neq 0$, so that the roots

$$\beta_1 = -a + \sqrt{a^2 - b}, \qquad \beta_2 = -a - \sqrt{a^2 - b}$$

of the auxiliary equation are distinct.

The solution of the homogeneous equation is then

$$y_{n,H} = c_1\beta_1^n + c_2\beta_2^n,$$

and the functions u_n and v_n in Eq. (4) for $y_{n,P}$ are

$$u_n = \beta_1^n, \qquad v_n = \beta_2^n.$$

We introduce these expressions for u_n and v_n in the first-order equations (9) for the coefficient functions $C_{1,n}$ and $C_{2,n}$. Since the determinant in (9) has the value

$$\begin{vmatrix} u_{n+1} & v_{n+1} \\ u_{n+2} & v_{n+2} \end{vmatrix} = \beta_1^{n+1}\beta_2^{n+1}(\beta_2 - \beta_1),$$

Eqs. (9) assume the form

$$C_{1,n+1} - C_{1,n} = \frac{1}{\beta_1 - \beta_2} \frac{q^n}{\beta_1^{n+1}},$$

$$C_{2,n+1} - C_{2,n} = \frac{1}{\beta_2 - \beta_1} \frac{q^n}{\beta_2^{n+1}}.$$

Application of Eqs. (15) and (16) in Section 7–2 then gives

$$C_{1,n} = \frac{1}{(\beta_1 - \beta_2)\beta_1} \sum_{j=0}^{n-1} \left(\frac{q}{\beta_1}\right)^j + c_1 = \frac{1}{(\beta_1 - \beta_2)\beta_1} \frac{1 - (q/\beta_1)^n}{1 - (q/\beta_1)} + c_1$$

and

$$C_{2,n} = \frac{1}{(\beta_2 - \beta_1)\beta_2} \frac{1 - (q/\beta_2)^n}{1 - (q/\beta_2)} + c_2.$$

In view of (4) we now have as a particular solution of the given difference equation

$$y_{n,P} = \frac{1}{\beta_1 - \beta_2} \left(\frac{\beta_1^n - q^n}{\beta_1 - q} - \frac{\beta_2^n - q^n}{\beta_2 - q}\right).$$

This solution remains valid when $q = \beta_1$ or $q = \beta_2$, in which case l'Hôpital's rule leads to the appropriate form of the result.

EXERCISES

In Exercises 1 through 3 use the method of undetermined coefficients to obtain particular solutions.

1. $y_{n+2} - 5y_{n+1} + 6y_n = 1 + n^2$

2. $y_{n+2} - \sqrt{2}y_{n+1} + y_n = q^n$ (For what values of q does this solution cease to be valid?)

3. $y_{n+2} - \frac{5}{2}y_{n+1} + y_n = q^n(q \neq ?)$

In Exercises 4 and 5 use the method of variation of parameters to obtain particular solutions.

4. $y_{n+2} - 5y_{n+1} + 6y_n = n^k$

5. $y_{n+2} - (\beta_1 + \beta_2)y_{n+1} + \beta_1\beta_2 y_n = 1/n!$

6. Given that u_n is a particular solution of the homogeneous equation $y_{n+2} + 2a_n y_{n+1} + b_n y_n = 0$. Show that the assumption $y_n = C_n u_n$ reduces the problem of determining the general solution to two successive first-order difference equations. [Hint. Transform the given difference equation into a first-order equation for $D_n = C_{n+1} - C_n$.]

7. Use the result of Exercise 6 to obtain the general solution of $y_{n+2} - 2\beta y_{n+1} + \beta^2 y_n = 0$.

8. Given that $y_n = 1$ is a particular solution of $y_{n+2} + (\alpha_n - 1)y_{n+1} - \alpha_n y_n = 0$, obtain the general solution of this equation.

9. Given the system of simultaneous nonhomogeneous difference equations

$$y_{n+1} = Ay_n + Bz_n + f_n, \qquad z_{n+1} = Cy_n + Dz_n + g_n$$

with solutions

$$y_{n,H} = c_1 u_{1,n} + c_2 u_{2,n}, \qquad z_{n,H} = c_1 v_{1,n} + c_2 v_{2,n}$$

of the associated homogeneous system, show that the assumption

$$y_{n,F} = C_{1,n} u_{1,n} + C_{2,n} u_{2,n}, \qquad z_{n,P} = C_{1,n} v_{1,n} + C_{2,n} v_{2,n}$$

reduces the problem of finding particular solutions of the nonhomogeneous system to two simultaneous linear algebraic equations for the differences $C_{1,n+1} - C_{1,n}$, $C_{2,n+1} - C_{2,n}$.

7–6 On approximating differential equations by difference equations.
Knowledge of the solution of finite difference equations permits us some interesting observations concerning methods of numerical solution for differential equations. We shall consider some typical examples.

EXAMPLE 1. The differential equation problem

$$y' = Ay, \qquad y(0) = y_0, \tag{1}$$

where A is a constant, has the solution

$$y = y_0 e^{Ax}. \tag{2}$$

A simple method of numerical solution (which of course is not actually needed since we have an exact solution) consists in writing instead of (1)

$$\frac{y_{n+1} - y_n}{h} = Ay_n, \tag{3}$$

where

$$y_n = y(x_n), \qquad x_{n+1} = x_n + h, \qquad x_0 = 0. \tag{4}$$

In this way we have as an approximation to (1) the finite difference equation

$$y_{n+1} = (1 + hA)y_n, \qquad n = 0, 1, 2, \ldots \tag{5}$$

The solution of (5) is

$$y_n = (1 + hA)^n y_0. \tag{6}$$

In order to see to what extent (6) is an approximation to (2), we recall the fact that $\lim_{\epsilon \to 0} (1 + \epsilon)^{1/\epsilon} = e$ and write (6) in the equivalent form

$$y_n = y_0[(1 + hA)^{1/hA}]^{Anh} = y_0[(1 + hA)^{1/hA}]^{Ax_n}. \tag{6'}$$

It is clear that as h tends to zero, the approximate solution (6') tends toward the exact solution (2).

EXAMPLE 2. The nonlinear problem

$$y' = Ay^2, \qquad y(0) = y_0 \neq 0 \tag{7}$$

has the solution

$$y = \frac{y_0}{1 - Ay_0x}. \tag{8}$$

We note that y becomes infinite as x approaches the value $1/Ay_0$.

Let us now see what the effect will be of replacing the derivative y' by the difference $(y_{n+1} - y_n)/h$. Equation (7) is then approximated by

$$y_{n+1} = y_n + hAy_n^2, \qquad n = 0, 1, 2, \ldots \tag{9}$$

It turns out that we are unable to solve this difference equation in explicit form. We can, however, starting with a given value of y_0, successively calculate y_1, y_2, etc., as follows:

$$y_1 = y_0 + hAy_0^2 = y_0(1 + hAy_0), \tag{10a}$$

$$y_2 = y_1 + hAy_1^2 = y_1(1 + hAy_1)$$

$$= y_0(1 + hAy_0)[1 + hAy_0(1 + hAy_0)], \tag{10b}$$

and so on. Evidently the successively calculated values of y_n will never assume infinite values. In this sense the approximate solution obtained ceases to be an acceptable approximation of the exact solution (8), for values of n in the vicinity of $1/hAy_0$.

EXAMPLE 3. We return to the linear differential equation (1), but now, instead of replacing $(dy/dx)_n$ by $(y_{n+1} - y_n)/h$, we make use of Simpson's formula,

$$y_{n+1} - y_{n-1} = \tfrac{1}{3}h(y'_{n+1} + 4y'_n + y'_{n-1}) + R, \tag{11}$$

in order to approximate (1). Omitting the remainder term R, we obtain the finite difference relation

$$y_{n+1} - y_{n-1} = \tfrac{1}{3}hA(y_{n+1} + 4y_n + y_{n-1}), \qquad n = 1, 2, \ldots \tag{12}$$

An immediately evident difficulty is the fact that in order to solve (12) we must know in advance not only the value of y_0 (which we assume we do) but also the value of y_1. We temporarily overlook this difficulty and instead find an explicit solution of the linear second-order difference equation (12). Setting, as in Section 7–3, $y_n = \beta^n$, we find admissible values of β from the auxiliary equation

$$(1 - \lambda)\beta^2 - 4\lambda\beta - (1 + \lambda) = 0, \tag{13}$$

in which

$$\lambda = \tfrac{1}{3}hA. \tag{14}$$

The solutions of (13) are

$$\beta_1 = \frac{2\lambda + \sqrt{1 + 3\lambda^2}}{1 - \lambda}, \qquad \beta_2 = \frac{2\lambda - \sqrt{1 + 3\lambda^2}}{1 - \lambda}, \tag{15}$$

and the general solution of (12) is

$$y_n = c_1\beta_1^n + c_2\beta_2^n. \tag{16}$$

In order to compare the difference equation solution (16) with the differential equation solution $y_n = y_0 e^{Ax_n}$ at the points $x = x_n$, we must now investigate the behavior of the terms β_1^n and β_2^n in (16). We particularly need to know what becomes of them for progressively smaller values of the interval length h. To this end we expand β_1 and β_2 in powers of $\lambda = \tfrac{1}{3}hA$:

$$\beta_1 = 1 + 3\lambda + \tfrac{9}{2}\lambda^2 + \cdots, \tag{17a}$$

$$\beta_2 = -1 + \lambda - \tfrac{1}{2}\lambda^2 + \cdots \tag{17b}$$

In order to have, as in the exact solution $y_0 e^{Ax_n}$, the quantity $Ax_n = nhA$ in the exponents, we now write (16) in the form

$$y_n = c_1[(1 + hA + \tfrac{1}{2}h^2A^2 + \cdots)^{1/hA}]^{Ax_n}$$
$$+ c_2(-1)^n[(1 - \tfrac{1}{3}hA + \tfrac{1}{18}h^2A^2 + \cdots)^{1/hA}]^{Ax_n}. \tag{18}$$

We recall again that $\lim_{\epsilon \to 0} (1 + \epsilon)^{1/\epsilon} = e$. This means that for sufficiently small values of h,

$$(1 + hA + \tfrac{1}{2}h^2A^2 + \cdots)^{1/hA} \approx e,$$
$$(1 - \tfrac{1}{3}hA + \tfrac{1}{18}h^2A^2 + \cdots)^{1/hA} \approx e^{-1/3}.$$

Accordingly, for sufficiently small values of h,

$$y_n \approx c_1 e^{Ax_n} + c_2(-1)^n e^{-Ax_n/3}. \tag{19}$$

We are now ready to arrive at some important conclusions. Evidently the *first* term in (16), with $c_1 = y_0$, represents the appropriate approximation to the differential equation solution. The second term is an "extra" solution, brought in because the approximating difference equation is of higher order than the original differential equation. The extra solution can be made to disappear by an appropriate choice of y_1 (this choice would be $y_1 = y_0\beta_1$). Suppose, however, that we did not know this value of y_1, as would be the case if we did not know the *explicit* solutions both of the differential equation and of the difference equation problem. In that case the *step-by-step solution* of the approximating difference equation (as described in Section 6–6) might or might not lead to a good approximation to the solution of the corresponding differential equation. It would lead to a good approximation if either (1) the exponent A was positive, or (2) y_1 was assumed correctly. If, however, A is negative and y_1 is chosen incorrectly, then instead of approximating the exact solution $y_0 e^{A x_n}$, this procedure would approximate *for sufficiently large* x_n an oscillating function with progressively larger amplitude, namely, $y_n \approx y_1(-1)^n e^{|A|x_n/3}$.

EXERCISES

1. Obtain a difference equation approximation to the solution of Eq. (1) on the basis of the approximation

$$y_{n+1} - y_n \approx \tfrac{1}{2}h(y'_{n+1} + y'_n).$$

2. The solution of the nonlinear differential equation (7), according to (8), assumes the values

$$y_n = \frac{y_0}{1 - Ahny_0}$$

for $x = x_n = nh$. Determine a first-order difference equation of which this is the solution, and show that this difference equation agrees with (9), except for terms of order $(hA)^2$.

3. The system of differential equations

$$y' = z, \qquad z' = -y$$

with initial conditions $y(0) = y_0$, $z(0) = 0$ has the solutions

$$y = y_0 \cos x, \qquad z = -y_0 \sin x.$$

Obtain the corresponding solution of the system of difference equations

$$y_{n+1} - y_n = hz_n, \qquad z_{n+1} - z_n = -hy_n$$

in terms of n, h, and the initial value y_0, assuming $z_0 = 0$.

4. Solve the approximating difference equation problem for $y' = z$, $z' = -y$; $y(0) = y_0$, $z(0) = 0$, on the basis of the formula

$$f_{n+1} - f_n \approx \tfrac{1}{2}h(f'_{n+1} + f'_n).$$

MISCELLANEOUS EXERCISES. CHAPTER 7

1. Obtain a difference equation for the determination of the coefficients a_n in the series solution $y = \sum_0^\infty a_n x^n$ for the linear differential equation $x^2 y'' - y' + 3xy = 0$.

2. Show that for the differential equation $x^2 y'' - 3xy' + 2y = 0$ the procedure used in Exercise 1 leads to the conditions

$$a_n(n^2 - 4n + 2) = 0, \qquad n = 0, 1, 2, \ldots,$$

and hence conclude that there is no solution of the desired form other than the identically zero one, $y \equiv 0$.

3. Obtain a first-order difference equation which is satisfied by $y_n = n^2 + cn$, c being an arbitrary constant.

4. (a) Show that $y_n = (c_1 + c_2 n)2^n + c_3(-2)^n$ satisfies the difference equation

$$y_{n+3} - 2y_{n+2} - 4y_{n+1} + 8y_n = 0.$$

(b) Show that this solution is the general solution in the sense that through suitable choice of the constants c_1, c_2, and c_3 the solution may assume arbitrarily prescribed initial values y_0, y_1, and y_2.

Solve the difference equations in Exercises 5 through 11.

5. $y_{n+1} = (y_n)^{1/3}$ 6. $y_{n+2} - 4y_{n+1} + 4y_n = 0$

7. $y_{n+2} - 6y_{n+1} + 5y_n = 0$ 8. $y_{n+2} - 3y_{n+1} + 3y_n = 0$

9. $y_{n+2} - 4y_{n+1} + 4y_n = 1 + 3n + n^2$

10. $y_{n+2} - 3y_{n+1} + 2y_n = n$

11. $q_n(t) = \lambda \int_0^t q_{n-1}(s)\, ds$, $q_0(t) = 1$

12. Solve the difference-differential equation

$$\frac{dp_n(t)}{dt} + \lambda p_n(t) = \lambda p_{n-1}(t)$$

for $n = 0, 1, 2, \ldots$, given $p_0(0) = 1$, $p_j(0) = 0$, $j = 1, 2, \ldots$, assuming $p_{-1}(t) \equiv 0$.

13. Solve $y_{n+1} = y_n - 3z_n$, $z_{n+1} = y_n + 5z_n$

14. (a) Solve $y_{n+6} - y_n = n + 3$

(b) Determine the constants in the solution of part (a) so that the solution satisfies the initial conditions

$$y_0 = y_1 = y_2 = 0, \qquad y_3 = y_4 = 1, \qquad y_5 = 2.$$

[*Hint.* First write the six equations corresponding to the six initial conditions. (Write $(-1 + i\sqrt{3})/2 = \omega$ and use the fact that $\omega^3 = 1$.) Then show that suitable combinations of pairs of the six equations lead to the three equations

$$c_1 + c_3 + c_5 = \tfrac{1}{8}, \quad c_1 + c_3\omega^2 + c_5\omega = -\tfrac{5}{24}, \quad c_1 + c_3\omega + c_5\omega^2 = -\tfrac{5}{24}.$$

Next solve these three equations for c_1, c_3, and c_5. (Use the relation $1 + \omega + \omega^2 = 0$.)

Similarly show that other combinations of the same pairs of the six conditions lead to the three equations

$$c_2 + c_4 + c_6 = -\tfrac{1}{8}, \quad c_2 + c_4\omega + c_6\omega^2 = -\tfrac{1}{8}, \quad c_2 + c_4\omega^2 + c_6\omega = -\tfrac{1}{8},$$

and solve these for c_2, c_4, and c_6.]

Exercise 14, and Exercises 15 through 22 which follow, arise in a topic in number theory known as the theory of partitions. In the study of properties of positive integers one sometimes asks about partitions of positive integers into a sum of positive integers. For example, one may seek to determine how many ways a positive integer n may be expressed as the sum of two positive integers. Denote this number by $p(n, 2)$. We consider a few examples:

$$n = 2: \quad 2 = 1 + 1 \qquad\qquad\qquad p(2, 2) = 1$$
$$n = 3: \quad 3 = 1 + 2 \qquad\qquad\qquad p(3, 2) = 1$$
$$n = 4: \quad 4 = 1 + 3 = 2 + 2 \qquad\quad p(4, 2) = 2$$
$$n = 5: \quad 5 = 1 + 4 = 2 + 3 \qquad\quad p(5, 2) = 2$$
$$n = 6: \quad 6 = 1 + 5 = 2 + 4 = 3 + 3 \quad p(6, 2) = 3$$

We shall now obtain a general formula for the number of ways a positive integer n may be expressed as the sum of two positive integers. We consider two cases, n even and n odd.

If n is even, say $n = 2m$, then we may write

$$n = 2m = 1 + (2m - 1) = 2 + (2m - 2) = 3 + (2m - 3) = \cdots = m + m$$

and one readily sees that

$$p(2m, 2) = m.$$

If n is odd, $n = 2m + 1$, then

$$n = 2m + 1 = 1 + (2m) = 2 + (2m - 1) = 3 + (2m - 2) = \cdots = m + (m + 1)$$

and hence

$$p(2m + 1, 2) = m.$$

Thus $p(n, 2)$ is always the integer nearest $\frac{1}{2}(n - \frac{1}{2})$; that is, $p(n, 2)$ has the value given for a_n in Exercise 17.

While it is more difficult, and another method of demonstration is used, it is known that the number of ways a positive integer n may be expressed as the sum of three positive integers is the integer nearest to $\frac{1}{12}n^2$. If we denote this number by $p(n, 3)$ then $p(n, 3)$ has the value given for a_n in Exercise 20.

More generally, if one denotes by $p(n, j)$ the number of ways a positive integer n may be expressed as the sum of exactly j positive integers, then in the theory of partitions it has been shown that for each value of n, $p(n, j)$ is the coefficient of x^n in the expansion

$$\frac{x^j}{(1 - x)(1 - x^2) \ldots (1 - x^j)} = \sum_{n=0}^{\infty} p(n, j)x^n, \qquad |x| < 1.$$

These properties account for the interest in Exercises 15 through 22.

15. Obtain a difference equation for the determination of the coefficients a_n in the power-series expansion $\sum_0^{\infty} a_n x^n$ for the function

$$\frac{x^2}{(1 - x)(1 - x^2)}, \qquad |x| < 1.$$

[*Hint.* Write $x^2 = \left(\sum_{n=0}^{\infty} a_n x^n\right)(1 - x - x^2 + x^3)$ and equate coefficients of corresponding powers of x on the two sides of the equation.]

16. Solve the difference equation problem

$$a_{n+3} - a_{n+2} - a_{n+1} + a_n = 0, \qquad n = 0, 1, 2, \ldots ;$$

$$a_0 = a_1 = 0, \qquad a_2 = 1.$$

17. Show that $a_n = \frac{1}{2}[n - \frac{1}{2} + (-1)^n \frac{1}{2}]$, $n = 0, 1, 2, \ldots$, is always an integer; indeed that it is the integer nearest to $\frac{1}{2}(n - \frac{1}{2})$. (Consider separately the two cases n even and n odd.)

18. Obtain a difference equation for the determinations of the coefficients a_n in the power-series expansion $\sum_0^{\infty} a_n x^n$ for the function

$$\frac{x^3}{(1 - x)(1 - x^2)(1 - x^3)}, \qquad |x| < 1.$$

19. Solve the difference equation problem

$$a_{n+6} - a_{n+5} - a_{n+4} + a_{n+2} + a_{n+1} - a_n = 0, \qquad n = 0, 1, 2, \ldots ,$$

$$a_0 = a_1 = a_2 = 0, \qquad a_3 = a_4 = 1, \qquad a_5 = 2.$$

[*Hint.* Show that the auxiliary equation

$$\beta^6 - \beta^5 - \beta^4 + \beta^2 + \beta - 1 = 0$$

may be written in the form $(\beta - 1)(\beta^2 - 1)(\beta^3 - 1) = 0$, and hence that the general solution of the difference equation is

$$a_n = c_1 n^2 + c_2 n + c_3 + (-1)^n c_4 + \omega^n c_5 + \omega^{2n} c_6,$$

where ω is a cube root of unity, $\omega = (-1 + i\sqrt{3})/2$. Having done this, use the six initial conditions to determine c_1 through c_6.]

20. Show that $a_n = \frac{1}{12}n^2 - \frac{7}{72} - \frac{1}{8}(-1)^n + \frac{1}{9}(\omega^n + \omega^{2n})$, $n = 0, 1, 2, \ldots$, is the integer nearest $\frac{1}{12}n^2$. [*Hint.* Consider separately the six cases $n = 6m$, $6m + 1$, $6m + 2$, $6m + 3$, $6m + 4$ and $6m + 5$. In each case compare the value of the two expressions a_n and $\frac{1}{12}n^2$.]

21. Show that the constants a_n of Exercise 20 satisfy the difference equation $a_{n+6} - a_n = n + 3$ (see also Exercise 14).

22. (a) Show that the coefficients a_n in the power-series expansion $\sum_0^\infty a_n x^n$ for the function

$$\frac{x^4}{(1 - x)(1 - x^2)(1 - x^3)(1 - x^4)}, \qquad |x| < 1$$

satisfy the difference equation

$$a_{n+10} - a_{n+9} - a_{n+8} + 2a_{n+5} - a_{n+2} - a_{n+1} + a_n = 0, \qquad n = 0, 1, 2, \ldots$$

with the initial conditions

$$a_0 = a_1 = a_2 = a_3 = 0, \quad a_4 = a_5 = 1, \quad a_6 = 2,$$

$$a_7 = 3, \quad a_8 = 5, \quad a_9 = 6, \quad a_{10} = 9.$$

(b) Determine the general solution of the difference equation.

CHAPTER 8

PARTIAL DIFFERENTIAL EQUATIONS

8–1 Introduction. In this chapter we shall consider differential equations of the form

$$F\left(x, y, z, \frac{\partial z}{\partial x}, \frac{\partial z}{\partial y}\right) = 0 \tag{1}$$

and

$$F\left(x, y, z, \frac{\partial z}{\partial x}, \frac{\partial z}{\partial y}, \frac{\partial^2 z}{\partial x^2}, \frac{\partial^2 z}{\partial x\,\partial y}, \frac{\partial^2 z}{\partial y^2}\right) = 0, \tag{2}$$

where F is a given function of its arguments, which are five in number for Eq. (1) and eight in number for Eq. (2). A solution of such a differential equation will be a relation between the dependent variable z and the independent variables x and y which does not contain any of the derivatives of z and which is compatible with the given differential equation.

For example, the solution of

$$\frac{\partial z}{\partial x} = xy \tag{3}$$

will be

$$z = \tfrac{1}{2}x^2 y + f(y), \tag{4}$$

where $f(y)$ is an arbitrary function.

Similarly, we find that the solution of

$$\frac{\partial^2 z}{\partial x\,\partial y} = 1 \tag{5}$$

will be

$$z = xy + f(y) + g(x), \tag{6}$$

where both $f(y)$ and $g(x)$ are arbitrary functions.

The two examples suggest that functions of integration should have the same significance for the solution of partial differential equations as constants of integration have for the solution of ordinary differential equations.

Exercises

Find solutions in terms of an arbitrary function of the differential equations of Exercises 1 through 4.

1. $\dfrac{\partial z}{\partial y} = x \cos y$ 2. $\dfrac{\partial z}{\partial x} = x \cos y$

3. $\dfrac{\partial z}{\partial x} - z = y$ 4. $y \dfrac{\partial z}{\partial y} + z = \cos{(xy)}$

Find solutions in terms of two arbitrary functions of the differential equations of Exercises 5 through 8.

5. $\dfrac{\partial^2 z}{\partial x^2} = 1$ 6. $\dfrac{\partial^2 z}{\partial y^2} - z = 0$

7. $x^2 \dfrac{\partial^2 z}{\partial x^2} - z = 0$ 8. $\dfrac{\partial^2 z}{\partial x \, \partial y} = 2e^{2x}$

8–2 First-order partial differential equations satisfied by expressions containing an arbitrary function.   Before further consideration of the problem of solving given partial differential equations, it is instructive, as in the discussion of ordinary differential equations, to consider the inverse problem of deriving the differential equation satisfied by a given expression.

Certain simple examples have shown us that the solution of a partial differential equation should contain one or more arbitrary functions. Let us consider given expressions containing arbitrary functions and see what partial differential equations these expressions satisfy.

As a first example, take the expression

$$z = f(x - y), \tag{1}$$

where f is an arbitrary differentiable function of the argument $x - y$. If, for the moment, we set

$$x - y = t, \tag{2}$$

then we have

$$\frac{\partial z}{\partial x} = \frac{df}{dt} \frac{\partial t}{\partial x} = \frac{df}{dt} \cdot 1,$$

$$\frac{\partial z}{\partial y} = \frac{df}{dt} \frac{\partial t}{\partial y} = \frac{df}{dt} \cdot (-1), \tag{3}$$

and from this, by elimination of df/dt, we obtain a differential equation which is satisfied by z:

$$\frac{\partial z}{\partial x} + \frac{\partial z}{\partial y} = 0. \tag{4}$$

As a second example, take the expression

$$z = x f(yx^{-1}), \tag{5}$$

where f is again an arbitrary function. Setting

$$\frac{y}{x} = t, \tag{6}$$

we have

$$\frac{\partial z}{\partial x} = f + x\frac{df}{dt}\frac{\partial t}{\partial x} = f + x\frac{df}{dt}\left(-\frac{y}{x^2}\right),$$

$$\frac{\partial z}{\partial y} = x\frac{df}{dt}\frac{\partial t}{\partial y} = \frac{df}{dt}. \tag{7}$$

We take df/dt from the second of Eqs. (7) and f from Eq. (5) and find that z is the solution of the following differential equation:

$$x\frac{\partial z}{\partial x} + y\frac{\partial z}{\partial y} - z = 0. \tag{8}$$

As a third, somewhat more complicated, expression take

$$z = xyf(x^2 + y^2 + z^2), \tag{9}$$

where now z is given *implicitly* in terms of the arbitrary function f. Denoting differentiation with respect to the argument $x^2 + y^2 + z^2$ by a prime, we have

$$\frac{\partial z}{\partial x} = yf + xyf' \cdot \left(2x + 2z\frac{\partial z}{\partial x}\right),$$

$$\frac{\partial z}{\partial y} = xf + xyf' \cdot \left(2y + 2z\frac{\partial z}{\partial y}\right). \tag{10}$$

By elimination of f and f' from (9) and (10), we obtain the following differential equation for z:

$$x(y^2 + z^2)\frac{\partial z}{\partial x} - y(x^2 + z^2)\frac{\partial z}{\partial y} = (y^2 - x^2)z. \tag{11}$$

We may note that the three differential equations (4), (8), and (11) have one thing in common. All of them are linear in the derivatives $\partial z/\partial x$ and $\partial z/\partial y$. However, while all of them are linear in the *derivatives* of the dependent variable z, only two of them are also linear in z. First-order partial differential equations which are linear in the derivatives of the dependent variable but not necessarily linear in the dependent variable itself form an important special class of differential equations, which are called *quasilinear* equations.

The fact that three examples of expressions involving an arbitrary function all lead to quasi-linear differential equations raises the question whether we will always obtain a quasi-linear differential equation by eliminating the arbitrary function f from an explicitly given functional relation involving x, y, and z. We shall now show that this is in fact so.

Consider the relation

$$f[u(x, y, z), v(x, y, z)] = 0, \tag{12}$$

where u and v are given functions of x, y, z and f is an arbitrary function of u and v. If we differentiate (12) partially with respect to x and y and observe that z is supposed to be a function of x and y, we obtain the following two relations:

$$\frac{\partial f}{\partial u}\left(\frac{\partial u}{\partial x} + \frac{\partial u}{\partial z}\frac{\partial z}{\partial x}\right) + \frac{\partial f}{\partial v}\left(\frac{\partial v}{\partial x} + \frac{\partial v}{\partial z}\frac{\partial z}{\partial x}\right) = 0,$$

$$\frac{\partial f}{\partial u}\left(\frac{\partial u}{\partial y} + \frac{\partial u}{\partial z}\frac{\partial z}{\partial y}\right) + \frac{\partial f}{\partial v}\left(\frac{\partial v}{\partial y} + \frac{\partial v}{\partial z}\frac{\partial z}{\partial y}\right) = 0. \tag{13}$$

Equations (13) are a system of two homogeneous linear equations for $\partial f/\partial u$ and $\partial f/\partial v$. In order that there be a solution of this system other than the trivial solution for which both $\partial f/\partial u$ and $\partial f/\partial v$ vanish, it is necessary that the determinant of the system vanish:

$$\begin{vmatrix} \dfrac{\partial u}{\partial x} + \dfrac{\partial u}{\partial z}\dfrac{\partial z}{\partial x} & \dfrac{\partial v}{\partial x} + \dfrac{\partial v}{\partial z}\dfrac{\partial z}{\partial x} \\[2mm] \dfrac{\partial u}{\partial y} + \dfrac{\partial u}{\partial z}\dfrac{\partial z}{\partial y} & \dfrac{\partial v}{\partial y} + \dfrac{\partial v}{\partial z}\dfrac{\partial z}{\partial y} \end{vmatrix} = 0. \tag{14}$$

The developed form of this determinantal equation is

$$P\frac{\partial z}{\partial x} + Q\frac{\partial z}{\partial y} = R, \tag{15}$$

where the coefficient functions P, Q, and R are given in terms of u and v, as follows:

$$P = \begin{vmatrix} \dfrac{\partial u}{\partial z} & \dfrac{\partial u}{\partial y} \\[2mm] \dfrac{\partial v}{\partial z} & \dfrac{\partial v}{\partial y} \end{vmatrix}, \quad Q = \begin{vmatrix} \dfrac{\partial u}{\partial x} & \dfrac{\partial u}{\partial z} \\[2mm] \dfrac{\partial v}{\partial x} & \dfrac{\partial v}{\partial z} \end{vmatrix}, \quad R = \begin{vmatrix} \dfrac{\partial u}{\partial y} & \dfrac{\partial u}{\partial x} \\[2mm] \dfrac{\partial v}{\partial y} & \dfrac{\partial v}{\partial x} \end{vmatrix}. \tag{16}$$

We see that the relation (12) is indeed a solution of the quasi-linear partial differential equation (15).

EXERCISES

Determine a first-order partial differential equation satisfied by each of the following expressions. (In every case f represents an arbitrary function.)

1. $z = f(x^2 - y)$ 2. $z^2 = f(x^2 - y)$
3. $z = yf(y^2/x)$ 4. $f(x^2 + y^2, z) = 0$
5. $f(x^2 + y^2, y^2 + z^2) = 0$ 6. $f(x + 2y + z, x^2 + z^2) = 0$

8–3 Reduction of the quasi-linear partial differential equation of the first order to a system of ordinary differential equations. We shall now consider a very elegant method of solution for the quasi-linear equation through its reduction to a system of first-order ordinary differential equations. Since the method of solution is so elegant mathematically, it is regrettable that very few problems in the applications lead to partial differential equations of this type.

We have seen in the preceding section that the differential equation

$$P(x, y, z)\frac{\partial z}{\partial x} + Q(x, y, z)\frac{\partial z}{\partial y} = R(x, y, z) \tag{1}$$

has solutions of the form

$$f[u(x, y, z), v(x, y, z)] = 0, \tag{2}$$

where f is an arbitrary function of its two arguments u and v, provided the functions $u(x, y, z)$ and $v(x, y, z)$ can be determined from the relations

$$\begin{vmatrix} \dfrac{\partial u}{\partial z} & \dfrac{\partial u}{\partial y} \\ \dfrac{\partial v}{\partial z} & \dfrac{\partial v}{\partial y} \end{vmatrix} = P, \quad \begin{vmatrix} \dfrac{\partial u}{\partial x} & \dfrac{\partial u}{\partial z} \\ \dfrac{\partial v}{\partial x} & \dfrac{\partial v}{\partial z} \end{vmatrix} = Q, \quad \begin{vmatrix} \dfrac{\partial u}{\partial y} & \dfrac{\partial u}{\partial x} \\ \dfrac{\partial v}{\partial y} & \dfrac{\partial v}{\partial x} \end{vmatrix} = R. \tag{3}$$

We can avoid the necessity of solving these three simultaneous partial differential equations for u and v by the following argument. We consider the equations

$$u(x, y, z) = c_1, \quad v(x, y, z) = c_2, \tag{4}$$

where c_1 and c_2 are constants, as the equations of two surfaces in space. In general, these two surfaces will intersect along a curve in space. Let

$$x = x(t), \quad y = y(t), \quad z = z(t) \tag{5}$$

be the equations of such a curve in parametric form.

From (4) we have the following relations for the derivatives dx/dt, dy/dt, and dz/dt:

$$\frac{\partial u}{\partial x}\frac{dx}{dt} + \frac{\partial u}{\partial y}\frac{dy}{dt} + \frac{\partial u}{\partial z}\frac{dz}{dt} = 0,$$

$$\frac{\partial v}{\partial x}\frac{dx}{dt} + \frac{\partial v}{\partial y}\frac{dy}{dt} + \frac{\partial v}{\partial z}\frac{dz}{dt} = 0. \tag{6}$$

We may solve (6) for two of these derivatives in terms of the third, say for dx/dt and dy/dt in terms of dz/dt. This gives

$$\begin{vmatrix} \dfrac{\partial u}{\partial x} & \dfrac{\partial u}{\partial y} \\[2mm] \dfrac{\partial v}{\partial x} & \dfrac{\partial v}{\partial y} \end{vmatrix} \frac{dx}{dt} = - \begin{vmatrix} \dfrac{\partial u}{\partial z} & \dfrac{\partial u}{\partial y} \\[2mm] \dfrac{\partial v}{\partial z} & \dfrac{\partial v}{\partial y} \end{vmatrix} \frac{dz}{dt},$$

$$\begin{vmatrix} \dfrac{\partial u}{\partial x} & \dfrac{\partial u}{\partial y} \\[2mm] \dfrac{\partial v}{\partial x} & \dfrac{\partial v}{\partial y} \end{vmatrix} \frac{dy}{dt} = - \begin{vmatrix} \dfrac{\partial u}{\partial x} & \dfrac{\partial u}{\partial z} \\[2mm] \dfrac{\partial v}{\partial x} & \dfrac{\partial v}{\partial z} \end{vmatrix} \frac{dz}{dt}. \tag{7}$$

Now if u and v are to be such that they give the solution of the partial differential equation (1) in the form (2), they must satisfy Eqs. (3) and therefore (7) must be equivalent to the following system:

$$R\frac{dx}{dt} = P\frac{dz}{dt}, \qquad R\frac{dy}{dt} = Q\frac{dz}{dt}. \tag{8}$$

To avoid giving unequal treatment to dz/dt, in comparison with what was done for dx/dt and dy/dt, we also consider the solution of (6) for dx/dt and dz/dt in terms of dy/dt, and for dy/dt and dz/dt in terms of dx/dt. Of all the relations which we obtain in this way there is only one new one, namely,

$$P\frac{dy}{dt} = Q\frac{dx}{dt}. \tag{8'}$$

If P, Q, R are all different from zero, then Eqs. (8) and (8') imply the relations

$$\frac{dx/dt}{P} = \frac{dy/dt}{Q} = \frac{dz/dt}{R}. \tag{9}$$

It is customary to write Eqs. (9) in the form

$$\frac{dx}{P} = \frac{dy}{Q} = \frac{dz}{R}. \tag{10}$$

If we designate the common value of the terms in (9) by λ, then Eq. (9) is equivalent to the following three equations:

$$\frac{dx}{dt} = \lambda P, \qquad \frac{dy}{dt} = \lambda Q, \qquad \frac{dz}{dt} = \lambda R. \tag{11}$$

Equation (11) remains valid, and equivalent to (8) and (8'), even if one or more of the P, Q, R are zero.

In any given problem of solving the equation $P(\partial z/\partial x) + Q(\partial z/\partial y) = R$ our task is then reduced to finding solutions (4) of the system of ordinary differential equations (8) and (8') or, when this is more convenient, of (9), (10), or (11). Having the solutions $u(x, y, z) = c_1$, $v(x, y, z) = c_2$, the relation $f(u, v) = 0$ for f arbitrary represents a solution of the given partial differential equation (1).

EXAMPLE 1. For the differential equation

$$\frac{\partial z}{\partial x} + \frac{\partial z}{\partial y} = 0$$

we have as associated ordinary differential equations, from (8) and (8'),

$$dx = dy, \qquad dz = 0.$$

Two independent solutions of these are

$$x - y = c_1, \qquad z = c_2.$$

This means that we have a solution of the given partial differential equation of the form

$$f(x - y, z) = 0.$$

With another arbitrary function g, we may write this solution in the alternative form

$$z = g(x - y).$$

EXAMPLE 2. For the differential equation

$$x \frac{\partial z}{\partial x} + y \frac{\partial z}{\partial y} = az,$$

where a is a constant which is different from zero, we have from (10)

$$\frac{dx}{x} = \frac{dy}{y} = \frac{dz}{az}.$$

Two independent solutions of these ordinary differential equations are

$$\frac{y}{x} = c_1, \qquad \frac{z}{x^a} = c_2,$$

and this means that a solution of the given partial differential equation is

$$f\left(\frac{y}{x}, \frac{z}{x^a}\right) = 0.$$

With a different arbitrary function f this result may be written in the alternate form

$$z = x^a f\left(\frac{y}{x}\right).$$

When $a = 1$ this brings us back to Eqs. (5) and (8) of Section 8–2.

EXAMPLE 3. The equation

$$(1 + y^2 + z^2)\frac{\partial z}{\partial x} + \frac{\partial z}{\partial y} = 1$$

is associated with the ordinary differential equations

$$\frac{dx}{1 + y^2 + z^2} = dy = dz.$$

A first solution is

$$z - y = c_1,$$

and a second independent solution is obtained from

$$\frac{dx}{1 + y^2 + (c_1 + y)^2} = dy$$

first in the form

$$x - y - \tfrac{1}{3}y^3 - \tfrac{1}{3}(c_1 + y)^3 = c_2.$$

From this we eliminate c_1, giving us as the second independent solution

$$x - y - \tfrac{1}{3}y^3 - \tfrac{1}{3}z^3 = c_2.$$

Therewith we have as a solution of the given partial differential equation

$$f(z - y, x - y - \tfrac{1}{3}y^3 - \tfrac{1}{3}z^3) = 0.$$

EXAMPLE 4. The differential equation

$$2(y - z)\frac{\partial z}{\partial x} + z\frac{\partial z}{\partial y} + 2y = 0$$

may be associated with the ordinary system

$$\frac{dx}{dt} = 2\lambda(y - z), \qquad \frac{dy}{dt} = \lambda z, \qquad \frac{dz}{dt} = -2\lambda y.$$

By observing that $dx + 2\,dy + dz = 0$, a first solution of this follows readily, as

$$x + 2y + z = c_1.$$

A second solution follows from $2y\,dy + z\,dz = 0$, as

$$2y^2 + z^2 = c_2,$$

and a solution of the given partial differential equation is then

$$f(x + 2y + z, 2y^2 + z^2) = 0.$$

EXERCISES

Find solutions in terms of an arbitrary function for the quasi-linear partial differential equations in Exercises 1 through 5.

1. $yz\dfrac{\partial z}{\partial x} - xz\dfrac{\partial z}{\partial y} - xy = 0$ $\qquad\qquad$ 2. $2y\dfrac{\partial z}{\partial x} - \dfrac{\partial z}{\partial y} = 0$

3. $2y\dfrac{\partial z}{\partial x} - \dfrac{\partial z}{\partial y} = x$ $\quad$ 4. $\dfrac{\partial z}{\partial x} + 2x\dfrac{\partial z}{\partial y} = x^2 + y$ $\quad$ 5. $\dfrac{\partial z}{\partial x} + z\dfrac{\partial z}{\partial y} = 1$

6. Show that the general solution of the differential equation

$$\frac{\partial z}{\partial x} + [A(x)y + B(x)z]\frac{\partial z}{\partial y} = C(x)y + D(x)z$$

is of the form

$$f\left[\frac{yv_1(x) - zu_1(x)}{W(x)}, \frac{yv_2(x) - zu_2(x)}{W(x)}\right] = 0,$$

where

$$U(x) = c_1u_1(x) + c_2u_2(x), \qquad V(x) = c_1v_1(x) + c_2v_2(x)$$

is the general solution of the system of equations

$$\frac{dU}{dx} = AU + BV, \qquad \frac{dV}{dx} = CU + DV,$$

and where

$$W = \begin{vmatrix} u_1 & u_2 \\ v_1 & v_2 \end{vmatrix}.$$

Solve the differential equations in Exercises 7 and 8.

7. $\dfrac{\partial z}{\partial x} + (-y + 2z)\dfrac{\partial z}{\partial y} = 4y + z$ 8. $\dfrac{\partial z}{\partial x} + \dfrac{2y + z}{x}\dfrac{\partial z}{\partial y} = \dfrac{4y + 2z}{x}$

8–4 Determination of arbitrary functions in solutions of quasi-linear differential equations. Just as in the solution of ordinary differential equations the value of arbitrary constants is determined by certain conditions imposed on the solution of the differential equation, such as initial conditions, so for the solution of partial differential equations it is necessary to impose appropriate conditions in order to determine the arbitrary functions in the solutions.

To take a simple example, the form of the arbitrary function f in the solution

$$z = f(x) \tag{1}$$

of the equation

$$\frac{\partial z}{\partial y} = 0 \tag{2}$$

assumes the form $f(x) = x^2$ if we prescribe that the solution of (2) satisfies the additional condition that

$$\text{when } y = 0, \quad \text{then } z = x^2. \tag{3}$$

It is useful to interpret this simple situation geometrically. The equation $z = f(x)$ represents the family of cylindrical surfaces with generators in the y-direction. The equations $y = 0$, $z = x^2$ represent a (plane) curve in space, and the solution $z = x^2$ represents a parabolic cylinder. We see that in order to select one specific surface among all solution surfaces of the partial differential equation we may use a condition stating that the solution surface pass through a certain curve in space.

There is one exceptional set of space curves for which this procedure breaks down. This is the set of curves

$$x = c_1, \quad z = g(y), \tag{4}$$

where c_1 is a constant and g is a given function of the variable y. Combination of (4) and (1) gives

$$g(y) = f(c_1). \tag{5}$$

Either Eq. (5) is impossible of solution, namely when $g(y) \neq$ const, or it has solutions when $g(y) = c_2$, but these solutions do not determine the form of the arbitrary function f. The latter case is again easily understood geometrically. The equations $x = c_1$, $z = c_2$ represent a straight line in the direction of the generators of the cylindrical surfaces, and there is obviously an infinity of cylindrical surfaces which have one generator in common.

If we write the solution (1) in the alternate form

$$f(x, z) = 0, \tag{6}$$

where obviously the meaning of f differs from that in (1), the special significance of the curves

$$x = c_1, \qquad z = c_2 \tag{7}$$

suggests that in the solution

$$f[u(x, y, z), v(x, y, z)] = 0 \tag{8}$$

of the differential equation

$$P \frac{\partial z}{\partial x} + Q \frac{\partial z}{\partial y} = R \tag{9}$$

the curves

$$u(x, y, z) = c_1, \qquad v(x, y, z) = c_2 \tag{10}$$

should have a special significance. This is, in fact, the case. It can be shown that while, in general, a specific solution surface can be determined from the family of solution surfaces (8) by the requirement that this specific surface pass through a curve

$$x = x(t), \qquad y = y(t), \qquad z = z(t), \tag{11}$$

this is not possible if the curve (11) satisfies one or both of Eqs. (10). If one of Eqs. (10) is satisfied by (11) but the other is not, no solution exists. If both Eqs. (10) are satisfied by (11), an infinity of solutions exists and the form of the function f in the solution (8) remains undetermined.

We see that the curves $u = c_1$ $v = c_2$ occupy an exceptional position with reference to the differential equation (9). It is customary to designate these curves as *characteristic curves* of the given partial differential equation. Analogously, the ordinary differential equations $dx/P = dy/Q = dz/R$ which have the solutions $u = c_1, v = c_2$ are often called the *characteristic differential equations* associated with the partial differential equation (9).

EXERCISES

In Exercises 1 through 4 determine the solutions of the differential equations with initial conditions as given.

1. $2y\dfrac{\partial z}{\partial x} - \dfrac{\partial z}{\partial y} = 0;\quad x = t^2, y = t, z = t + 1$

2. $\dfrac{\partial z}{\partial x} + \dfrac{\partial z}{\partial y} = 0;\quad x = t^2 + 1, y = 2t, z = \cos t$

3. $x\dfrac{\partial z}{\partial x} + y\dfrac{\partial z}{\partial y} = 3z;\quad x = \cos t, y = \sin t, z = \sin^3 t$

4. $x\dfrac{\partial z}{\partial x} + y\dfrac{\partial z}{\partial y} = 3z;\quad x = \cos t, y = \sin t, z = \cos t \sin^2 t$

5. Find three distinct solutions of the differential equation

$$2y\frac{\partial z}{\partial x} - \frac{\partial z}{\partial y} = 0$$

with the initial conditions $x = 2 - t^2,\ y = t,\ z = 3$.

6. Determine the solution of the differential equation

$$\frac{\partial z}{\partial x} + \frac{\partial z}{\partial y} = 0$$

with the initial conditions

$$x = A_0 + A_1 t, \qquad y = B_0 + B_1 t, \qquad z = C_0 + C_1 t.$$

7. Determine the solution of the differential equation

$$yz\frac{\partial z}{\partial x} - xz\frac{\partial z}{\partial y} - xy = 0$$

with the initial conditions

$$x = 2t^{1/2}, \qquad y = t - 1, \qquad z = (2t - 1)^{1/2}.$$

[*Hint:* First write the general solution in the form $z^2 = g(x^2 + y^2) - y^2$.]

8–5 Second-order partial differential equations of physics. Relatively little is known, even today, concerning the general theory of second-order partial differential equations of the form

$$F\left(\frac{\partial^2 z}{\partial x^2}, \frac{\partial^2 z}{\partial x\,\partial y}, \frac{\partial^2 z}{\partial y^2}, \frac{\partial z}{\partial x}, \frac{\partial z}{\partial y}, z, x, y\right) = 0. \tag{1}$$

A somewhat simpler class of second-order equations is the class of *quasilinear* equations

$$A\frac{\partial^2 z}{\partial x^2} + B\frac{\partial^2 z}{\partial x\,\partial y} + C\frac{\partial^2 z}{\partial y^2} = D, \tag{2}$$

which is linear in the second derivatives and where the coefficients A, B, C, and D are given functions of x, y, z, $\partial z/\partial x$, and $\partial z/\partial y$. But even here the theory is difficult and much further progress remains to be made. We might mention that a special form of Eq. (2) governs the problem of steady two-dimensional potential flow of a compressible fluid. This problem is of great practical significance, since it describes important effects of compressibility of the atmosphere on the characteristics of high-speed flight of aircraft.

Certain aerodynamic effects may be analyzed approximately by a very much simplified version of Eq. (2), namely, the equation

$$(1 - M^2) \frac{\partial^2 z}{\partial x^2} + \frac{\partial^2 z}{\partial y^2} = 0, \tag{3}$$

where M is a constant which is called the *Mach number* at which the flight takes place. This Mach number is defined as the ratio of the speed of the aircraft to the speed of sound in the medium in which the aircraft travels. When $M < 1$, we have subsonic flight; when $M > 1$, we have supersonic flight.*

In many problems it is necessary to take account of changes in all three space directions x, y, and z. The variable z is then one of the independent variables, and we must use a different symbol for the dependent variable. Let us denote this dependent variable by the letter w.

The approximate differential equation for steady subsonic and supersonic flow depending on all three space coordinates is

$$(1 - M^2) \frac{\partial^2 w}{\partial x^2} + \frac{\partial^2 w}{\partial y^2} + \frac{\partial^2 w}{\partial z^2} = 0. \tag{4}$$

In problems of nonsteady flow (such as flight through a gust) time t becomes a fourth independent variable. The appropriate approximate differential equation is then

$$(1 - M^2) \frac{\partial^2 w}{\partial x^2} + \frac{\partial^2 w}{\partial y^2} + \frac{\partial^2 w}{\partial z^2} - M^2 \left(\frac{2}{U} \frac{\partial^2 w}{\partial x\, \partial t} + \frac{1}{U^2} \frac{\partial^2 w}{\partial t^2} \right) = 0, \tag{5}$$

where U is the constant velocity of flight.

Equations (3), (4), and (5) have to be solved in such a way that certain boundary and initial conditions are satisfied. These conditions follow from

---

* Equation (3) ceases to be applicable even approximately when M is near unity, say for $0.9 < M < 1.1$. For values of M in this range, which is called the *transonic* range, a less simple differential equation must be used. The same is true when M is large compared with unity, say $M > 10$. We are then in what is called the *hypersonic* range.

a consideration of the specific problem of flow for which a solution is desired. Since an understanding of these flow problems requires a more detailed knowledge of the theory of flow of fluids (*fluid dynamics*) than can be given here, we shall not pursue this particular subject. Instead, we shall consider the differential equations of certain other problems of a more classical nature.

8-6 Heat conduction in solids. The differential equation of heat conduction in solids may be obtained on the basis of two fundamental laws. The first of these laws states that the *heat content* of a volume V of the solid is given by

$$\int_V \rho c T \, dV,$$

where T is the temperature distribution, ρ is the density, and c is the specific heat of the material of the solid.

The second law states that the rate of heat flow through a surface S with normal direction n is given by

$$-\int_S k \frac{\partial T}{\partial n} \, dS,$$

where k is the thermal conductivity of the material of the solid. The minus sign indicates that the flow takes place in the direction of decreasing temperatures.

If S is the closed surface surrounding the volume V, we have that the rate of change of heat content of V must equal the rate of heat flow through S. This means that we have the relation

$$\frac{\partial}{\partial t} \int_V \rho c T \, dV = \int_S k \frac{\partial T}{\partial n} \, dS \tag{1}$$

for the volume V bounded by the surface S. We shall show that evaluation of this relation leads to the differential equation of heat conduction.

We shall here assume that ρ, c, and k are the same throughout the body; that is, we shall restrict our attention to *homogeneous* solids.

For homogeneous solids Eq. (1) may be written in the form

$$\int_S \frac{\partial T}{\partial n} \, dS = \frac{\rho c}{k} \int_V \frac{\partial T}{\partial t} \, dV. \tag{2}$$

Let us apply Eq. (2) in the case where V is the volume of the infinitesimal parallelepiped $dx \, dy \, dz$ with sides parallel to the coordinate planes. We then have, for the term on the right of (2),

$$\int_V \frac{\partial T}{\partial t} \, dV = \frac{\partial T}{\partial t} \, dx \, dy \, dz. \tag{3}$$

There are six contributions to the surface integral on the left of (2), one from each face of the parallelepiped. From the face $x =$ const, where the outward normal direction is the negative x-direction, we have

$$\int \frac{\partial T}{\partial n}\, dS = -\frac{\partial T}{\partial x}\, dy\, dz.$$

From the face $x + dx =$ const, where the outward normal direction is the positive x-direction, we have, considering the change in values in going from x to $x + dx$,

$$\int \frac{\partial T}{\partial n}\, dS = +\frac{\partial T}{\partial x}\, dy\, dz + \frac{\partial}{\partial x}\left(\frac{\partial T}{\partial x}\, dy\, dz\right) dx.$$

Corresponding contributions come from the other two pairs of faces. Altogether, if S is the surface of the parallelepiped $dx\, dy\, dz$,

$$\int_S \frac{\partial T}{\partial n}\, dS = \left(\frac{\partial^2 T}{\partial x^2} + \frac{\partial^2 T}{\partial y^2} + \frac{\partial^2 T}{\partial z^2}\right) dx\, dy\, dz. \qquad (4)$$

Introduction of (3) and (4) into the relation (2) shows that the differential equation for the conduction of heat in homogeneous isotropic solids is of the form

$$\lambda\left(\frac{\partial^2 T}{\partial x^2} + \frac{\partial^2 T}{\partial y^2} + \frac{\partial^2 T}{\partial z^2}\right) = \frac{\partial T}{\partial t}. \qquad (5)$$

The coefficient $\lambda = k/\rho c$ is sometimes called the *thermometric conductivity*.

In a mathematically precise derivation of the differential equation (5) from the basic relation (2) we would proceed as follows. Instead of considering the infinitesimal parallelepiped $dx\, dy\, dz$, consider a parallelepiped with vertices

$$(x, y, z),\ (x + \Delta x, y, z),\ \ldots,\ (x + \Delta x, y + \Delta y, z + \Delta z).$$

Applying the mean value theorem of the integral calculus to the volume integral in (2), we have

$$\int_V \frac{\partial T}{\partial t}\, dV = \left(\frac{\partial T}{\partial t}\right)_{\xi, \eta, \zeta} \Delta x\, \Delta y\, \Delta z,$$

where (ξ, η, ζ) represents some point belonging to the parallelepiped.

Similar statements apply to the surface integrals over the six faces of the parallelepiped. We substitute the formulas obtained in this way into the relation (2), divide on both sides by the product $\Delta x\, \Delta y\, \Delta z$, and then let $\Delta x, \Delta y,$ and Δz tend to zero.

To solve a specific problem of heat conduction, we must know, in addition to the differential equation which governs the flow of heat in the interior of the body, what happens on the surface of the body. The conditions which state what happens on the surface of the body are called *boundary conditions*. These boundary conditions may be of various forms. The problem may be such that the temperature is prescribed over the surface, or the rate of heat flow $k(\partial T/\partial n)$ across the surface may be prescribed. A special case of the latter condition is given when the surface is *insulated* so that no heat flows across the surface. Still another condition might be that the rate of heat flow across the surface is a given function of the difference between the surface temperature of the body and the temperature of the surrounding medium.

Further consideration shows that in addition to boundary conditions we also need an *initial condition*. This means that in order to determine the temperature distribution in a solid for times $t > t_0$ we must know not only what happens on the surface of the solid for $t > t_0$, but also the temperature distribution in the interior of the body when $t = t_0$.

EXERCISES

1. Given a homogeneous, nonisotropic solid with thermal conductivities k_x, k_y, k_z in the x-, y-, z-directions, respectively, show that the differential equation for the distribution of temperature T in the solid is of the form

$$k_x \frac{\partial^2 T}{\partial x^2} + k_y \frac{\partial^2 T}{\partial y^2} + k_z \frac{\partial^2 T}{\partial z^2} = c\rho \frac{\partial T}{\partial t}.$$

2. Given that the thermal conductivities in the x-, y-, z-directions are k_x, k_y, k_z, respectively, show that the heat flow intensity through an element dS the normal n of which encloses angles α, β, γ with the x-, y-, z-axes, respectively, is given by

$$k_x \cos \alpha \frac{\partial T}{\partial x} + k_y \cos \beta \frac{\partial T}{\partial y} + k_z \cos \gamma \frac{\partial T}{\partial z}.$$

[*Hint:* Apply Eq. (1) to an infinitesimal tetrahedron with sides perpendicular to x, y, z, and n.]

3. Show that the differential equation of heat conduction in homogeneous isotropic solids, when written in cylindrical coordinates r, θ, z, is of the form

$$\lambda \left(\frac{\partial^2 T}{\partial r^2} + \frac{1}{r} \frac{\partial T}{\partial r} + \frac{1}{r^2} \frac{\partial^2 T}{\partial \theta^2} + \frac{\partial^2 T}{\partial z^2} \right) = \frac{\partial T}{\partial t}.$$

8–7 One-dimensional heat flow. It is natural to begin by considering problems of heat flow for which the temperature distribution is a function of one of the space variables only, say of the variable x. In this case the differential equation for T reduces to the following form:

$$\lambda \frac{\partial^2 T}{\partial x^2} = \frac{\partial T}{\partial t}. \tag{1}$$

Equation (1) determines the temperature distribution in a solid which has the form of an infinite slab bounded by two planes $x = $ const, under the assumption that over each of the two boundary planes the temperature is a function of time only.

Equation (1) may also be applied to the study of the temperature distribution along the axis of a cylindrical rod, under the assumption that the sides of the rod are insulated.

Let us first take up very briefly the *steady-state* problem, that is, the problem of the temperature distribution independent of time. Equation (1) in this case reduces to the ordinary differential equation

$$\frac{d^2T}{dx^2} = 0,$$

whose solution is obviously

$$T = c_0 + c_1 x.$$

The two constants c_0 and c_1 may be determined in such a way that T assumes given values T_1 and T_2 at two bounding sections $x = x_1$ and $x = x_2$. Problems of this sort have been discussed in more detail and from a different point of view in Section 1–5.

We turn now to the problem of time-dependent temperature distributions. A basic problem of heat conduction which serves to illustrate one of the most useful procedures for the solution of the differential equation (1) is the following. At time $t = 0$ the temperature T of the slab is a given function $T_0(x)$ of the distance x across the thickness of the slab (or along the length of the rod with insulated sides). Beginning at time $t = 0$, and from then on, the boundary planes of the slab (or the ends of the rod) are kept at zero temperature.

Let the bounding planes of the slab (or the ends of the rod) be at $x = 0$ and $x = L$. We then have the *initial condition*

$$0 \leq x \leq L, \quad t = 0: \quad T = T_0(x) \tag{2}$$

and the *boundary conditions*

$$0 < t, \quad x = 0, \quad x = L: \quad T = 0. \tag{3}$$

Suitable solutions of the differential equation for T may be found by the *method of separation of variables*. In this method we seek particular solutions T_p of the form

$$T_p = f(x)g(t). \tag{4}$$

Substitution of (4) in (1) gives

$$\lambda \frac{d^2 f}{dx^2} g = f \frac{dg}{dt} \tag{5}$$

or

$$\lambda \frac{d^2 f/dx^2}{f} = \frac{dg/dt}{g}. \tag{6}$$

Now the left side of (6) is independent of t and the right side of (6) is independent of x. This can be so only if both sides are equal to a constant. Let k be the value of this constant, which may be called the *separation constant*. We then have

$$\lambda \frac{d^2 f}{dx^2} = kf \tag{7a}$$

and

$$\frac{dg}{dt} = kg. \tag{7b}$$

Equations (7) may readily be solved for any value of the separation constant k.

Suppose we determine k in such a way that the particular solution T_p satisfies the boundary conditions at $x = 0$ and $x = L$. The solution of (7a) must then satisfy the conditions

$$\begin{aligned} f(0) &= 0, \\ f(L) &= 0. \end{aligned} \tag{8}$$

If we take the general solution of the second-order equation (7a) and make it satisfy (8), we find that the separation constant k must have one of the following values:

$$k = -\frac{\lambda \pi^2}{L^2} n^2, \qquad n = 1, 2, 3, \ldots \tag{9}$$

Corresponding to each such value of k we have a function f of the form

$$f = C \sin \frac{n\pi}{L} x, \tag{10}$$

where C is an arbitrary constant.

With k given by (9), the time function g becomes

$$g = C^* e^{-\lambda \pi^2 n^2 t/L^2}, \tag{11}$$

where C^* is another arbitrary constant.

We now combine (10) and (11) in product form according to (4) and set $CC^* = C_n$. This gives us the following family of particular solutions of the partial differential equation (1):

$$T_p = C_n \sin \frac{n\pi x}{L} e^{-\lambda \pi^2 n^2 t/L^2}, \qquad n = 1, 2, \ldots \qquad (12)$$

Each one of the solutions (12) satisfies the differential equation (1) and the boundary conditions (3). The only condition which remains to be satisfied is the initial condition (2).

When $t = 0$, we have from (12)

$$T_p(x, 0) = C_n \sin \frac{n\pi x}{L}, \qquad (13)$$

and consequently the initial condition (2) is satisfied by the particular solution (12) if the initial temperature distribution is of the form $T_0(x) = C_n \sin n\pi x/L$.

We see that we have solved the given problem for the class of initial temperature distributions consisting of n half-sine waves, but as yet not for more general distributions, such as $T_0 = cx(x - L)$.

Since the differential equation (1) is linear, the superposition principle holds and any linear combination of particular solutions (12) is also a solution of (1). The most general linear combination of particular solutions (12) is

$$T = \sum_{n=1}^{\infty} C_n \sin \frac{n\pi x}{L} e^{-\lambda \pi^2 n^2 t/L^2}. \qquad (14)$$

The solution (14) satisfies the boundary conditions (3) term by term. The initial condition (2) becomes

$$\sum_{n=1}^{\infty} C_n \sin \frac{n\pi x}{L} = T_0(x). \qquad (15)$$

Evidently we have solved our heat-conduction problem whenever $T_0(x)$ is as in (15), with suitable values of the constants C_n.

There is no question as to the nature of the function $T_0(x)$ for which we have solved our heat-conduction problem in the event that the *trigonometric series* on the left of (15) contains a finite number of terms only. Of more interest is the question of what can be accomplished when we have an infinite number of series terms. Briefly, the answer to this question is that all functions $T_0(x)$ which are sectionally continuous in the interval $0 < x < L$ can be represented by a series of the form (15).

To determine the coefficients C_n for a given function $T_0(x)$, we proceed as follows. We multiply both sides of (15) by a factor $\sin m\pi x/L$ and then integrate between 0 and L. We then have

$$\int_0^L \sin \frac{m\pi x}{L} \sum_{n=1}^{\infty} C_n \sin \frac{n\pi x}{L}\, dx = \int_0^L \sin \frac{m\pi x}{L}\, T_0(x)\, dx. \qquad (16)$$

We now interchange integration and summation on the left of (16) and take account of the following relation:

$$\int_0^L \sin \frac{m\pi x}{L} \sin \frac{n\pi x}{L}\, dx = \begin{cases} 0, & n \neq m, \\ \frac{1}{2}L, & n = m. \end{cases} \qquad (17)$$

Therewith Eq. (16) becomes

$$C_m = \frac{2}{L} \int_0^L T_0(x) \sin \frac{m\pi x}{L}\, dx, \qquad (18)$$

and we have determined all elements in our infinite series of particular solutions of the one-dimensional heat flow equation.

Equation (15), *with coefficients as in* (18), *is an example of a Fourier series, called a Fourier sine series. The coefficients C_n as determined in* (18) *are called Fourier coefficients of the function $T_0(x)$.* We remarked earlier that all sectionally continuous functions in the interval $0 < x < L$ may be represented by the Fourier sine series. We must add that this does not mean that the series obtained is necessarily convergent. [For convergence we need slightly stronger restrictions on $T_0(x)$.] However, even if this series diverges, use of it in connection with the solution of differential equations is possible, as continued study of the subject reveals.

Returning now to our original problem, combination of (18) and (14) shows that the solution of the heat-flow problem stated in Eqs. (1) through (3) is of the form

$$T = \frac{2}{L} \sum_{n=1}^{\infty} \left(\int_0^L T_0(x) \sin \frac{n\pi x}{L}\, dx \right) \sin \frac{n\pi x}{L}\, e^{-\lambda \pi^2 n^2 t / L^2}. \qquad (19)$$

If we distinguish the variable of integration from the free variable x by writing ξ instead of x for the former, we may write (19) without parentheses as follows:

$$T = \frac{2}{L} \sum_{n=1}^{\infty} \int_0^L T_0(\xi) \sin \frac{n\pi \xi}{L}\, d\xi \sin \frac{n\pi x}{L}\, e^{-\lambda \pi^2 n^2 t / L^2}. \qquad (19')$$

As an example of the use of the general solution (19), we determine the distribution of temperature in a slab of thickness L the faces of which are at zero temperature and for which the distribution of temperature for $t = 0$ is of the form

$$T_0(x) = \begin{cases} T_1 \dfrac{x}{\frac{1}{2}L}, & 0 < x < \frac{1}{2}L, \\[2mm] T_1 \left(2 - \dfrac{x}{\frac{1}{2}L}\right), & \frac{1}{2}L < x < L, \end{cases}$$

where T_1 is a constant.

We have

$$\int_0^L T_0(x) \sin \frac{n\pi x}{L} \, dx$$

$$= T_1 \int_0^{L/2} \frac{2}{L} x \sin \frac{n\pi x}{L} \, dx + T_1 \int_{L/2}^L \left(2 - \frac{2x}{L}\right) \sin \frac{n\pi x}{L} \, dx$$

$$= T_1 L \frac{\sin \frac{1}{2}n\pi}{\frac{1}{4}\pi^2 n^2},$$

and therewith

$$T(x, t) = \frac{8}{\pi^2} T_1 \sum_{n=1}^{\infty} \frac{\sin \frac{1}{2}n\pi}{n^2} \sin \frac{n\pi x}{L} e^{-\lambda \pi^2 n^2 t / L^2}.$$

EXERCISES

1. Determine the distribution of temperature in a slab of thickness L if the faces $x = 0$ and $x = L$ are at temperature zero and the distribution of temperature at time $t = 0$ is

(a) $T_1 \sin \dfrac{\pi x}{L} + T_3 \sin \dfrac{3\pi x}{L}$,   (b) $4T_1 \dfrac{x}{L}\left(1 - \dfrac{x}{L}\right)$,

(c) 0 for $0 \leq x \leq x_1$, T_1 for $x_1 < x < x_2$, 0 for $x_2 \leq x \leq L$.

2. Determine the distribution of temperature in a slab of thickness L if the face $x = 0$ is at a constant temperature A and the face $x = L$ at a constant temperature B and if for $t = 0$ we have $T = T_0(x)$. [*Hint:* Show that by setting $T(x, t) = A + (B - A)(x/L) + U(x, t)$ the function U may be determined by the method explained in the text.]

3. Show that the differential equation

$$d^2f/dx^2 + \mu f = 0$$

has solutions which satisfy the boundary conditions

(a) $f(0) = f(L) = 0$,   (b) $f'(0) = f'(L) = 0$,   (c) $f(0) = f'(L) = 0$, only for the following values of the coefficient μ:

(a) $\mu = \dfrac{n^2\pi^2}{L^2}$,   (b) $\mu = \dfrac{n^2\pi^2}{L^2}$,   (c) $\mu = \dfrac{(2n+1)^2\pi^2}{4L^2}$,

where $n = 0, 1, 2, 3, \ldots$, and that the corresponding solutions f are

(a) $f = C \sin \dfrac{n\pi x}{L}$,   (b) $f = C \cos \dfrac{n\pi x}{L}$,   (c) $f = C \sin \dfrac{(2n+1)\pi x}{2L}$.

4. Show that

$$T = \sum_{n=0}^{\infty} C_n \cos \frac{n\pi x}{L} e^{-\lambda(\pi/L)^2 n^2 t}$$

satisfies the differential equation $\lambda(\partial^2 T/\partial x^2) = \partial T/\partial t$ and the boundary conditions $(\partial T/\partial x)_0 = (\partial T/\partial x)_L = 0$, and obtain the temperature distribution in a slab of thickness L when the faces $x = 0$ and $x = L$ are insulated and the temperature distribution at time $t = 0$ is $T(x, 0) = \frac{1}{2}T_1(1 - \cos 2\pi x/L)$.

5. Show that when $\sum_{n=0}^{\infty} C_n \cos n\pi x/L = T_0(x)$, the coefficient C_n may be expressed in terms of the function T_0 by means of the formulas

$$LC_0 = \int_0^L T_0(x)\, dx, \qquad \tfrac{1}{2}LC_n = \int_0^L T_0(x) \cos (n\pi x/L)\, dx.$$

[Hint: Multiply the given relation by $\cos m\pi x/L$ and integrate between $x = 0$ and L.]

6. Use the result of Exercise 5 to solve Exercise 4 with the initial condition of Exercise 4 replaced by the condition $T(x, 0) = T_0(x)$, where $T_0(x)$ is a given function.

8–8 Flow of heat in circular cylindrical bodies. Among problems of heat conduction in solids which are of some practical importance and for which an exact solution can be obtained are many problems for bodies of the form of a right circular cylinder. The boundaries of a circular cylindrical body are, of course, most conveniently described in terms of cylindrical coordinates, and we shall see that the use of cylindrical coordinates in such cases is an essential element of the method of solution.

Let r, θ, z be cylindrical coordinates defined in the usual way. The boundary of a cylindrical body of radius a and length L may then be given by the two planes $z = 0$ and $z = L$, and by the cylindrical surface $r = a$.

As a specific example, let us assume that we have at initial time $t = 0$ a given temperature throughout the interior of the cylindrical body, and for all later times $t > 0$ we have given temperatures over the entire bounding surface of the body. The first of these conditions, the initial condition, may be written in the form

$$t = 0; \quad 0 \le r \le a, \quad 0 \le \theta < 2\pi, \quad 0 \le z \le L, \quad T = f_1(r, \theta, z), \quad (1)$$

where f_1 is an arbitrarily given function. The second of these conditions, the boundary condition, may be stated in mathematical terms as follows:

$$z = 0, \quad 0 \leq r \leq a, \quad T = f_2(r, \theta, t),$$

$$t > 0; \quad z = L, \quad 0 \leq r \leq a, \quad T = f_3(r, \theta, t), \tag{2}$$

$$r = a, \quad 0 < z < L, \quad T = f_4(\theta, z, t),$$

where the functions f_2, f_3, and f_4 are arbitrarily prescribed.

The differential equation of heat conduction for isotropic homogeneous solids in terms of cylindrical coordinates is

$$\lambda \left(\frac{\partial^2 T}{\partial r^2} + \frac{1}{r} \frac{\partial T}{\partial r} + \frac{1}{r^2} \frac{\partial^2 T}{\partial \theta^2} + \frac{\partial^2 T}{\partial z^2} \right) = \frac{\partial T}{\partial t}, \tag{3}$$

and the problem now is to obtain a solution of this differential equation which satisfies the conditions (1) and (2). It will be instructive to consider a number of special cases, instead of the general problem (1) through (3).

8–9 Steady-state temperature distribution in circular cylindrical bodies. Determination of steady-state temperature distributions in circular cylindrical bodies requires the determination of solutions of the differential equation

$$\frac{\partial^2 T}{\partial r^2} + \frac{1}{r} \frac{\partial T}{\partial r} + \frac{1}{r^2} \frac{\partial^2 T}{\partial \theta^2} + \frac{\partial^2 T}{\partial z^2} = 0, \tag{1}$$

subject to suitable boundary conditions. Since the function T is independent of time t, we have no initial condition.

The following examples will illustrate the nature of the problem and methods of solution.

(a) *Infinite cylinder with T independent of θ and z.* Equation (1) reduces to

$$\frac{d^2 T}{dr^2} + \frac{1}{r} \frac{dT}{dr} = 0, \tag{2}$$

whose solution is

$$T = c_0 + c_1 \ln r. \tag{3}$$

For the determination of c_0 and c_1 we distinguish two separate cases:

(i) *Solid cylinder of radius a.* Since $T(0)$ must not be infinite, we must set

$$c_1 = 0,$$

and the only steady-state distribution is a uniform distribution $T = \text{const.}$

(ii) *Hollow cylinder.* Let $r = a$ and $r = b$ be the walls of the cylinder. We may prescribe

$$T(a) = T_1, \qquad T(b) = T_2,$$

and determine c_0 and c_1 in terms of T_1 and T_2. The fact that the expression (3) for $T(r)$ becomes infinite for $r = 0$ is now of no consequence, since $r = 0$ is not part of the solid in which the distribution of temperature is to be determined.

(b) *Infinite cylinder with T independent of z.* We must now solve the equation

$$\frac{\partial^2 T}{\partial r^2} + \frac{1}{r}\frac{\partial T}{\partial r} + \frac{1}{r^2}\frac{\partial^2 T}{\partial \theta^2} = 0. \tag{4}$$

As for the equation $\lambda(\partial^2 T/\partial x^2) = \partial T/\partial t$, we utilize the method of separation of variables by looking for particular solutions of the form

$$T = f(r)g(\theta). \tag{5}$$

Introduction of (5) into (4) gives

$$\left[f''(r) + \frac{1}{r}f'(r)\right]g(\theta) + \frac{1}{r^2}f(r)g''(\theta) = 0,$$

or, separating variables,

$$\frac{f''(r) + r^{-1}f'(r)}{r^{-2}f(r)} = -\frac{g''(\theta)}{g(\theta)}. \tag{6}$$

Since the left side of (6) is independent of θ and the right side is independent of r, *both* sides must be independent of r *and* θ. We then have

$$\frac{g''(\theta)}{g(\theta)} = -k, \qquad \frac{f''(r) + r^{-1}f'(r)}{r^{-2}f(r)} = k$$

or

$$g''(\theta) + kg(\theta) = 0 \tag{7a}$$

and

$$f''(r) + \frac{1}{r}f'(r) - \frac{k}{r^2}f(r) = 0. \tag{7b}$$

According to Section 3–6, Eq. (7a) has the general solution

$$\begin{aligned}
g(\theta) &= c_1 \cos \sqrt{k}\,\theta + c_2 \sin \sqrt{k}\,\theta, & k &\neq 0, \\
g(\theta) &= c_1 + c_2\theta, & k &= 0,
\end{aligned} \tag{8a}$$

and according to Section 3–7, the general solution of the equidimensional
equation (7b) is

$$f(r) = c_3 r^{\sqrt{k}} + c_4 r^{-\sqrt{k}}, \qquad k \neq 0,$$
$$f(r) = c_3 + c_4 \ln r, \qquad k = 0. \tag{8b}$$

Up to now we have said nothing concerning the values of the separation
constant k. Restrictions on the possible values of this constant follow from
a physical consideration.

We know that one and the same given physical point in the cross
section of the cylinder may have the coordinates (r, θ) and $(r, \theta + 2\pi)$. In
order that $T(r, \theta)$ have the same value, regardless of which of the two repre-
sentations of the point (r, θ) we choose, we require that the function $g(\theta)$
be of such form that

$$g(\theta) = g(\theta + 2\pi).$$

When $k = 0$, this requires that $c_2 = 0$, and when $k \neq 0$, it requires that

$$\cos \sqrt{k}\theta = \cos \sqrt{k}(\theta + 2\pi), \qquad \sin \sqrt{k}\theta = \sin \sqrt{k}(\theta + 2\pi)$$

for all values of θ. These relations are satisfied if and only if

$$1 = \cos \sqrt{k}\, 2\pi,$$

and this can be so if and only if

$$\sqrt{k} = n, \qquad n = 0, 1, 2, \ldots$$

We now have particular solutions $T = T_n(r, \theta)$ of Eq. (4) of the form

$$T_n = (c_1 \cos n\theta + c_2 \sin n\theta)(c_3 r^n + c_4 r^{-n}), \qquad n = 1, 2, 3, \ldots,$$
$$T_0 = c_1(c_3 + c_4 \ln r), \tag{9}$$

and it remains to see what we can do with them.

Let us assume, for the sake of simplifying the discussion, that we are
dealing with a solid cylinder, so that the line $r = 0$ is part of it. As we
see no reason for the temperature at $r = 0$ to be infinite, we set in (9)

$$c_4 = 0.$$

We incorporate the constant c_3 in c_1 and c_2 and indicate that we still have
n at our disposal by writing

$$c_1 c_3 = A_n, \qquad c_2 c_3 = B_n.$$

This leaves us with the following class of particular solutions:

$$T_n = (A_n \cos n\theta + B_n \sin n\theta)r^n, \qquad n = 0, 1, 2, \ldots \tag{10}$$

Let $r = a$ be the boundary of the cylinder. The particular solution T_n assumes the value

$$T_n(a, \theta) = (A_n \cos n\theta + B_n \sin n\theta)a^n \tag{11}$$

at this boundary. This means that this class of particular solution solves our heat-conduction problem provided the boundary condition is that for $r = a$ the surface temperature varies with the angle θ in the special manner indicated in Eq. (11).

Suppose that we have the more general condition of arbitrarily given values of T for $r = a$:

$$T(a, \theta) = f(\theta). \tag{12}$$

To illustrate, the function $f(\theta)$ might be

$$f(\theta) = |\cos \theta|$$

or

$$f(\theta) = \begin{cases} 1 \text{ for } -\pi/2 \leq \theta \leq \pi/2, \\ 0 \text{ elsewhere.} \end{cases}$$

Problems of this sort may be solved—and this was a major discovery some 150 years ago—by superposing particular solutions of the form (10) as follows:

$$T(r, \theta) = A_0 + \sum_{n=1}^{\infty} (A_n \cos n\theta + B_n \sin n\theta)r^n. \tag{13}$$

Expression (13) is a solution of the given differential equation (4). The arbitrary constants A_n and B_n must be determined from the boundary condition (12). This is simple to do if the function $f(\theta)$ in (12) is directly given as a trigonometric sum:

$$f(\theta) = a_0 + a_1 \cos \theta + b_1 \sin \theta + a_2 \cos 2\theta + b_2 \sin 2\theta + \cdots \tag{14}$$

Introduction of (13) and (14) into (12) then gives

$$A_0 + \sum(A_n \cos n\theta + B_n \sin n\theta)a^n = a_0 + \sum(a_n \cos n\theta + b_n \sin n\theta). \tag{15}$$

Equation (15) is to be considered as an identity in θ. It seems reasonable, therefore, and it can be proved rigorously, that the only solution which is possible is one where we equate corresponding coefficients of the trigonometric functions on the left and on the right as follows:

$$A_0 = a_0, \qquad A_n = \frac{a_n}{a^n}, \qquad B_n = \frac{b_n}{a^n}. \tag{16}$$

With (16) we have as an expression for T

$$T(r, \theta) = a_0 + \sum (a_n \cos n\theta + b_n \sin n\theta)(r/a)^n, \tag{17}$$

and this expression does, in fact, satisfy the boundary condition (12) with f given by (14).

There still remains the question of what to do if $f(\theta)$ is not directly given by the series (14). The answer to this fundamental question is as follows. Any physically reasonable function $f(\theta)$ can be *developed* in a series of the form (14). To carry out this development, we multiply both sides of (14) by a factor $\cos m\theta$ and integrate with respect to θ from 0 to 2π, then multiply both sides of (14) by $\sin m\theta$ and integrate as before. In both sets of integration we make use of the fact that of all the integrals which arise in this way the only nonvanishing ones are

$$\int_0^{2\pi} d\theta = 2\pi, \quad \int_0^{2\pi} \cos^2 m\theta \, d\theta = \int_0^{2\pi} \sin^2 m\theta \, d\theta = \pi, \quad m = 1, 2, \ldots$$

With this we obtain the following fundamental formulas for the series coefficients a_n and b_n:

$$a_0 = \frac{1}{2\pi} \int_0^{2\pi} f(\theta) \, d\theta, \qquad a_n = \frac{1}{\pi} \int_0^{2\pi} f(\theta) \cos n\theta \, d\theta,$$

$$b_n = \frac{1}{\pi} \int_0^{2\pi} f(\theta) \sin n\theta \, d\theta, \qquad n = 1, 2, 3, \ldots \tag{18}$$

The series (14), with coefficients determined by Eqs. (18), is called a Fourier series, and the coefficients a_n and b_n are the Fourier coefficients of the function $f(\theta)$. Earlier, in Section 8–7, we encountered a special case of such series, namely, a Fourier sine series. We do not in this text consider the question of convergence of Fourier series, which is a problem of great interest. For practical purposes the application of Fourier series methods is possible in all cases in which the functions to be expanded in such a series have the property that the integrals defining its Fourier coefficients exist.

Fourier series in an interval of length P. The Fourier series (14) with coefficients (18) is for a function given in the interval $0 \leq \theta < 2\pi$. It is easily seen that formula (14) also applies for intervals $\theta_0 < \theta < \theta_0 + 2\pi$ provided a corresponding change in the limits of the integrals in (18) is made. Finally, if we make the substitution

$$\frac{x - x_0}{P} = \frac{\theta - \theta_0}{2\pi} \tag{19}$$

we are led to the general Fourier series

$$F(x) = A_0 + A_1 \cos \frac{2\pi}{P} x + B_1 \sin \frac{2\pi}{P} x$$

$$+ A_2 \cos \frac{2\pi}{P} 2x + B_2 \sin \frac{2\pi}{P} 2x + \cdots \tag{20}$$

for functions $F(x)$ defined in an interval $x_0 \le x < x_0 + P$. The coefficients in this series, called Fourier coefficients, are given by the formulas

$$A_0 = \frac{1}{P} \int_{x_0}^{x_0+P} F(x) \, dx, \qquad A_n = \frac{2}{P} \int_{x_0}^{x_0+P} F(x) \cos \frac{2n\pi x}{P} \, dx,$$

$$\tag{21}$$

$$B_n = \frac{2}{P} \int_{x_0}^{x_0+P} F(x) \sin \frac{2n\pi x}{P} \, dx, \qquad n = 1, 2, 3, \ldots$$

The individual functions $\cos 2n\pi x/P$ and $\sin 2n\pi x/P$ are periodic, of period P. This means that the series (20) also represents a function $F^*(x)$ which exists for *all* x, which is periodic of period P, and which coincides with $F(x)$ in the interval of definition of $F(x)$.

Exercises

In Exercises 1 and 2, consider an infinite solid circular cylinder of radius a and a steady-state temperature distribution which is independent of the axial coordinate z.

1. Determine $T(r, \theta)$ if the boundary condition is

(a) $T(a, \theta) = \frac{1}{2}T_0(1 + \cos \theta)$,   (b) $T(a, \theta) = \frac{1}{2}T_0(1 + \cos^3 \theta)$.

2. Determine $T(r, \theta)$ for the following cases of prescribed rate of heat flow through the surface:

(a) $(\partial T/\partial r)_{r=a} = A \cos \theta$,   (b) $(\partial T/\partial r)_{r=a} = A \cos \theta + B \cos^3 \theta$.

State a physical reason why we must have $\int_0^{2\pi} (\partial T/\partial r)_{r=a} \, d\theta = 0$.

3. The expression $T(r, \theta) = A_0 + \sum(A_n \cos n\theta + B_n \sin n\theta)r^{-n}$ may be used for the determination of steady-state temperatures in an infinite body bounded internally by a surface $r = a$. Use this fact to determine the temperature distribution in such a body, provided the boundary conditions are

$$|z| \le \infty, r = a: \quad T = C_m \cos m\theta \quad (m \text{ a fixed positive integer}),$$
$$|z| \le \infty, r = \infty: \quad T = 0.$$

4. Given a solid circular cylinder of finite radius a and finite axial length L. Let the ends $z = 0$ and $z = L$ be at zero temperature. Show that Eq. (1) has particular solutions of the form

$$T_m = \sin (m\pi z/L) f_m(r, \theta)$$

which satisfy the boundary conditions at both ends of the cylinder.

Show further that the remaining differential equation for f_m has solutions of the form

$$f_m(r, \theta) = \cos n\theta \, g_{m,n}(r) \qquad \text{and} \qquad f_m(r, \theta) = \sin n\theta \, g_{m,n}(r),$$

and determine the nature of the ordinary differential equation for $g_{m,n}(r)$.

5. Using the result of Exercise 4, solve the following boundary-value problems for a steady-state temperature distribution:

(a) $0 < r < a$, $\quad z = 0, L$; $\qquad T = 0$

$\quad 0 < z < L$, $\quad r = a$; $\qquad T = T_0 \sin \pi z/L$

(b) $0 < r < a$, $\quad z = 0, L$; $\qquad T = 0$

$\quad 0 < z < L$, $\quad r = a$; $\qquad T = \frac{1}{2}T_0(1 + \cos \theta) \sin \pi z/L$

6. Obtain the coefficients A_n and B_n in the Fourier series (20) for functions $F(x)$ defined in the interval $0 \leq x < P$ as follows:

(a) $F = \begin{cases} Q^{-1}, & 0 \leq x < Q \\ 0, & Q < x < P \end{cases}$

(b) $F = \begin{cases} 0, & 0 \leq x < R \\ Q^{-1}, & R \leq x < R + Q \\ 0, & R + Q \leq x < P \end{cases}$

(c) $F = \sin (\pi x/P)$

(d) $F = \begin{cases} x, & 0 \leq x < \frac{1}{2}P \\ \frac{1}{2}P - x, & \frac{1}{2}P \leq x < P \end{cases}$

7. By sketches on the same graph, compare the functions F^* corresponding to the functions F in Exercises 6(c) and 6(d).

8–10 Infinite cylinder with temperature distribution independent of θ and z but varying with time.

The change from steady-state problems for the circular cylinder to problems where time variations are to be considered complicates the analysis somewhat. In view of this fact, we shall here content ourselves with the treatment of a class of special cases of the problem for which T is a function of r and t only.

We assume that at time $t = 0$ the temperature in the interior of the solid is a function of the radial coordinate r only and that for $t > 0$ the temperature on the surface $r = a$ of the solid is a given function of t, the ends of the cylinder being at $z = \pm\infty$. Under these conditions T will be independent of θ and z and the differential equation (3) of Section 8–8 reduces to the following form:

$$\lambda\left(\frac{\partial^2 T}{\partial r^2} + \frac{1}{r}\frac{\partial T}{\partial r}\right) = \frac{\partial T}{\partial t}. \tag{1}$$

The initial condition for the solution $T(r, t)$ may be written

$$r \le a: \quad T(r, 0) = T_0(r), \tag{2}$$

where $T_0(r)$ is a given function.

The boundary condition for $T(r, t)$ may be written

$$t > 0: \quad T(a, t) = T_1(t), \tag{3}$$

where $T_1(t)$ is another given function. To describe the method of solution which is suitable for this problem, we shall limit ourselves to the special case

$$T_1(t) \equiv 0. \tag{4}$$

We should expect that when $T(a, t) = 0$ for all $t > 0$, the temperature T would gradually tend to zero also in the interior of the solid, regardless of the magnitude of the initial temperatures $T_0(r)$. In other words, we should expect that the solution of our problem satisfies the limit relation

$$\lim_{t\to\infty} T(r, t) = 0$$

for all $r \le a$. The actual solution of the heat-flow problem will tell us in addition at what rate this limiting value will be approached.

To solve the problem as stated by Eqs. (1) through (4), we again employ the method of separation of variables. We first look for particular solutions of Eq. (1) of the form

$$T_p(r, t) = f(r)g(t). \tag{5}$$

Substitution of (5) into (1) gives

$$\lambda\left(\frac{d^2 f}{dr^2} + \frac{1}{r}\frac{df}{dr}\right)g = f\frac{dg}{dt}, \tag{6}$$

or, separating functions of the variables r and t,

$$\lambda\frac{(d^2 f/dr^2) + (1/r)(df/dr)}{f} = \frac{dg/dt}{g}. \tag{7}$$

In (7) the left side is a function of r only, the right side a function of t only. This can be so only when both sides are equal to a constant, the separation constant k:

$$\lambda \frac{(d^2f/dr^2) + (1/r)(df/dr)}{f} = k, \qquad \frac{dg/dt}{g} = k. \qquad (8)$$

The first-order equation for $g(t)$ has the solution

$$g(t) = Ce^{kt}. \qquad (9)$$

For the determination of the function $f(r)$ we have the second-order equation

$$\frac{d^2f}{dr^2} + \frac{1}{r}\frac{df}{dr} - \frac{k}{\lambda}f = 0. \qquad (10)$$

Since we expect that as t increases the temperature T decreases, we should expect that suitable values of the exponent k in (9) would be negative. Let us assume that this will indeed be so and, in view of the form of Eq. (10), set

$$k = -\kappa^2\lambda, \qquad (11)$$

where κ is real, even though as yet we cannot be sure that this is appropriate. If, however, we do in fact obtain the solution of our problem by restricting attention to negative values of the separation constant k, we shall then have justified, a *posteriori*, our restriction regarding values of k.

Equation (10) now reads

$$f''(r) + \frac{1}{r}f'(r) + \kappa^2 f(r) = 0, \qquad (10')$$

and this equation was considered when we studied power-series solutions of second-order ordinary linear differential equations. Its solution is of the form

$$f(r) = c_1 J_0(\kappa r) + c_2 Y_0(\kappa r), \qquad (12)$$

where J_0 and Y_0 are the Bessel functions of zeroth order and of the first and second kind, respectively.

We see that by combining (9) and (12) in accordance with (5) we have found particular solutions of the partial differential equation (1) of the form

$$T_p(r, t) = [c_1 J_0(\kappa r) + c_2 Y_0(\kappa r)]e^{-\kappa^2\lambda t}, \qquad (13)$$

where we have incorporated the constant C in (9) into the arbitrary constants c_1 and c_2 in (12).

We know from our earlier study of Bessel's differential equation (10′) that

$$\lim_{r \to 0} J_0(\kappa r) = 1, \qquad \lim_{r \to 0} Y_0(\kappa r) = \infty. \tag{14}$$

Since we see no reason why T should be infinite when $r = 0$, we reject that part of solution (13) which becomes infinite when $r = 0$ by setting in it*

$$c_2 = 0. \tag{15}$$

This leaves us with the following class of particular solutions of the partial differential equation (1):

$$T_p = c_1 J_0(\kappa r) e^{-\kappa^2 \lambda t}. \tag{16}$$

To select from the class of particular solutions (16) those which are suitable for our purposes, we now proceed in the same way as when solving problems of one-dimensional heat flow in slabs by the method of separation of variables. We require that the particular solutions (16) satisfy the boundary condition $T(a, t) = 0$. This means that we must have

$$J_0(\kappa a) = 0. \tag{17}$$

Investigation of the properties of Bessel functions shows that Eq. (17) is satisfied for an infinite sequence of values κ_n of κ.

Let x_n be the nth root of the equation $J_0(x) = 0$, arranged so that $x_n < x_{n+1}$. The first few of these roots are, numerically,

$$x_1 = 2.40 \ldots, \qquad x_2 = 5.52 \ldots, \qquad x_3 = 8.65 \ldots \tag{18}$$

In view of (17), we have

$$\kappa_n = \frac{x_n}{a}, \tag{19}$$

and if we replace c_1 by c_n in order to indicate with which value of κ we are concerned, the particular solutions (16) assume the form

$$T_p = c_n J_0 \left(x_n \frac{r}{a} \right) e^{-x_n^2 \lambda t / a^2}. \tag{16′}$$

When $t = 0$, the particular solutions (16′) become

$$T_p(r, 0) = c_n J_0 \left(x_n \frac{r}{a} \right). \tag{20}$$

---

* Note that when $r = 0$ is not part of the physical region under consideration, as for a *hollow* cylindrical solid, we are not entitled to omit the part of the particular solution containing the function Y_0.

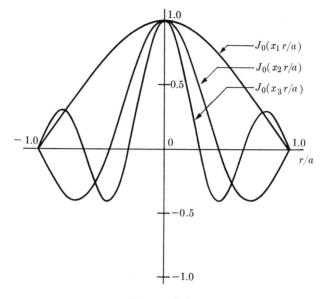

FIGURE 8-1

In view of the initial condition (2), this means that our heat-flow problem is solved completely by the particular solution (16′) provided that the function $T_0(r)$ in the initial condition is a constant multiple of the Bessel function $J_0(x_n r/a)$. The initial temperature distributions along each diameter of the circular cross section of the solid which are described by these functions are as indicated in Fig. 8-1. We would expect that of these only $J_0(x_1 r/a)$ would be of practical interest by itself. However, just as in the problem of the slab, we may obtain the solution of more general problems by the superposition principle. If we write

$$T(r,\, t) \;=\; \sum_{n=1}^{\infty} c_n J_0\left(x_n \frac{r}{a}\right) e^{-x_n^2 \lambda t / a^2}, \tag{21}$$

we have a solution of the differential equation (1) which satisfies the boundary condition as stated in (3) and (4) term by term. Since

$$T(r,\, 0) \;=\; \sum_{n=1}^{\infty} c_n J_0\left(x_n \frac{r}{a}\right), \tag{22}$$

it also satisfies the initial condition (2), provided that the constant coefficients c_n are such that the infinite series $\sum c_n J_0(x_n r/a)$ represents the function $T_0(r)$.

When $T_0(r)$ is directly given as a sum of the form (22), the solution of the problem is completed. However, even when this is not the case, as for instance when $T_0(r) = C[1 - (r/a)^2]$, we may obtain a solution of the form (21), by way of expressing $T_0(r)$ as an infinite series of this form,

$$T_0(r) = \sum_{n=1}^{\infty} c_n J_0\left(x_n \frac{r}{a}\right). \tag{23}$$

In analogy to what was described for trigonometric series in Section 8–7, there is a theory for the development of suitable functions in terms of series of the form (23). A discussion of this possibility is given in books on Advanced Calculus, and also in other books which treat what are called series of orthogonal functions. For our part, we shall merely mention that for a rather large class of functions $T_0(r)$, including all of practical interest, there is a development of the form (23), valid in the interval $0 < r < a$, and the coefficients c_n are determined by the following expressions:

$$c_n = \frac{2}{a^2} \frac{1}{[J_1(x_n)]^2} \int_0^a r T_0(r) J_0\left(x_n \frac{r}{a}\right) dr. \tag{24}$$

We note that the factors multiplying the integrals in these expressions do not depend upon the particular function $T_0(r)$ which is being considered. Values for the first few expressions $J_1(x_n)$ which occur in the denominators of (24) are as follows:

$$J_1(x_1) = 0.52\ldots, \qquad J_1(x_2) = 0.34\ldots, \qquad J_1(x_3) = 0.27\ldots \tag{25}$$

To summarize, introduction of Eq. (24) into the series (21) leads to a series solution of the problem as stated in Eqs. (1) through (4), this series solution being

$$T(r, t) = \frac{2}{a^2} \sum_{n=1}^{\infty} \frac{\int_0^a r T_0(r) J_0(x_n r/a)\, dr}{[J_1(x_n)]^2} J_0\left(x_n \frac{r}{a}\right) e^{-x_n^2 \lambda t/a^2}, \tag{26}$$

where the quantities x_n are the successive positive roots of the transcendental equation $J_0(x) = 0$.

EXERCISES

1. Write the expression for $T(r, t)$ for a solid circular cylinder, provided that $T(a, t) = 0$ for $t > 0$, and $T(r, 0) = A J_0(\kappa_1 r) + B J_0(\kappa_2 r)$.

2. Given a hollow circular cylinder with radii a and b, show that the constants c_1 and c_2 in the particular solution (13) can be chosen so as to satisfy the boundary conditions $T(a, t) = 0$ and $T(b, t) = 0$, provided κ satisfies the equation

$$J_0(\kappa b) Y_0(\kappa a) - J_0(\kappa a) Y_0(\kappa b) = 0.$$

MISCELLANEOUS EXERCISES. CHAPTER 8

Find solutions in terms of an arbitrary function of the differential equations
of Exercises 1 through 9.

1. $\dfrac{\partial z}{\partial x} = xe^{y}$

2. $\dfrac{\partial z}{\partial y} = xe^{y}$

3. $(x + e^{z})\dfrac{\partial z}{\partial x} + x^{2} + z = 0$

4. $\dfrac{\partial z}{\partial x} + 3x^{2}z = 1$

5. $\dfrac{\partial z}{\partial x} = (y - 1)(y - 4)\dfrac{\partial z}{\partial y}$

6. $\dfrac{\partial z}{\partial x} - y\dfrac{\partial z}{\partial y} + z = 0$

7. $x\dfrac{\partial z}{\partial x} + y\dfrac{\partial z}{\partial y} = z$

8. $y\dfrac{\partial z}{\partial x} + 2x\dfrac{\partial z}{\partial y} = y^{3} - 2x^{2}y + xy$

9. $x\dfrac{\partial z}{\partial x} + y\dfrac{\partial z}{\partial y} = x^{2}$

Find solutions in terms of two arbitrary functions of the differential equations
of Exercises 10 through 13.

10. $\dfrac{\partial^{2} z}{\partial x^{2}} = x + y$

11. $\dfrac{\partial^{2} z}{\partial x \, \partial y} = 6x^{2}y^{3}$

12. $y\dfrac{\partial^{2} z}{\partial y^{2}} + \dfrac{\partial z}{\partial y} = 0$

13. $\dfrac{\partial^{2} z}{\partial y^{2}} - 3x\dfrac{\partial z}{\partial y} + 2x^{2}y = 0$

Determine a first-order partial differential equation satisfied by each of the
following expressions. (In each case f represents an arbitrary function.)

14. $z = f(x^{2} + y)$

15. $z^{2} = f(x^{2} + xy)$

16. $z = f(x + e^{y})$

17. $f(x^{2} + z^{2}, xy) = 0$

18. $f(xz, yz) = 0$

19. $z = xf(y^{2} + x)$

20. $z = xf(xy^{2})$

21. $z = xy^{2} + f(x^{2} + y^{3})$

22. $z = f(x + y + z)$

In Exercises 23 through 25 determine the solution of the differential equation
with initial conditions as given.

23. $\dfrac{\partial z}{\partial x} - y\dfrac{\partial z}{\partial y} + z = 0;\quad x = \ln t,\quad y = t^{-1/2},\quad z = t\,(t > 0)$

24. $2xy\dfrac{\partial z}{\partial x} - x\dfrac{\partial z}{\partial y} = 2yz;\quad x = t^{2}\cos^{2} t,\quad y = t\sin t,\quad z = t^{4}\cos^{3} t$

25. $\dfrac{\partial z}{\partial x} + 2x\dfrac{\partial z}{\partial y} = x^{2} + y;\quad x = t - 1,\quad y = -4t,$

$$z = 1 + 12t - \tfrac{1}{3}(t - 1)^{3}$$

In Exercises 26 and 27 determine a first-order partial differential equation satisfied by the given expressions.

26. $z = (x + c_1)(y + c_2)$ 27. $z = (x + c_1 y)^3 + c_2$

In Exercises 28 and 29 determine a second-order partial differential equation satisfied by the given expressions, where f and g are arbitrary functions and a is a fixed constant.

28. $z = f(x + ay) + g(x - ay)$ 29. $z = f(x^2 + ay) + g(x^2 - ay)$

30. Solve the boundary-value problem

$$\frac{\partial^2 z}{\partial x^2} = 0; \quad z(0, y) = \sin y, \quad z(a, y) = b \quad (a \neq 0)$$

31. By separation of variables obtain a class of solutions of

$$\frac{\partial^2 z}{\partial x^2} - \frac{\partial z}{\partial y} + z = 0$$

32. By separation of variables obtain particular solutions $z(x, y)$, satisfying the conditions $z(0, y) = z(\pi, y) = 0$, of the equations

(a) $\partial^2 z/\partial x^2 + \partial^2 z/\partial y^2 = 0$ (b) $\partial^2 z/\partial x^2 + y^2 \partial^2 z/\partial y^2 = 0$

33. Determine the one-dimensional flow of heat in the interval $0 \leq x < \pi$, for $t \geq 0$, with the boundary conditions $T(0, t) = 0$, $T(\pi, t) = kt$, and the initial condition $T(x, 0) = 0$. [*Hint:* Assume the solution in the form $T = kt + u(x, t)$ and represent the constant k by a Fourier sine series.]

34. Given the differential equation $\lambda \, \partial^2 T/\partial x^2 = \partial T/\partial t$ in the region $0 \leq x < \infty, 0 \leq t < \infty$, with the boundary conditions $T(0, t) = T_0(t)$, $T(\infty, t) = 0$ and the initial condition $T(x, 0) = 0$. Show that the Laplace transform $\overline{T}(x, p)$ of $T(x, t)$ is given in terms of the Laplace transform $\overline{T}_0(p)$ of $T_0(t)$, by means of the equation $\overline{T} = \overline{T}_0 \exp(-\sqrt{p/\lambda}\, x)$.

ANSWERS TO EXERCISES

ANSWERS TO EXERCISES

CHAPTER 1

2. (a) $y = 2x + c$ (b) $y = \frac{2}{3}e^{3x} + c$ (c) $y = 2\sin^{-1}x + c$
   (d) $y = \int e^{x^2}\,dx + c$ (e) $y = \frac{1}{2}e^{x^2} + c$
   (f) $y = x\sin^{-1}x + \sqrt{1-x^2} + c$
3. (a) $y = ce^{x^2/2}$ (b) $y = -3/(x^3 + c)$ (c) $y = \ln\,[2/(c + x^2)]$
   (d) $y = \cos^{-1}\frac{1}{3}(c - x^3)$ (e) $y = \sin\,[\ln\,(cx)]$
   (f) $(y - ce^x)(y - ce^{-x}) = 0$ (g) $(y - 2x - c)(y - x - c) = 0$
   (h) $y = \tan^{-1}x + c$ (i) $y = \ln\,|\csc x - \cot x| + c$
4. (a) $(dy/dx) - y + x = c$ (b) $y + \frac{1}{2}x^2 = c_1 x + c_2$
   (c) $(dy/dx) + 2y = \frac{1}{2}x^2 + c$ (d) $y + \frac{1}{3}x^3 = c_1 x^2 + c_2 x + c_3$
   (e) $y'' + 2y = \frac{1}{2}x^2 + c_1 x + c_2$ (f) $y''' - y = \frac{1}{2}x^2 + c$

1. $y'y(a^2 - y^2)^{-1/2} \pm 1 = 0$ 2. $(y')^2(x^2 - 3y^2) - 4y^2 = 0$
3. (a) $(y')^2 = (R^2 - y^2)/y^2$ (b) $(x - y)^2[1 + (y')^2] = R^2(1 + y')^2$
4. $r = ce^{\theta\cot\alpha}$
5. $r = ce^{\pm\theta/\sqrt{k^2-1}}$, $k > 1$; where k is the proportionality constant and c
is arbitrary.
6. $xy = c$ 7. $xy = c$ 8. $y = a\cosh\,[(x + c)/a]$

1. 96% 2. (a) 34.7 (b) 23.1 (c) 17.3

3. (a) $\dfrac{\pi R^2}{CA_{\mathrm{or}}}\sqrt{\dfrac{2L}{g}}$ (b) $\dfrac{8LR^{3/2}}{3CA_{\mathrm{or}}\sqrt{g}}$

4. $N = N_0\left(\dfrac{N_1}{N_0}\right)^{(t-t_0)/(t_1-t_0)}$

5. $\dfrac{1 + (\mu/x)}{1 + (\mu/x_0)} = \left[\dfrac{1 + (\mu/x_1)}{1 + (\mu/x_0)}\right]^{(t-t_0)/(t_1-t_0)}$,   where $\mu = M - x_0$.

6. $N = \dfrac{M}{1 + \dfrac{M - N_0}{N_0}\left[\dfrac{N_0(M - N_1)}{N_1(M - N_0)}\right]^{(t-t_0)/(t_1-t_0)}}$

SECTION 1–5

1. 1.27×10^6 cal/m^2 2. 3.05×10^6 cal/m

3. $Q = \dfrac{1}{(h_1/k_1) + (h_2/k_2)} A(T_i - T_0); \quad 0 < x < h_1, \quad T = T_i - \dfrac{Q}{k_1 A} x;$

$h_1 < x < h_1 + h_2, \quad T = T_0 + \dfrac{Q}{k_2 A} (h_1 + h_2 - x)$

5. $\dfrac{h_1 + h_2 + \cdots + h_n}{k} = \dfrac{h_1}{k_1} + \dfrac{h_2}{k_2} + \cdots + \dfrac{h_n}{k_n}$

6. $Q = \dfrac{2\pi k(T_i - T_0)}{\ln (r_0/r_i)}, \quad T = T_i + \dfrac{\ln (r/r_i)}{\ln (r_0/r_i)} (T_0 - T_i)$

7. $Q = \dfrac{2\pi(T_i - T_0)}{\dfrac{1}{k_1} \ln \dfrac{r_i + h_1}{r_i} + \dfrac{1}{k_2} \ln \dfrac{r_0}{r_i + h_1}};$

$r_i < r < r_i + h_1, \quad T = T_i - \dfrac{Q}{2\pi k_1} \ln \dfrac{r}{r_i};$

$r_i + h_1 < r < r_0, \quad T = T_0 + \dfrac{Q}{2\pi k_2} \ln \dfrac{r_0}{r}$

8. $Q = \dfrac{2\pi k_i(T_i - T_0)}{\ln \dfrac{[1 + (\alpha r_i/h)]r_0}{[1 + (\alpha r_0/h)]r_i}}, \quad T = T_i + \dfrac{\ln \dfrac{[1 + (\alpha r/h)]r_i}{[1 + (\alpha r_i/h)]r}}{\ln \dfrac{[1 + (\alpha r_i/h)]r_0}{[1 + (\alpha r_0/h)]r_i}} (T_1 - T_0),$

$\alpha = \dfrac{k_0 - k_i}{k_i}$

SECTION 1–6

1. $h = \dfrac{mv_0}{k} - \dfrac{m^2 g}{k^2} \ln \left(1 + \dfrac{kv_0}{mg}\right), \quad T = \dfrac{m}{k} \ln \left(1 + \dfrac{kv_0}{mg}\right)$

3. $k = k_1 + k_2$ 4. $k^{-1} = k_1^{-1} + k_2^{-1}$

5. $m\dddot{x} + (mk/c)\ddot{x} + k\dot{x} = F_0[(k/c) \sin \omega t + \omega \cos \omega t]$

SECTION 1–7

1. $v_1 = v_0 + \dfrac{cr}{r + q} \ln \dfrac{m_0}{m_p} - \dfrac{m_{f0} g}{r}$

2. $v = v_0 \left(1 - \dfrac{rt}{m_0}\right)^{k/r} + \dfrac{cr}{k} \left[1 - \left(1 - \dfrac{rt}{m_0}\right)^{k/r}\right]$

4. $F = wv_0 t + wv_0^2/g$

SECTION 1–9

1. $k = (cr_0/m)^{1/2}, \quad \epsilon = (\omega_0/k)^{1/2}r_0 - 1$

2. $T = 2\pi\sqrt{\dfrac{mr_0}{-F(r_0)}}, \quad T_s = 2\pi\sqrt{\dfrac{R}{g}}\left(1 + \dfrac{H}{R}\right)^3$

3. $\dfrac{d^2\rho}{dt^2} + \left(\dfrac{3k^2}{r_0^4} - \dfrac{F_r'(r_0)}{m}\right)\rho = 0, \quad F_r(r_0) = -\dfrac{mk^2}{r_0^3}$

4. $\eta'' + \left(3 - \dfrac{r_0^4 F_r'(r_0)}{k^2 m}\right)\eta = 0$

SECTION 1–10

For the circuits of Fig. 1–15:

(a) $\dfrac{de}{dt} = R\dfrac{d}{dt}(i_1 - i_2) + \dfrac{1}{C}(i_1 - i_2), \quad e = L\dfrac{di_2}{dt}$

(b) $\dfrac{de}{dt} = R\dfrac{d}{dt}(i_1 - i_2) + \dfrac{1}{C}(i_1 - i_2), \quad e = L\dfrac{di_2}{dt} + R_2 i_2$

(c) $\dfrac{de}{dt} = R_b\dfrac{d}{dt}(i_1 - i_2) + \dfrac{1}{C_b}(i_1 - i_2) + L_b\dfrac{d^2}{dt^2}(i_1 - i_2) + \dfrac{1}{C_a}i_1$

$\dfrac{de}{dt} = R_a\dfrac{di_2}{dt} + L_a\dfrac{d^2 i_2}{dt^2} + \dfrac{1}{C_a}i_1$

(d) $\dfrac{de_1}{dt} = \dfrac{1}{C}i_1 + R\dfrac{d}{dt}(i_1 - i_2), \quad e_2 = -R(i_1 - i_2) + L\dfrac{di_2}{dt}$

MISCELLANEOUS EXERCISES, CHAPTER 1

2. (a) $y(c - \tfrac{1}{2}x^2) = 1$ (b) $y = ce^{x^3/3}$ (c) $y^2 - x^2 = c$

(d) $y = c_1 e^x + c_2$ (e) $y = \tan^{-1}x$

3. $y = \tfrac{1}{4}(x + c)^2$ 4. $y = 2x$ 5. $y = 3e^{x-2}$

6. $yy'' + y'^2 + 1 = 0$ 7. $x + yy' = 0$ 8. $yy' + 2x = 0$

9. $2n$ seconds

10. $\dfrac{2L^{1/2}(8R_2^2 + 4R_1 R_2 + 3R_1^2)}{15R_2^2 c\sqrt{2g}}$

11. $(25\sqrt{2})\% \approx 35.35\%$

12. $y = ce^x - x$

13. $2y^2 = x$

14. $y = \pm 1$

15. $y = c/x$

16. $(x + 2)y' = y$

17. $(x^2 - y^2 - a^2)\,dy = 2xy\,dx$

CHAPTER 2

SECTION 2–1

1. $y - x\,dy/dx = 0$ 2. $dy/dx = m$

3. $(x^2 - y^2)(dy/dx) - 2xy = 0$ 4. $y - x(dy/dx) + \frac{1}{3}(dy/dx)^3 = 0$

5. $y - x(dy/dx) + \sin^2(dy/dx) = 0$ 6. $dy/dx = \pm\sqrt{1 - y^2}$

7. $dy/dx + (y - 1)\cos x = 0$ 8. $y = 2x(dy/dx) - 4y(dy/dx)^2$

9. Yes

10. $p = n/(n - 1), \qquad A^{n-1} = (p - 1)/p^n$

13. p_1/p_0 and q/p continuous in $a < x < b$. In particular, $p_0(x) \neq 0$ in the interval unless p_0, p_1, and q are all zero for the same value of x in such a way that p_1/p_0 and q/p_0 remain finite.

SECTION 2–2

5. $y' = x/y$

SECTION 2–3

1. $y = \ln|cx|$ 2. $y = \sin(x + c)$ 3. $y = 1 + ce^{-\sin x}$

4. $y = \dfrac{c - x}{1 + cx}$ 5. $y = c(1 + x)^{-3}$ 6. $y = c\cosh x$

7. $y = c\cos x$ 8. $y = c\sec x$ 9. $y + 1 = cxy$

10. $y = x\tan(\ln|cx|)$ 11. $y = x\dfrac{cx^2 - 1}{cx^2 + 1}$ 12. $xy^3 - x^3y = c$

13. $\ln(x^2 + y^2) + 2\tan^{-1}(y/x) = c$

14. $y = ce^{ax}, \qquad y = ce^{bx}$ 15. $2y = x^2 + c, \qquad y = ce^{2x}$

17. (a) $3(y - 1)^2 + 4(y - 1)(x + 1) + 3(x + 1)^2 = c$

(b) $(5x + 2)^2 + 4(5x + 2)(5y + 4) - (5y + 4)^2 = c$

18. $x = ce^{xy^2}$ 19. $y = cxe^{-xy}$

21. $x\sqrt{1 - y^2} + y\sqrt{1 - x^2} = c$ 23. $x_0\exp(-e^{y_0/x_0}) < x$

SECTION 2–4

1. $x\sin y + y^3 = c$ 2. $x^3 + 3xy + 3e^y = c$

3. $4xy - y^4 = c$ 4. $\cos x\cos y = c$

5. $x^3e^y + \cos y - x^2 = c$ 6. $x^3\ln|y| = c$

7. $a = 1, b$ arbitrary; $\quad 4xy + x^4 + by^4 = c$

8. $a = m, b$ arbitrary; $\quad x^2 + 2mxy + by^2 = c$

9. $a = 0; \quad y = e^{c/x}$

10. Not exact for any values of a and b.

11. a arbitrary, $b = 2; \quad \sin(xy^2) + ax + y^3 = c$

SECTION 2–5

2. $(x^{-1} + y^2 - 2y + 2)e^y = c$ 3. $x^3 e^y + x^2 y = c$

4. $y^2 \ln x - x^2 e^y = c$ 5. $\ln(x^2 + y^2) + 2\tan^{-1}(x/y) = c$

6. $\phi(y) = 1/y$; $x \ln y - x^2 + y = c$ 7. $n = -2$; $1 + xy^3 = cxy$

8. $m = 1, n = 2$; $x^3 + 7x^2 y^2 + x^5 y^5 + y^4 = c$

SECTION 2–7

1. $y = ce^x + e^{2x}$ 2. $y = ce^x + xe^x$

3. $y = \begin{cases} cx^a + \dfrac{1}{m - a + 1}x^{m+1}, & a \neq m + 1 \\ cx^{m+1} + x^{m+1}\ln|x|, & a = m + 1 \end{cases}$

4. $y = 1 + ce^{-e^x}$ 5. $y = ce^{-x} + e^{-x}\ln(1 + e^x)$

6. $x = c\csc y - \csc y \ln|\cos y|$ 7. $y(1 + x^2)^2 - 2\ln|x| - x^2 = c$

8. $xy^{-3} - y = c$ 10. $1/y = 1 - x + ce^{-x}$

11. $y = x^2/(c - x)$ 12. $1/y = cx + \ln|x| + 1$

13. $\sin y = ce^{-x} + x - 1$ 14. $\cos y = 1 + ce^{-\cos x}$

SECTION 2–8

1. $y = cx - e^c$, $y = x \ln x - x$

2. $y = cx - \frac{1}{2}(c - 4)^2$, $y = \frac{1}{2}x^2 + 4x$

3. $y = cx + c^2$, $y = -x^2/4$

4. $y = cx \pm (c/\sqrt{1 + c^2})$, $x^{2/3} + y^{2/3} = 1$

SECTION 2–9

1. $y = c_0\left[1 - x + \dfrac{1}{2!}x^2 - \dfrac{1}{3!}x^3 + \cdots\right]$

$\qquad + 2\left[\dfrac{1}{3!}x^3 - \dfrac{1}{4!}x^4 + \dfrac{1}{5!}x^5 - \cdots\right]$

$\qquad = ce^{-x} + 2 - 2x + x^2$

2. $y = \left[x + \dfrac{x^5}{5} + \dfrac{x^9}{5 \cdot 9} + \dfrac{x^{13}}{5 \cdot 9 \cdot 13} + \cdots\right]$

$\qquad + c\left[1 + \dfrac{x^4}{4} + \dfrac{x^8}{4 \cdot 8} + \cdots\right]$

$\qquad = \left[x + \dfrac{x^5}{5} + \dfrac{x^9}{5 \cdot 9} + \dfrac{x^{13}}{5 \cdot 9 \cdot 13} + \cdots\right] + ce^{x^4/4}$

3. $y = c[1 + 4x + 8x^2 + 12x^3 + \cdots]$

4. $y = c_0(1 + 3x + 3x^2 + x^3) = c_0(1 + x)^3$

5. $y = -\frac{1}{3} + c_0(1 + x)^3$

6. $y = -\frac{2}{3} + x + c_0(1 + x)^3$

7. $\alpha = -\sqrt[3]{3/a}\, b, \quad \beta = -\sqrt[3]{3/a}$

$z/b = [t + \frac{1}{4}at^4 + \cdots] + c[1 + \frac{1}{3}at^3 + \frac{1}{2}(\frac{1}{3}a)^2 t^6 + \cdots]$

8. $y = c + (1 - c)(x - 1) + \frac{1}{2}(1 + c)(x - 1)^2 + \cdots$

9. $y = c + (1 - 3c)(x - 1) - \frac{3}{2}(1 - c)(x - 1)^2 + \cdots$

10. $y = c_0 + (1 - 2c_0)(x - 1) + c_0(x - 1)^2 + \cdots$

SECTION 2-10

1. $y = c_0(1 - x) + \frac{1}{2}x^2 - \frac{1}{6}x^3 - \frac{1}{12}x^4 - \cdots$

2. $y = c_0 + x + \frac{1}{2}(1 - c_0)x^2 + 0x^3 + \cdots$

3. $y = c_0(1 + x + \frac{1}{2}x^2 + \frac{1}{2}x^3 + \frac{3}{8}x^4 + \frac{3}{8}x^5 + \cdots) + x + \frac{1}{2}x^2 + \frac{1}{6}x^3$
   $\qquad + \frac{7}{24}x^4 + \frac{19}{120}x^5 + \cdots$

4. $y = c_0 x^{-1}[1 - \frac{1}{2}x^2 - \frac{1}{8}x^4 - \frac{1}{16}x^6 - \cdots]$

5. (a) $y = c_0(x^{-1} - 1) = c_0(1 - x)/x$

   (b) $y = c_0 x \left(1 + \frac{x^2}{2} + \frac{3x^4}{2 \cdot 4} + \frac{3 \cdot 5 x^6}{2 \cdot 4 \cdot 6} + \cdots \right) = c_0 x(1 - x^2)^{-1/2}$

6. $y_P = 1 - \frac{1}{3}x^2 - \frac{2 \cdot 1}{5 \cdot 3}x^4 - \frac{4 \cdot 2 \cdot 1}{7 \cdot 5 \cdot 3}x^6 - \cdots$

9. $A_{00} = 1, \qquad A_{01} = A_{02} = A_{10} = 0, \qquad A_{11} = a_0/(1 - m),$
   $A_{12} = a_1/(2 - m), \qquad A_{20} = A_{21} = 0, \qquad A_{22} = a_0^2/[2(1 - m)^2]$

SECTION 2-11

1. (a) $y = x - \frac{2}{3}x^3 + \cdots$

   (b) $y = \frac{\pi}{4} + \frac{\sqrt{2}}{2}x - \frac{1 + \sqrt{2}}{4}x^2 - \frac{1 + \sqrt{2}}{12}x^3 + \cdots$

   (c) $y = \frac{1}{2}\pi - \frac{1}{2}x^2 + \frac{1}{6}x^3 + \cdots$

2. $y = 2\tan^{-1}(x + c) - x$

3. (a) $y = x - \frac{1}{6}x^3 + \cdots$ \qquad (b) $y = \frac{1}{2}\pi - \frac{1}{3}x^3 + \cdots$

4. (a) $y = \frac{1}{3}x^3 + \frac{1}{63}x^7 + \cdots$ \qquad (b) $y = 1 + x + x^2 + \frac{4}{3}x^3 + \cdots$

5. (a) $y = x + \frac{1}{3}x^3 + \frac{1}{15}x^5 - \frac{1}{70}x^7 + \cdots$

   (b) $y = \frac{1}{2} + x + \frac{1}{4}x^2 + \frac{1}{3}x^3 + \cdots$

6. (a) $y = x + \frac{1}{2}x^2 + \frac{1}{3}x^3 + \frac{1}{4}x^4 + \cdots,$

   (b) $y = 1 + 2x + \frac{5}{2}x^2 + 3x^3 + 4x^4 + \cdots$

7. (a) $y = x + \frac{2}{3}x^3 + \frac{4}{15}x^5 + \cdots,$

   (b) $y = 1 + 2x + 2x^2 + 3x^3 + \frac{7}{2}x^4 + \frac{23}{5}x^5 + \cdots$

SECTION 2–12

1. $y = \frac{1}{2}x^2 + \frac{1}{20}x^5 + \cdots$

2. $y = x + \frac{1}{2}x^2 - \frac{1}{8}x^4 - \frac{1}{10}x^5 + \cdots$

3. $y = x - \frac{1}{6}x^3 - \frac{1}{4}x^4 - \frac{7}{120}x^5 + \cdots$

4. (a) $y = x + \frac{1}{3}x^3 + \frac{1}{6}x^5 + \frac{2}{21}x^7 + \cdots$

   (b) $y = 1 + x + \frac{1}{2}x^2 + \frac{1}{2}x^3 + \frac{5}{12}x^4 + \cdots$

5. $y = 2x + \frac{1}{2}x^2 - \frac{2}{3}x^3 - \frac{1}{4}x^4 + \frac{3}{8}x^5 + \cdots$

6. $y = x + x^2 + \frac{1}{3}x^3 + \frac{1}{24}x^4 + \cdots$

7. $\cos(x^2 + y) = \cos 2 - (2\sin 2)(x - 1) - (\sin 2)(y - 1)$
$$- (\sin 2 + 2\cos 2)(x - 1)^2 - (2\cos 2)(x - 1)(y - 1)$$
$$- (\tfrac{1}{2}\cos 2)(y - 1)^2 + \cdots$$

8. $y = 1 + (\cos 2)(x - 1) - \frac{1}{2}(\sin 2)(2 + \cos 2)(x - 1)^2$
$$- \tfrac{1}{6}\{(2 + \cos 2)^2 \cos 2 + [2 - (2 + \cos 2)\sin 2]\sin 2\}(x - 1)^3 + \cdots$$

9. $y = \pi/2 + 2(x - 1) + \frac{1}{2}(x - 1)^2 - \frac{2}{3}(x - 1)^3 - \frac{1}{4}(x - 1)^4$
$$+ \frac{3}{8}(x - 1)^5 + \cdots$$

10. (a) $d\eta/d\xi = 5 + \xi + 4\eta + \eta^2$ (b) $d\eta/d\xi = 3 + \xi + 2\eta + \eta^2$

11. (a) $d\eta/d\xi = 1 - (\xi + 1)\sin \eta$ (b) $d\eta/d\xi = 1 - (\xi - 1)\cos \eta$

12. $y = \pi - (x + 1) + (x + 1)^2 - \frac{1}{3}(x + 1)^3 + \frac{1}{24}(x + 1)^4 + \cdots$

SECTION 2–13

1. $-\infty < x < \infty$ 2. $-\infty < x < \infty$ 3. $-\infty < x < \infty$

4. $-1 < x < 1$ 5. $-1 < x < 1$ 6. $-\frac{1}{2}y_0^2 < x < \frac{1}{2}y_0^2$

7. $-\sqrt{2/|y_0|} < x < \sqrt{2/|y_0|}$

8. $-\frac{1}{4}y_0^4 < x < \frac{1}{4}y_0^4$ 9. $-e^{-y_0} < x < e^{-y_0}$

SECTION 2–14

1. $\rho_0 = a(1 - e^{-1/2a^2})$; $a \approx 0.63$

2. $\rho_0 = a[1 - \exp(-1/2k^2 a^{1+p/q})]$

   (a) $\rho_0 = a[1 - \exp(-1/2a^{3/2})]$, $\rho_{0,\text{max}} \approx 0.40$

   (b) $\rho_0 = a[1 - \exp(-1/8a^2)]$, $\rho_{0,\text{max}} \approx 0.23$

   (c) $\rho_0 = a[1 - \exp(-1/2a^2)]$, $\rho_{0,\text{max}} \approx 0.45$

SECTION 2–15

1. $s = 1$, $k = p + q$

2. (a) $y = x + \frac{1}{2}x^2 + \frac{1}{12}x^3 + \cdots$ (b) $y = 2x + \frac{2}{5}\sqrt{2}\, x^{5/2} + \frac{1}{20}x^4 + \cdots$

3. $c_0 = 2$, $c_1 = 8/5$, $c_2 = 64/45$

4. $a = 1 - m$, $b = 3 - 2m$, $c_0^2 = (1 - m)^{-1}$, $c_1 = (4 - 3m)^{-1}c_0$

MISCELLANEOUS EXERCISES, CHAPTER 2

1. $y(x^2 + 1) = \frac{1}{6}x^6 + \frac{1}{4}x^4 + c$

2. $x^3 y^2 = c$

3. $y = 1 + ce^{\cos x}$

4. $y = \frac{2}{3}e^{3x} + c$

5. $xy^4 = c(x - 4y)$

6. $xye^{y/(x+y)} = c(x + y)$

7. $\ln|y| + g(x/y) = c$, where $g(v) = \displaystyle\int \frac{e^v + v^2}{ve^v + v^3 + \sin v}\, dv$

8. $y = e^x/2 + ce^{-x}$

9. $e^x \cos y + x^3 = c$

10. $x^2 y^3 + \sin y = c$

11. $x^2 y^3 + x^3 y = c$

12. $y = ce^{2x}, \ y = ce^x$

13. $y = 2/9 - 2x/3 + ce^{-3x}$

14. $y = 3/2 + c/x^2$

15. $y = cx + \frac{1}{4}c^4, \ y = -\frac{3}{4}x^{4/3}$

16. $\ln|x| = \tan^{-1} y + c$

17. $x^2 = c\dfrac{y + 1}{y - 1}$

18. $\dfrac{y - 1}{y + 1}\cos^2 x = c$

19. $y - x - \ln[(x + y + 1)^2 + 1] = c$

20. $x^4 \ln|y| = c$

21. $\sin(x^2 y) + y^3 = c$

22. $y = -2(1 + x) + (\sin x - \cos x)/2 + ce^x$

23. $x^2 + y^2 = cx$

24. $y = (\sin x + c)\cos x$

25. $y \cos x = c - \frac{2}{3}\cos^3 x$

26. $y + xe^{y/x} = c$

27. $x \sin(y^2 + 1) = c$

28. $y = (x^3 + c)(1 + x)$

29. $3xy = x^3 + c$

30. $y^3 + 1 = cx^3 y^3$

31. $3x^2 + y^3 + 3\sin^{-1}(x/y) = c$

32. $\ln|x| + xy = c$

33. $4x^2 y - x^4 = c$

34. $x^3 + y^2 = cx$

35. $\ln(x^2 + y^2 + 1) = 2x + c$

36. $y^4 + 4x^3 y = c$

37. $y(1 - \ln y/x) = c$

38. $y^2 + 3x^2 e^{-y/x} = c$

39. $(x^2 + 3)\ln(y^2 + 2) = c$

40. $y = cxe^x + x^2$

41. $y = ce^x - 5 - 2x$

42. $y = cx - 3 + 2x \ln|x|$

43. $\sqrt{x^2 + y^2} = 3x \ln|x| + c$

44. $y^2(\ln x^2 + c) + x^2 = 0$

45. $y = ce^{x^2/2} - 1, \ y = c + \frac{1}{2}x^2$

46. $y = x^3(c + 3 \ln|x|)$

47. $y \sin x + \ln \cos^2 x = c$

48. $y = 4 + 4x + ce^{4x}(y - 4x)$

49. $\frac{1}{4}x^4 + x^2 y + y^3 x + \frac{1}{5}y^5 = c$

50. $y^2 = \frac{1}{3}(x - \frac{1}{6}) + ce^{-6x}$

51. $y(\ln|x| + c) = x$

52. $yx^3 + x = cy$

53. $y(x^2 + c) = 2x$

54. $y = c(x + 2)^2 - 3x - 3$

55. $(x^3 + y^3)e^y = c$

56. $\sin y + 1 = ce^{-\cos x}$

57. $y^{1/2} = \pm(x - 1)^{1/2} + c$

58. $y = x + c, \ y = 2x + c, \ y = -2x + c$

59. $y = \frac{1}{2}a^{-1}e^{ax} + ce^{-ax}$

60. $y - a \tan^{-1}\dfrac{x + y}{a} = c$

61. $y = 2 \sin ax + 2a + c \exp(a^{-1} \sin ax)$ 62. $y = -\dfrac{1}{a} + \dfrac{x}{1-a} + cx^a$

63. $Q(x) = g'(x)P[g(x)]$

64. (a) $xy' = 3y$ (b) $yy' = x$ (c) $xy' + y = 0$

65. $a = 2, b = 3$; $x^2 y + \sin x + 3xe^y = c$

66. $a = -3, b = 2$; $x^3 y - y^3 x + 2e^{xy} = c$

67. $x^2 + y^2 = cx$ 68. $(x-1)y = cx$

69. (a) $y = \ln x^2 + c$ (b) $3y = x^3 + c$ (c) $y = ce^x$

70. $n = 2$; $x^3 y^2 + x^2 y^5 = c$

71. $m = 2, n = 1$; $x^4 y^3 + x^3 y^2 = c$

72. (a) $x = y \ln |y|$ (b) $x = y \ln \left| \dfrac{y}{2} \right|$ (c) $x = y(\ln |y| + 1)$

73. $y = c\left(1 + x^2 + \dfrac{x^4}{2!} + \dfrac{x^6}{3!} + \cdots\right) = ce^{x^2}$

74. $y = c\left(1 + x^3 + \dfrac{x^6}{2!} + \dfrac{x^9}{3!} + \cdots\right) = ce^{x^3}$

75. $y = c - 1 + (2-c)x + c\dfrac{x^2}{2!} - c\dfrac{x^3}{3!} + \cdots = ce^{-x} + 2x - 1$

76. $y = c(1 - x + x^2) + (\tfrac{1}{3} - c)x^3 + (c - \tfrac{1}{12})x^4 + \cdots$

$$= \left(c + \dfrac{x^3}{3} + \dfrac{x^4}{4}\right)/(1+x)$$

77. $y = c + (1-c)x + (c-2)\dfrac{x^2}{2} + \tfrac{2}{3}x^3 + \cdots$

78. $y = 2 + 4x + 9x^2 + \tfrac{52}{3}x^3 + \tfrac{106}{3}x^4 + \cdots$

79. $y = c_0 + 3(x-1) + \tfrac{1}{2}(1 - c_0)(x-1)^2 + \cdots$

80. $y = c_0 + \tfrac{1}{2}(x-1)^2 - c_0(x-1)^3 + \cdots$

81. $y = c_0 x^{1/2}(1 + 2x + 4x^2 + 8x^3 + \cdots) = c_0 \dfrac{x^{1/2}}{1-2x}$

82. $-\dfrac{|y_0|^3}{3} < x < \dfrac{|y_0|^3}{3}$ (Solution: $y^3 = 3x + y_0^3$)

83. $-\infty < x < \infty$ (Solution: $y = y_0 e^{x^2}$)

CHAPTER 3

SECTION 3–1

1. $xy'' - y' + 6 = 0$ 2. $y'' + 4y = 0$

3. $y'' - 4y = 0$ 4. $y'' - 4y' + 4y = 0$

5. $(1 - \cot x)y'' - 2y' + (1 + \cot x)y = 0$

6. $yy'' + y'^2 = 0$

7. $xy'' + y' = 1$

8. $y'' - y(y')^2 = 0$

9. $x^2 y'' + xy' - y = 0$

10. $xyy'' + x(y')^2 - yy' = 0$

11. $y - y'x + \frac{1}{2}x^2 y'' + (y'')^n = 0$

12. $yy'' + y'^2 = 1$

13. (1) Not compatible.

    (2) $c_1 = 0$, $c_2 = \frac{1}{2}$

    (3) $c_1 = \frac{1}{4}$, $c_2 = -\frac{1}{4}$

    (6) Not compatible

14. (1) $c_1 = -3$, $c_2 = -2$

    (2) $c_1 = \cos 2$, $c_2 = \sin 2$

    (3) $c_1 = \frac{1}{2}e^{-2}$, $c_2 = \frac{1}{2}e^2$

    (6) $c_1 = 1$, $c_2 = 0$

15. (1) $c_1 = -3/a$, $c_2 = -3a$; $a \neq 0$

    (2) $c_1 = 0$, $c_2 = 0$

    (3) $c_1 = 0$, $c_2 = 0$

    (6) $c_1 = 0$, $c_2 = 0$

16. (1) $c_1 = -7$, $c_2 = 1$

    (2) $c_1 = 1$, $c_2 = -\cot 2$

    (3) $c_1 = 1/(1 - e^4)$, $c_2 = -e^4/(1 - e^4)$

    (6) $c_1 = 1$, $c_2 = -1$

17. (1) Solution is possible only if $b = 6$; in this case c_1 is arbitrary and $c_2 = a$.

    (7) Solution is possible only if $b = 1$; in this case $c_1 = 0$ and $c_2 = a$.

18. $m = \dfrac{2n}{n-1}$, $A^{n-1} = \dfrac{\frac{3}{2}m - \frac{1}{2}m^2 - 1}{m^n(m-1)^n}$

SECTION 3–2

1. $y = c_1 \ln|x| + c_2$

2. $y = x + c_1 \ln|x| + c_2$

3. $y = \ln|x| + c_1 x^{-1} + c_2$

4. $y = \ln|x + c_1| + c_2$

5. $y = \ln|e^x + c_1 e^{-x}| + c_2$

6. $y = c_1 e^{kx} + c_2 e^{-kx}$

7. $y = c_1 \cos kx + c_2 \sin kx$

8. $\displaystyle\int \frac{dy}{\sqrt{c_1 + \frac{2}{3}k^2 y^3}} + c_2 = \pm x$

9. $\displaystyle\int \frac{dy}{\sqrt{c_1 - \frac{2}{3}k^2 y^3}} + c_2 = \pm x$

10. $\displaystyle\int \frac{dy}{\sqrt{c_1 + \frac{1}{2}k^2 y^4}} + c_2 = \pm x$

11. $\displaystyle\int \frac{dy}{\sqrt{c_1 - \frac{1}{2}k^2 y^4}} + c_2 = \pm x$

12. $\displaystyle\int \frac{dy}{y - 1 + c_1 e^{-y}} + c_2 = x$

13. $c_1 \int e^{-y^2/2}\, dy + c_2 = x$

14. $y^2 = c_1 x + c_2$

15. $y = c_2 e^{c_1 x}$

16. $y = \tanh x$

17. $f\dfrac{\partial R}{\partial y'} + y'\dfrac{\partial R}{\partial y} + \dfrac{\partial R}{\partial x} = 0$,   identically in x, y, y'

SECTION 3–3

1. $y = c_1 + c_2 \ln|x|$

2. No

3. $A = \frac{3}{4}$; $y = c_1 + c_2 \ln|x| + \frac{3}{4}x^2$

4. $A = \frac{1}{12}$; $y = c_1 x^{-1} + c_2 + \frac{1}{3}x^3 - 7\ln|x|$

5. $y = c_1 e^x + c_2 e^{2x}$

6. $A = 2$, $B = 3$; $y = 2x + 3 + c_1 e^x + c_2 e^{2x}$

9. $v = \exp\left[-\frac{1}{2}\int(Q/P)\,dx\right]$,

   $u'' + [(R/P) - \frac{1}{4}(Q/P)^2 - \frac{1}{2}(Q/P)']u = (S/P)\exp\left[\frac{1}{2}\int(Q/P)\,dx\right]$

10. $W = \text{const}$

12. $z' + hz^2 + [(h'/h) + f]z + (g/h) = 0$

SECTION 3–4

1. $y = c_1 e^x + c_2 e^{2x}$

2. $y = e^{-x/2}[c_1 \cos(\frac{1}{2}\sqrt{7}\,x) + c_2 \sin(\frac{1}{2}\sqrt{7}\,x)]$

3. $y = c_1 e^{2x} + c_2 e^{3x}$ 4. $y = c_1 \cos 2x + c_2 \sin 2x$

5. $y = c_1 e^{2x} + c_2 e^{-2x}$ 6. $y = c_1 e^{-2x} + c_2 e^{-3x}$

7. $y = c_1 e^{-3x} + c_2$

8. $y = (c_1 \cos \sqrt{2}\,x + c_2 \sin \sqrt{2}\,x)e^{-x}$

SECTION 3–5

1. $y = (c_1 + c_2 x)e^x$ 2. $y = (c_1 + c_2 x)e^{-5x/2}$

3. $y = (c_1 + c_2 x)e^{-x}$ 4. $y = (c_1 + c_2 x)e^{\sqrt{3}x}$

SECTION 3–6

4. $y = c_1 e^{ix} + c_2 e^{-x}$ 5. $y = (c_1 + c_2 x)e^{ix}$

6. $y = c_1 e^{(1-i)x/\sqrt{2}} + c_2 e^{(-1+i)x/\sqrt{2}}$

7. $y = \cos \frac{1}{2}\sqrt{2}\,x\,[c_1 e^{\sqrt{2}x/2} + c_2 e^{-\sqrt{2}x/2}]$,

   $z = \sin \frac{1}{2}\sqrt{2}\,x\,[c_1 e^{\sqrt{2}x/2} - c_2 e^{-\sqrt{2}x/2}]$

8. $y_1'' + 2a_1 y_1' - 2a_2 y_2' + b_1 y_1 - b_2 y_2 = 0$,

   $y_2'' + 2a_2 y_1' + 2a_1 y_2' + b_2 y_1 + b_1 y_2 = 0$

9. $z = -x\,\dfrac{\sinh x + c \cosh x}{\cosh x + c \sinh x}$

12. $y = c_1 \cosh(\lambda x^n) + c_2 \sinh(\lambda x^n)$

13. $y = c_1 \cosh(\lambda e^{kx}) + c_2 \sinh(\lambda e^{kx})$

14. $y = c_1 \cos(\lambda e^{kx}) + c_2 \sin(\lambda e^{kx})$

15. $y = c_1 \cosh(\lambda e^{kx^n}) + c_2 \sinh(\lambda e^{kx^n})$

SECTION 3–7

1. $y = x^{-1/2}[c_1 \cos(\frac{1}{2}\sqrt{11}\ln x) + c_2 \sin(\frac{1}{2}\sqrt{11}\ln x)]$

2. $y = \begin{cases} c_1 + c_2 \ln x, & n = 0 \\ c_1 x^n + c_2 x^{-n}, & n \text{ real}, n \neq 0 \\ c_1 x^\mu\,[\cos(\nu \ln x) + i \sin(\nu \ln x)] \\ \qquad\qquad + c_2 x^{-\mu}\,[\cos(\nu \ln x) - i \sin(\nu \ln x)], \\ \qquad n \text{ complex}, n = \mu + i\nu \neq 0 \end{cases}$

3. $y = c_1 x^{1/2} + c_2 x^{-1}$

4. $y = x^{1/2}[c_1 \cos (\frac{1}{2}\sqrt{3} \ln x) + c_2 \sin (\frac{1}{2}\sqrt{3} \ln x)]$

5. $\gamma = -2, \delta = 2$ 6. $\gamma = 4, \delta = 2$ 7. $\gamma = 1, \delta = -\frac{1}{4}$

8. $\gamma = 1, \delta = -4$ 9. $\gamma = -1, \delta = 1$ 10. $\gamma = 3, \delta = 1$

11. $\gamma = 1, \delta = 4$ 12. $\gamma = 3, \delta = 2$

13. $p = 1 \pm \sqrt{(\gamma - 1)^2 - 4\delta}, \quad q = \frac{1}{2}[\gamma - 1 \mp \sqrt{(\gamma - 1)^2 - 4\delta}]$

14. $y = \dfrac{x^{m+2}}{(m + 2)^2 - n^2} + c_1 x^n + c_2 x^{-n}$

15. $z'' = z' + f(z', z)$

SECTION 3–8

1. $y = c_1 e^{3x} + c_2 e^{-x} - \frac{2}{3}e^{2x} - \frac{3}{5}\sin x + \frac{3}{10}\cos x$

2. $y = c_1 e^{\frac{1}{2}(-5+\sqrt{17})x} + c_2 e^{\frac{1}{2}(-5-\sqrt{17})x} + e^{\sqrt{2}x}/(5 + 2\sqrt{2})$
   $\qquad - \frac{1}{76}\sqrt{3} \cos (\sqrt{3} x) + \frac{15}{76} \sin (\sqrt{3} x)$

3. $y = (c_1 + c_2 x)e^{-x} + \frac{3}{4}e^x$

4. $y = (c_1 + c_2 x)e^{-x} + 2x^2 e^{-x}$

5. $y = (c_1 + c_2 x)e^x - \frac{2}{25} \cos 2x - \frac{11}{25} \sin 2x + \frac{1}{2}e^{-x}$

6. $y = c_1 \cos 2x + c_2 \sin 2x + \frac{1}{2}x \sin 2x + \frac{1}{3} \sin x + \frac{2}{5}e^{-x}$

7. $y = e^{-x/2}[c_1 \cos (\frac{1}{2}\sqrt{3} x) + c_2 \sin (\frac{1}{2}\sqrt{3} x)] + x^3 - x^2 - 4x + 6$

8. $y = c_1 + c_2 e^{-x} + \frac{1}{4}x^4 - \frac{1}{3}x^3 + x^2 - 2x$

9. $y = (c_1 - \frac{1}{2}x) \cos x + c_2 \sin x$

10. $y = (c_1 - x^2) \cos x + (c_2 + x) \sin x$

SECTION 3–9

1. $y = c_1 x + c_2 x e^{1/x}$

2. $y = c_1 x^2 + c_2 x^2 \displaystyle\int \frac{e^{-x^2/4}}{x^3} \, dx$

3. $y = c_1 x + c_2(\sqrt{1 - x^2} + x \sin^{-1} x)$

4. $y = c_1 e^x + c_2 e^x \displaystyle\int \sqrt{\frac{1 - x}{1 + x}} \, e^{-2x} \, dx$

5. $y = \left(c_1 + c_2 \displaystyle\int \frac{x^2 e^x}{(x + 2)^2} \, dx\right) (x + 2)$

6. $y = c_1 x + c_2 x \int [x^{-2} e^{-\int xf(x)dx}] \, dx$

7. $y = c_1 e^x + c_2 e^x \int [e^{-x-\int f(x)dx}] \, dx$

8. $y = c_1 e^{4x} + c_2 e^{4x} \int e^{-[x^3/3 + 4x]} \, dx$

9. $y = c_1 x^n + c_2 x^n \int [x^{-(n+1)} e^{-\int f(x)dx}] \, dx$

SECTION 3–10

1. $y = c_1 \cos 2x + c_2 \sin 2x + \cos x \cos 2x$
   $\qquad + \sin 2x \left[\sin x - \frac{1}{2} \ln |\tan (\frac{1}{4}\pi + \frac{1}{2}x)|\right]$

2. $y = c_1 \cos \sqrt{3}\, x + c_2 \sin \sqrt{3}\, x$
   $\qquad - \dfrac{\cos \sqrt{3}\, x}{\sqrt{3}} \displaystyle\int \dfrac{\sin \sqrt{3}\, x}{\cos x}\, dx + \dfrac{\sin \sqrt{3}\, x}{\sqrt{3}} \displaystyle\int \dfrac{\cos \sqrt{3}\, x}{\cos x}\, dx$

3. $y = [c_1 - \frac{1}{2}x + \frac{1}{2} \ln (e^x + 1)]e^x + [c_2 - \frac{1}{2} \ln (e^x + 1)]e^{-x} - \frac{1}{2}$

4. $y = (c_1 + c_2 x)e^x + x^2 e^x (\frac{1}{2} \ln |x| - \frac{3}{4})$

5. $y = c_1 x^{1/2} + c_2 x^{-1} - \frac{1}{3}x^{-1} \ln |x|$

6. $y = c_1 \cos kx + c_2 \sin kx$
   $\qquad - \dfrac{\cos kx}{k} \displaystyle\int \tan x \sin kx\, dx + \dfrac{\sin kx}{k} \displaystyle\int \tan x \cos kx\, dx$

7. $y = c_1 x + c_2 x^2 + \frac{1}{2}x^3$

8. $y = c_1 x + c_2 x^2 - x \ln |x|$

9. $y_p = x \iint f\, dx - (1 - x^2)^{1/2} \int f x (1 - x^2)^{-1/2}\, dx$

10. $W = c/x$
    $\qquad\qquad\qquad\qquad$ 11. $W = c/(1 - x^2)$

SECTION 3–12

1. $y = c_0 \left[1 + \dfrac{x^3}{6} - \dfrac{x^4}{24} + \dfrac{x^5}{120} + \cdots\right]$
   $\qquad + c_1 \left[x - \dfrac{x^2}{2} + \dfrac{x^3}{6} + \dfrac{x^4}{24} - \dfrac{x^5}{30} + \cdots\right]$

2. $y = c_0[1 - 3x^2] + c_1[x - \frac{2}{3}x^3 - \frac{1}{5}x^5 - \cdots]$

3. $y = c_0 \left[1 + \dfrac{x^2}{2} - \dfrac{x^4}{24} + \cdots\right] + c_1 \left[x + \dfrac{x^3}{6} - \dfrac{x^5}{24} + \cdots\right]$

4. $c_{2n} = \dfrac{c_0}{2 \cdot 4 \cdot 6 \cdots (2n)} = \dfrac{c_0}{n! 2^n}$,
   $\quad c_{2n+1} = \dfrac{c_1}{1 \cdot 3 \cdot 5 \cdots (2n + 1)} = \dfrac{n! 2^n c_1}{(2n + 1)!}$

5. $y = c_0 \left[1 + \dfrac{x^4}{12} - \dfrac{x^5}{60} - \dfrac{x^6}{120} + \cdots\right]$
   $\qquad + c_1 \left[x - \dfrac{x^2}{2} + \dfrac{x^4}{12} + \dfrac{x^5}{30} - \dfrac{x^6}{30} + \cdots\right]$

6. $y = c_0 \left[1 - \dfrac{x^4}{12} + \cdots\right] + c_1 \left[x - \dfrac{x^5}{20} + \cdots\right]$

7. $z = \dfrac{c(\frac{1}{2}x^2 + \frac{1}{30}x^5 + \frac{1}{1440}x^8 + \cdots) + (1 + \frac{1}{3}x^3 + \frac{1}{72}x^6 + \cdots)}{c(1 + \frac{1}{6}x^3 + \frac{1}{180}x^6 + \cdots) + (x + \frac{1}{12}x^4 + \frac{1}{504}x^7 + \cdots)}$

8. $y = c_0\left[1 + \dfrac{1}{3!}kx^3 + \dfrac{1\cdot 4}{6!}k^2x^6 + \dfrac{1\cdot 4\cdot 7}{9!}k^3x^9 + \cdots\right]$

$\quad + c_1\left[x + \dfrac{2}{4!}kx^4 + \dfrac{2\cdot 5}{7!}k^2x^7 + \dfrac{2\cdot 5\cdot 8}{10!}k^3x^{10} + \cdots\right]$

SECTION 3–13

1. (a) $r = -1$ (c) $r = -2, +2$ (d) $r = 1, 2$

2. (a) Ordinary point (b) Ordinary point
   (c) Regular singular point (d) Irregular singular point

3. $r^2 + 3 = 0, r = i\sqrt{3}, -i\sqrt{3}$

4. (a) $r(r - 2) = 0$ (b) $r^2 = 0$

5. Regular: $x = 0, 1$; irregular: $x = -1$

6. Regular: $x = 1$; irregular: $x = 0$

7. Irregular: $x = 0$ 8. Regular: $x = 0$

9. $y = C_1x[1 + \frac{1}{5}x + \frac{1}{70}x^2 + \cdots] + C_2x^{-1/2}[1 - x - \frac{1}{2}x^2 + \cdots]$

10. $y = C_1x^{1/2}\left[1 - \dfrac{x^2}{3!} + \dfrac{x^4}{5!} - \cdots\right] + C_2x^{-1/2}\left[1 - \dfrac{x^2}{2!} + \dfrac{x^4}{4!} - \cdots\right]$

$\quad = x^{-1/2}[C_1 \sin x + C_2 \cos x]$

11. $y = C_1\left[1 - \dfrac{x^2}{6} + \dfrac{x^4}{120} + \cdots\right] + C_2x^{-1}\left[1 - \dfrac{x^2}{2} + \dfrac{x^4}{24} + \cdots\right]$

12. $y = C_1\left[1 + \dfrac{a}{c}x + \dfrac{a}{c}\dfrac{a+1}{c+1}\dfrac{x^2}{2} + \cdots\right]$

$\quad + C_2x^{1-c}\left[1 + \dfrac{1+a-c}{2-c}x + \dfrac{1+a-c}{2-c}\dfrac{2+a-c}{3-c}\dfrac{x^2}{2} + \cdots\right]$

$\quad = C_1M(a, c; x) + C_2x^{1-c}M(1 + a - c, 2 - c; x)$

13. $y = c_0\left(1 - \dfrac{x^2}{2^2} + \dfrac{x^4}{2^2\cdot 4^2} - \dfrac{x^6}{2^2\cdot 4^2\cdot 6^2} + \cdots\right)$

15. $c_1 = \frac{1}{2}p(p + 1)c_0, \qquad c_2 = \frac{1}{16}c_0(p - 1)p(p + 1)(p + 2)$

SECTION 3–14

1. No.

3. $y = C_1x^{3/4}[1 - \frac{1}{5}x^2 + \frac{1}{90}x^4 + \cdots] + C_2x^{1/4}[1 - \frac{1}{3}x^2 + \frac{1}{42}x^4 + \cdots]$

4. $y = C_1x^{-1/2}[1 + \beta x + \cdots] + C_2x^{3/2}[1 - \frac{1}{3}\beta x + \cdots]$

5. $u_2 = -1 + x \ln |x| + x \int_0^x \dfrac{e^t - 1 - t}{t^2} \, dt$

$= -1 + x \ln |x| + \dfrac{1}{2!} x^2 + \dfrac{1}{3!} \dfrac{x^3}{2} + \dfrac{1}{4!} \dfrac{x^4}{3} + \cdots + \dfrac{1}{n!} \dfrac{x^n}{n-1} + \cdots$

6. $k = 2, 3, \ldots ; \quad k = 1$

SECTION 3–15

2. $I_0(x) = 1 + (\tfrac{1}{2}x)^2 + \dfrac{(\tfrac{1}{2}x)^4}{1^2 \cdot 2^2} + \cdots$

4. $J_1(x) = \tfrac{1}{2}x - \dfrac{(\tfrac{1}{2}x)^3}{1^2 \cdot 2} + \dfrac{(\tfrac{1}{2}x)^5}{1^2 \cdot 2^2 \cdot 3} + \cdots$

5. $y = x^{-1/2}[C_1 \cos x + C_2 \sin x], \quad p = \tfrac{1}{2}$

SECTION 3–16

1. $y = c_1 J_0(\lambda x) + c_2 Y_0(\lambda x);$ 2. $c = 2/\pi$

(a) $J_0(\lambda) = 0$

(b) $\begin{vmatrix} J_0(\tfrac{1}{2}\lambda) & Y_0(\tfrac{1}{2}\lambda) \\ J_0(\lambda) & Y_0(\lambda) \end{vmatrix} = 0$

3. $y = \tfrac{1}{2}\pi a \{y_a[Y_0'(a)J_0(x) - J_0'(a)Y_0(x)] - y_a'[Y_0(a)J_0(x) - J_0(a)Y_0(x)]\}$

MISCELLANEOUS EXERCISES, CHAPTER 3

1. (a) $y'' - 3y' + 2y = 0$ (b) $y'' + y = 0$
   (c) $y'' + y = 0$ (d) $y'' + y = 3$
   (e) $y'' - 5y' + 6y = 12x + 14$ (f) $y'' - 4y' + 4y = 2 - 8x + 4x^2$

2. (a) $yy'' + 2(y')^2 = 0$ (b) $xy'' - y' = 8x^3$
   (c) $xy'' - (2x + 1)y' + (x + 1)y = 0$
   (d) $x^2(1 + x^2)y'' + (1 + 2x - x^4)y' - (1 + x)^2 y = 0$

3. (a) $y = xy' - \tfrac{1}{2}x^2 y''$ (b) $y^2 = 2xyy' - x^2 yy'' - x^2(y')^2$

4. $y'' (\tan x - 2 \tan 2x) + 3y' + 2(2 \tan x - \tan 2x)y = 0$

5. $y^2 = (x + c_1)^2 + c_2$

6. $y = (c_1 - x) \cos x + (c_2 + \ln | \sin x|) \sin x$

7. $y = c_1 x + c_1^2 \ln |x - c_1| + c_2$

8. $y = (c_1 + c_2 x)e^x (\cos x + i \sin x)$

9. $y = c_1 x + c_2 x^2$ 10. $y = (c_1 + c_2 \ln |x|)/x$

11. $y = c_1 x + c_2 x^3$

12. $y = c_1 x + c_2 x^2 + \dfrac{x^n}{(n - 1)(n - 2)}$

13. $\begin{cases} y = (c_1 + c_2 \ln |x|)x \text{ for } n = 1 \\ y = c_1 x + c_2 x^n \text{ for } n \neq 1 \end{cases}$

14. $y = c_1 \cos (\ln x^2) + c_2 \sin (\ln x^2)$

15. $y = c_1 \cos x + c_2 \sin x + e^{-x} + 3x$

16. $y = (c_1 + c_2 x + x^2)e^x + x + 2$

17. $y = c_1 e^{4x} + (c_2 - \frac{11}{9}x - \frac{1}{3}x^2)e^x + \frac{1}{4}x^2 + \frac{5}{8}x + \frac{21}{32}$

18. $y = c_1 \sin x + c_2 \cos x + \frac{1}{2}e^x - \frac{2}{3} \sin 2x$

19. $y = c_1 \sin x + (c_2 - x) \cos x + \frac{1}{5}e^{2x}$

20. $y = c_1 x^{1/\sqrt{2}} + c_2 x^{-1/\sqrt{2}} - 1$

21. $y = \sin^{-1} (c_1 x) + c_2$ 22. $y = c_1 \sin^{-1} x + c_2$

23. $y = c_1 \cos x + (c_2 - \ln |\csc x - \cot x|) \sin x$

24. $y = (c_1 - \frac{1}{2}x) \cos 2x + (c_2 + \frac{1}{4} \ln | \sin 2x|) \sin 2x$

25. $y = c_1 e^{-x} + (c_2 - \sin e^x)e^{-2x}$

26. $y = (c_1 + \int e^{-x} \ln x \cdot dx)e^x + (c_2 - \int e^{2x} \ln x \cdot dx)e^{-2x}$

27. $y = \frac{1}{2} \ln x - \frac{1}{2} + x^{-1}[c_1 \cos (\ln x) + c_2 \sin (\ln x)]$

28. $y = c_1 + (c_2 + 2x)e^x - x^3 - 3x^2 - 11x - \frac{1}{2}e^{-x}$

29. $y = c_1 x + (c_2 + 3 \ln |x|)x^2$

30. $y = \frac{1}{4} \ln |x^2 + c_1| + c_2$ 31. $y = \frac{1}{2}x^2 + c_1 \ln |x| + c_2$

32. $y = \frac{1}{9}x^3 + 3x + c_1 \ln |x| + c_2$ 33. $y = \left(c_1 + c_2 \int \frac{e^{x^2/2}}{x^2} \, dx \right)x$

34. $y = \dfrac{c_1 c_2 e^{c_1 x}}{1 - c_2 e^{c_1 x}}, \ y = c$ 35. $y = \tan^{-1} x$

36. $y = \dfrac{1}{2} \ln \left| \dfrac{1 - x}{1 + x} \right|$ 37. $y = \frac{1}{3}(x^3 - 1)$

38. $y = e^x(1 - x)$

39. (a) $y = \frac{1}{16}x^4 + c_1 \ln |x| + c_2$ (b) $y = \int \dfrac{e^x}{x^2} \, dx + \dfrac{c_1}{x} + c_2$

(c) $y = c_1 x^2 + c_2$

40. $\dfrac{d^2 z}{ds^2} + \left(2ag' - \dfrac{g''}{g'} \right) \dfrac{dz}{ds} + b(g')^2 z = 0$

41. $p = 2\dfrac{h'}{h} - \dfrac{g''}{g'}, \ q = -\dfrac{h''}{h} - 2\left(\dfrac{h'}{h} \right)^2 + \dfrac{h'}{h}\dfrac{g''}{g'} - (g')^2$

42. $z = c_1 s^m \cosh (\lambda s^n) + c_2 s^m \sinh (\lambda s^n)$

43. $\alpha = -15; \ a = 2, \ b = -5, \ c = 2, \ d = 7$

44. $a = \frac{1}{2}, \ b = 1, \ c = 1; \ y = \left[c_1 + c_2 \int \dfrac{x^2 e^x \, dx}{(1 + x + \frac{1}{2}x^2)^2} \right](1 + x + \frac{1}{2}x^2)$

47. $y = c_1 x + c_2(x^2 - 1)$ 48. $y = (c_1 e^x + c_2 e^{-x})/x$

49. $y = (c_1 e^x + c_2 e^{-x})/x - x^2$

50. $y = c_0(1 + x) + c_2 \left(\dfrac{x^2}{2!} + \dfrac{x^3}{3!} + \dfrac{x^4}{4!} + \cdots \right) = c_0(1 + x) + c_2(e^x - 1 - x)$

51. $y = c_0 \left(1 + \dfrac{x^2}{2} - \dfrac{x^4}{2 \cdot 4} + \dfrac{1 \cdot 3 x^6}{2 \cdot 4 \cdot 6} - \cdots \right) + c_1 x$

   $= c_0(1 + x^2)^{1/2} + c_1 x$

52. $y = c_0(1 + \frac{1}{2}x^2 + \frac{1}{8}x^4 + \cdots) + c_1(x + \frac{1}{6}x^3 + \cdots)$

53. $y = c_0 \left(1 - \dfrac{x^2}{2} + \dfrac{x^4}{2 \cdot 4} - \dfrac{x^6}{2 \cdot 4 \cdot 6} + \cdots \right)$

   $+ c_1 \left(x - \dfrac{x^3}{3} + \dfrac{x^5}{1 \cdot 3 \cdot 5} - \cdots \right)$

54. $y = c_0 + c_1 x - \frac{1}{2} c_1 x^2 + \frac{1}{6}(c_1 - c_0)x^3 + \frac{1}{24}(c_0 - 3c_1)x^4 + \cdots$

55. $y = c_0 + c_1 x + \frac{1}{4} c_0 x^2 - \frac{1}{24} c_0 x^3 + 0 \cdot x^4 + \cdots$

56. $y = c_0 \left(1 - \dfrac{x^3}{3!} + \dfrac{4^2 x^6}{6!} - \dfrac{4^2 7^2 x^9}{9!} + \cdots \right)$

   $+ c_1 \left(x - \dfrac{2^2 x^4}{4!} + \dfrac{2^2 5^2 x^7}{7!} - \cdots \right)$

57. $y = C_1 \left(1 - \dfrac{x}{2!} + \dfrac{x^2}{4!} - \cdots \right) + c_2 x^{1/2} \left(1 - \dfrac{x}{3!} + \dfrac{x^2}{5!} - \cdots \right)$

   $= C_1 \cos \sqrt{x} + c_2 \sin \sqrt{x}$

58. $y = C_1(1 - 2x + \frac{1}{3}x^2 + \cdots) + C_2 x^{4/5}(1 - \frac{2}{9}x + \frac{1}{63}x^2 + \cdots)$

59. $y = C_1(1 + \frac{1}{3}x^2 + \frac{1}{42}x^4 + \cdots) + C_2 x^{1/2}(1 + \frac{1}{3}x + \frac{1}{5}x^2 + \cdots)$

60. $y = C_1 \left(\dfrac{1}{x} - \dfrac{1}{2} \right) + C_2 x^2 \left(1 - \dfrac{2}{1 \cdot 4} x + \dfrac{2 \cdot 3}{1 \cdot 4 \cdot 2 \cdot 5} x^2 + \cdots \right)$

61. $y = C_1(1 + \frac{1}{3}x^2 + \cdots) + C_2 x^{1/2}(1 + \frac{1}{5}x^2 + \cdots)$

62. $y = 1 - \dfrac{1}{2!}(x - 1)^2 + \dfrac{1}{4!}(x - 1)^4 + \cdots = \cos(x - 1)$

63. $y = 1 + 2(x - 1) + (x - 1)^2 + \frac{5}{6}(x - 1)^3 + \frac{1}{2}(x - 1)^4 + \cdots$

64. $y = (x - 2) + \frac{3}{4}(x - 2)^2 + \frac{1}{12}(x - 2)^3 + \cdots$

65. $z'' = (2q + 1)z' - (q^2 + q)z + f(z' - qz, z)$

CHAPTER 4

SECTION 4–1

1. $y^{\mathrm{iv}} - 3y''' + 2y'' = 4$

2. $yy''' + 3y'y'' - yy'' - (y')^2 = 0$

3. $y''' + 3y'y'' + (y')^3 - 6e^{-y} = 0$

4. $(1 - x)y''' + xy'' - y' + 1 = 0$

5. $y''' + 4y' = 0$ 10. a and b arbitrary; $c = b - 1$

SECTION 4–2

1. $y = (c_1 + c_2x + c_3x^2)e^{-x}$
2. $y = c_1e^{-x} + (c_2 \cos \frac{1}{2}\sqrt{3}\,x + c_3 \sin \frac{1}{2}\sqrt{3}\,x)e^{x/2}$
3. $y = c_1e^{x} + (c_2 \cos \frac{1}{2}\sqrt{3}\,x + c_3 \sin \frac{1}{2}\sqrt{3}\,x)e^{-x/2}$
4. $y = c_1e^{kx} + c_2e^{-kx} + c_3 \cos kx + c_4 \sin kx$
5. $y = \sum_{n=1}^{4} e^{kx \cos (2n-1)\pi/8}$
   $\times\ [c_{2n-1} \cos (kx \sin \frac{1}{8}(2n - 1)\pi) + c_{2n} \sin (kx \sin \frac{1}{8}(2n - 1)\pi)]$
6. $y = (c_1 + c_2x)e^{kx} + (c_3 + c_4x)e^{-kx}$
7. $y = c_1e^{\gamma x} + c_2e^{-\gamma x} + c_3 \cos \gamma x + c_4 \sin \gamma x + (c_5 \cos \delta x + c_6 \sin \delta x)e^{\delta x}$
   $+ (c_7 \cos \delta x + c_8 \sin \delta x)e^{-\delta x},$
   where $\gamma = (\sqrt{a^8 + 1} - a^4)^{1/4}$, $\delta = \frac{1}{2}\sqrt{2}\,(\sqrt{a^8 + 1} + a^4)^{1/4}$
8. $y = (c_1 + c_2x + c_3x^2 + c_4x^4)e^{x}$
9. $y = (c_1 + c_2x) \cos ax + (c_3 + c_4x) \sin ax$
10. $y = c_1e^{x} + c_2e^{2x} + c_3e^{3x}$
11. $y = (c_1 + c_2x)e^{2x} + (c_3 + c_4x)e^{-2x} + c_5e^{6x}$
12. $y = c_1e^{-x} + c_2u_2(x) + c_3u_3(x) + (c_4 \cos \frac{1}{2}\sqrt{3}\,x + c_5 \sin \frac{1}{2}\sqrt{3}\,x)e^{x/2}$
   where

$$c_2u_2(x) + c_3u_3(x) = \begin{cases} c_2e^{ax} + c_3e^{-ax} & \text{if} \quad a \neq 0, \pm 1 \\ c_2xe^{-x} + c_3e^{x} & \text{if} \quad a = \pm 1 \\ c_2 + c_3x & \text{if} \quad a = 0 \end{cases}$$

13. $y^{\text{iv}} - 10y''' + 35y'' - 50y' + 24y = 0$
14. $y^{\text{iv}} - y''' - \frac{7}{4}y' + \frac{15}{16}y = 0$
15. $y^{\text{iv}} + 0.68y''' + 0.253y'' + 0.5067y' + 0.1605y = 0$

SECTION 4–3

1. $c_1 = \frac{1}{2}$, $\ c_2 = -\frac{1}{4}$, $\ c_3 = \frac{1}{2}$, $\ c_4 = \frac{1}{4}$
2. The system of linear equations is solvable, since its determinant, $e^2 - 6 + e^{-2}$, is different from zero.
3. $k = n\pi/a, n = \pm 1, \pm 2, \ldots$ 4. (a) 2 (b) e^{-x} (c) -2

SECTION 4–5

1. $y_p = (3 \sin kx + 4 \cos kx)/(1 + k^2)^2$
2. $y_p = \frac{1}{10} \sin 2x + \frac{3}{4}x^2 + \frac{1}{4} + \frac{4}{5}e^{x}$
3. $y_p = x^2 + 4x$ 4. $y_p = -x^2 - 2x + \frac{3}{2}xe^{x}$
5. $y_p = (x/4k^3)(K_1e^{kx} - K_2 \sin kx)$
6. $y_p = \frac{1}{8}K_1k^{-2}x^2e^{kx} + \frac{1}{4}K_2k^{-4} \cos kx$
7. $y_p = \frac{5}{18}xe^{3x} - \frac{1}{3}x - \frac{1}{9}x^2$ 8. $y_p = x^2$

SECTION 4–7

1. $\dfrac{b}{p^2 + b^2}$

2. $\dfrac{p}{p^2 - a^2}$

3. $\dfrac{a}{p^2 - a^2}$

4. $G(p)/p$

5. $\dfrac{1 - e^{-pa}}{p}$

6. $\dfrac{p + a}{(p + a)^2 + b^2}$

7. $\dfrac{b}{(p + a)^2 + b^2}$

8. $3e^{-4x}$

9. $e^x - 1$

10. $a^{-1} \sin ax$

11. $1 - \cos bx$

12. $(\sinh ax - \sin ax)/a$

SECTION 4–8

1. $y = (1 - e^{-ax})/a$

2. $y = e^{-ax}(x + 1)$

3. $y = \cos ax$

4. $y = \begin{cases} \dfrac{1}{\sqrt{b - a^2}} \displaystyle\int_0^x f(x - s)e^{-as} \sin (\sqrt{b - a^2}\, s)\, ds, & \text{if } b - a^2 \neq 0 \\[2ex] \displaystyle\int_0^x f(x - s)se^{-as}\, ds, & \text{if } b - a^2 = 0 \end{cases}$

5. $y = \frac{1}{3}[e^x - e^{-x/2}\,(\cos \frac{1}{2}\sqrt{3}\, x - \sqrt{3} \sin \frac{1}{2}\sqrt{3}\, x)]$

6. $y = \frac{1}{2}y_0''x^2 e^x$

7. $y(x) = \displaystyle\int_0^x g(s)e^{a(x-s)}\, ds$

8. $\dfrac{y_0 p^3 + y_0'p^2 + y_0''p + y_0'''}{p^4 + 4k^4} = \dfrac{A_1(p - k) + A_2}{(p - k)^2 + k^2} + \dfrac{A_3(p + k) + A_4}{(p + k)^2 + k^2}$

with suitable constants A_j gives

$$y = (A_1 \cos kx + k^{-1}A_2 \sin kx)e^{kx} + (A_3 \cos kx + k^{-1}A_4 \sin kx)e^{-kx}$$

SECTION 4–9

1. $y = c_0[1 + (x^4/4!) + \cdots] + c_1[x + (x^5/60) + \cdots]$
   $+ c_2 [x^2 + (x^6/120) + \cdots]$

2. $y = c_0[1 + (x^6/360) + \cdots] + c_1[x + (x^7/840) + \cdots]$
   $+ c_2 [x^2 + (x^8/8 \cdot 7 \cdot 6 \cdot 5) + \cdots] + c_3[x^3 + (x^9/9 \cdot 8 \cdot 7 \cdot 6) + \cdots]$

3. $y = c_0[1 - (x^3/2) - (x^4/8) - (x^5/20) + (x^6/80) + \cdots]$
   $+ c_1[x - (5x^4/24) - (x^5/12) - (x^6/24) + \cdots]$
   $+ c_2[x^2 - (7x^5/60) - (7x^6/120) + \cdots]$

4. (a) $s = k^{1/4}x$; (b) $s = k^{1/6}x$

SECTION 4–10

1. $y = c_1 x^{1/2} + c_2 x^{(5-\sqrt{13})/4} + c_3 x^{(5+\sqrt{13})/4}$

SECTION 4–11

1. $x^{\beta_2}e^{\alpha x}y = c_1\int x^{(\beta_2-\beta_1-1)}e^{2\alpha x}\,dx + c_2$

2. $x^\beta y = c_1\int x^{\beta-1}e^{-\alpha x}\,dx + c_2$

3. Result follows by writing second-order equation as $(pD + q + \lambda_1)$ $(pD + q + \lambda_2)y = 0$ and by observing that the first-order operators commute.

6. $p = (x + c)^2$, $q = -(x + c)$, $r = (x + c)^4$

7. $y = x(c_1e^{1/x} + c_2e^{-1/x})$

8. $x^2\,Dy_1 = (x + \lambda_1)y_1$, $x^2\,Dy_2 = (x + \lambda_2)y_2$

11. $k = 1 \pm \sqrt{1 + 16m^2 - 8m}$

12. $2l = n + m + k$, $4a = 3k + m - n$
    $7k^2 + m^2 + n^2 + 10km + 6kn - 2mn = 12n = 4m = 12k$

13. $m = 1$, $(xD^2 + 2D \pm i)y = 0$

14. $p_1P_1 = pP$, $p_1P_1' + p_1Q_1 + q_1P_1 = 2p'P + qP + pQ$
    $p_1Q_1' + p_1R_1 + q_1Q_1 = p''P + 2q'P + p'Q + qQ + pR$
    $p_1R_1' + q_1R_1 = q''P + q'Q + qR$

MISCELLANEOUS EXERCISES, CHAPTER 4

1. $y''' + y''\tan x - 2\tan x = 0$

2. $y''' - 3y'' + 3y' - y = -2$

3. $y'''\cos y - 3y'y''\sin y - (y')^3\cos y = e^x$

5. $y = c_1 + c_2e^{3x} + c_3\cos x + c_4\sin x$

6. $y = c_1 + c_2x + c_3e^x + c_4e^{-x}$

7. $y = c_1e^x + (c_2\sin\frac{1}{2}\sqrt{3}\,x + c_3\cos\frac{1}{2}\sqrt{3}\,x)e^{-x/2} - x$

8. $y = c_1 + c_2x + c_3\cos x + c_4\sin x$

9. $y = c_1 + c_2x + c_3x^2 + c_4x^4 + c_5e^{-x}$

10. $y = c_1 + c_2x + c_3x^5 + x^6/30$

11. $y = c_1e^x + c_2e^{-x} + c_3\cos x + c_4\sin x + c_5e^{2x}$
    $\quad + (c_6\cos\sqrt{3}\,x + c_7\sin\sqrt{3}\,x)e^{-x}$

12. $y = x + c_1e^{-x} + (c_2 + c_3x)e^{2x}$

13. $y = \pm\frac{1}{15}(2x + c_1)^{5/2} + c_2x + c_3$

14. $y = \pm\frac{1}{105}(2x + c_1)^{7/2} + c_2x^2 + c_3x + c_4$

15. $y = (c_1 + c_2x)e^x + (c_3 + x^2)e^{-x}$

16. $y = (c_1 + x)e^x + (c_2 + c_3x)e^{-x} - x^2 + 2x - 4$

17. $y = x^3 - 3x^2 + c_1x + c_2 + c_3e^{-x}$

18. $y = x^2 + c_1 + c_2\cos x + c_3\sin x$

19. $y = c_1 + c_2 e^x + c_3 e^{5x}$

20. $y = \frac{1}{6}x^3 + c_1 x^2 + c_2 x + c_3 + c_4 x^2 \ln|x|$

21. $y = 2x^2 + c_1 + (c_2 + x)e^x + c_3 e^{-x}$

22. $y = c_1 e^{-x} + (c_2 + c_3 x + x^2)e^{2x}$

23. $y = \frac{1}{15}\cos 2x + c_1 e^x + c_2 e^{-x} + c_3 \cos x + c_4 \sin x$

24. $y = c_1 e^{-2x} + (c_2 \cos\sqrt{7}\,x + c_3 \sin\sqrt{7}\,x + \frac{1}{21})\,e^x$

25. $y = \frac{1}{9}e^{2x} + (c_1 + c_2 x)e^x + (c_3 + c_4 x)e^{-x} + c_5 \cos x + c_6 \sin x$

26. $y = 3x^2 - 12 + (c_1 + c_2 x)\cos x + (c_3 + c_4 x)\sin x$

27. $y = c_1 + c_2 x^{3/2} + c_3 \ln|x|$

29. $m = 1, 2, -2;\quad y = c_1 x + c_2 x^2 + c_3 x^{-2}$

30. $y = -1 + \frac{1}{4}e^x + (\frac{3}{4} + \frac{1}{2}x)e^{-x}$

31. $y = c_0\left(1 + \frac{2!}{5!}x^5 + \cdots\right) + c_1\left(x + \frac{3!}{6!}x^6 + \cdots\right)$

$$+ c_2\left(x^2 + \frac{4!}{7!}x^7 + \cdots\right)$$

32. $y = c_0\left(1 + \frac{3!}{7!}x^7 + \cdots\right) + c_1\left(x + \frac{4!}{8!}x^8 + \cdots\right)$

$$+ c_2\left(x^2 + \frac{5!}{9!}x^9 + \cdots\right) + c_3\left(x^3 + \frac{6!}{10!}x^{10} + \cdots\right)$$

33. $y = \frac{1}{2}x^2 + 2x^3 + \frac{1}{8}x^4 - \frac{1}{240}x^6 - \frac{3}{140}x^7 + \cdots$

34. $y = c_1 e^{(1-\lambda)x^2/2} + c_2 e^{-(1+\lambda)x^2/2}$

CHAPTER 5

SECTION 5–1

1. $y'_1 = y_2,\quad y'_2 = f(x) - by_1 - 2ay_2$

2. $x' = u,\quad y' = v,\quad u' = ax + by,\quad v' = \alpha x + \beta y$

3. $y' = -y/3 + 2z/3,\quad z' = 4y/3 + z/3$

4. $2xy' = (2x - 3)y + z;\quad 2xz' = -15y + (2x + 5)z$

5. $(1 + x + 3y^2)y' + (1 + 2xz + 3z^2)z' = y + z^2$

$\qquad (1 + x + 3xy^2)y' + (x + 2z + 3xz^2)z' = y + y^3 + z + z^3$

6. $y = z' + xy',\quad z = xz' + y'$

7.
$$\begin{vmatrix} u_1 & u_2 \\ v_1 & v_2 \end{vmatrix} y' = \begin{vmatrix} u'_1 & u'_2 \\ v_1 & v_2 \end{vmatrix} y - \begin{vmatrix} u'_1 & u'_2 \\ u_1 & u_2 \end{vmatrix} z$$

$$\begin{vmatrix} u_1 & u_2 \\ v_1 & v_2 \end{vmatrix} z' = \begin{vmatrix} u_1 & u_2 \\ v'_1 & v'_2 \end{vmatrix} z - \begin{vmatrix} v_1 & v_2 \\ v'_1 & v'_2 \end{vmatrix} y$$

8. $y = c_1 + c_2 x,\quad z = c_1 x + c_2$

SECTION 5–2

1. $y = A_1 e^{3x} + A_2 e^{-3x}, \quad z = 2A_1 e^{3x} - A_2 e^{-3x}$

2. $y = (A_1 x + A_2) e^{2x}, \quad z = A_1 e^{2x}$

3. $y = A_1 e^x + A_2 e^{-x}, \quad z = A_1 e^x - A_2 e^{-x}$

4. $y = A_1 e^{3x} + A_2 e^{2x}, \quad z = A_1 e^{3x} + 2A_2 e^{2x}$

5. $y = 2A_1 e^{2x} + 2A_2 e^{-2x}, \quad z = A_1 e^{2x} - A_2 e^{-2x}$

6. $y = 2A_1 e^{-x} + A_2 e^{2x}, \quad z = -A_1 e^{-x} + A_2 e^{2x}$

SECTION 5–3

1. $x = A_1 e^{2t} + (A_2 \cos \sqrt{3}\, t + A_3 \sin \sqrt{3}\, t) e^{-t}$

$\quad y = A_1 e^{2t} + [\frac{1}{2}(A_3\sqrt{3} - A_2) \cos \sqrt{3}\, t - \frac{1}{2}(A_2\sqrt{3} + A_3) \sin \sqrt{3}\, t] e^{-t}$

$\quad z = A_1 e^{2t} - [\frac{1}{2}(A_2\sqrt{3} + A_3) \cos \sqrt{3}\, t - \frac{1}{2}(A_2\sqrt{3} - A_3) \sin \sqrt{3}\, t] e^{-t}$

2. $x = A_1 e^{2t}, y = \frac{3}{4}A_1 e^{2t} + A_2 e^{-2t}, z = -\frac{3}{2}A_1 e^{2t} - \frac{2}{5}A_2 e^{-2t} + A_3 e^{3t}$

3. $x = A_1 + (A_2 + A_3 t) e^t, y = -A_1 + A_3 e^t,$

$\quad z = A_1 + (A_2 + A_3 + A_3 t) e^t$

4. $y_1 \approx A_1 e^{5.5x} + A_2 e^{0.38x} + A_3 e^{-1.88x}$

$\quad y_2 \approx (21/31) A_1 e^{5.5x} + (269/7) A_2 e^{0.38x} - (39/83) A_3 e^{-1.88x}$

$\quad y_3 \approx (32.5/31) A_1 e^{5.5x} - (180.8/7) A_2 e^{0.38x} - (55.3/83) A_3 e^{-1.88x}$

SECTION 5–4

1. $y_1 = \frac{1}{2}(e^x + e^{-x}), \quad y_2 = \frac{1}{2}(e^x - e^{-x})$

2. $y_1 = -\frac{1}{2}e^x + \frac{1}{6}e^{-x} + \frac{1}{3}e^{2x}, \quad y_2 = -\frac{1}{2}e^x - \frac{1}{6}e^{-x} + \frac{2}{3}e^{2x}$

3. $y_1 = -\frac{1}{4}e^x + \frac{1}{4}e^{-x} + \frac{1}{2}xe^x, \quad y_2 = \frac{1}{4}e^x - \frac{1}{4}e^{-x} + \frac{1}{2}xe^x$

4. $y_1 = \frac{1}{3}e^{2t} + \frac{2}{3}(\cos \sqrt{3}\, t) e^{-t}$

$\quad y_2 = \frac{1}{3}e^{2t} - \frac{1}{3}(\cos \sqrt{3}\, t + \sqrt{3} \sin \sqrt{3}\, t) e^{-t}$

$\quad y_3 = \frac{1}{3}e^{2t} - \frac{1}{3}(\cos \sqrt{3}\, t - \sqrt{3} \sin \sqrt{3}\, t) e^{-t}$

5. $y_1 = -e^{3x} + e^{2x}, \quad y_2 = -e^{3x} + 2e^{2x}$

6. $y_1 = \frac{3}{2}e^{2x} - \frac{1}{2}e^{-2x}, \quad y_2 = \frac{3}{4}e^{2x} + \frac{1}{4}e^{-2x}$

SECTION 5–5

1. (a) $y = \frac{1}{3}(e^{3x} - e^{-3x}), \quad z = \frac{1}{3}(2e^{3x} + e^{-3x})$

  (b) $y = e^{3(x-1)}, \quad z = 2e^{3(x-1)}$

2. (a) $y = xe^{2x}, \quad z = e^{2x}$ (b) $y = (2x - 1)e^{2(x-1)}, \quad z = 2e^{2(x-1)}$

3. (a) $y = \frac{1}{2}(e^x - e^{-x})$, $z = \frac{1}{2}(e^x + e^{-x})$

(b) $y = \frac{3}{2}e^{x-1} - \frac{1}{2}e^{-(x-1)}$, $z = \frac{3}{2}e^{x-1} + \frac{1}{2}e^{-(x-1)}$

6. $x = \frac{1}{3}e^{2t} + \frac{2}{3}(\cos\sqrt{3}\,t)e^{-t}$,

$y = \frac{1}{3}e^{2t} - \frac{1}{3}(\cos\sqrt{3}\,t + \sqrt{3}\sin\sqrt{3}\,t)e^{-t}$,

$z = \frac{1}{3}e^{2t} - \frac{1}{3}(\cos\sqrt{3}\,t - \sqrt{3}\sin\sqrt{3}\,t)e^{-t}$

7. $x = e^{2t}$, $y = \frac{3}{4}e^{2t} - \frac{3}{4}e^{-2t}$, $z = -\frac{3}{2}e^{2t} + \frac{3}{10}e^{-2t} + \frac{6}{5}e^{3t}$

8. $x = -1 + (2 - t)e^t$, $y = 1 - e^t$, $z = -1 + (1 - t)e^t$

SECTION 5-6

1. $y_1 = (A_1 - \frac{1}{3}x - \frac{1}{9})e^{3x} + A_2e^{-3x}$, $y_2 = (2A_1 - \frac{2}{3}x + \frac{1}{9})e^{3x} - A_2e^{-3x}$

2. $y_1 = (A_1 + x - \frac{1}{2})e^x + A_2e^{-x} - \frac{1}{2}\cos x$,

$y_2 = (A_1 + x + \frac{1}{2})e^x - A_2e^{-x} + \frac{1}{2}\sin x$

3. $y_1 = (A_1 - \frac{1}{4} + \frac{1}{2}\ln|x|)x + A_2/x$,

$y_2 = (A_1 + \frac{1}{4} + \frac{1}{2}\ln|x|)x - A_2/x$

4. $y_1 = (2A_1 + x + \frac{1}{4})e^{2x} + 2A_2e^{-2x}$

$y_2 = (A_1 + \frac{1}{2}x - \frac{1}{8})e^{2x} - A_2e^{-2x}$

5. $y_1 = y_{1,h} - \frac{1}{4} - \frac{1}{2}x$, $y_2 = y_{2,h} - \frac{3}{4}x$, $y_3 = y_{3,h} + \frac{1}{6} + \frac{1}{2}x$

SECTION 5-7

1. $y = a_0(1 + \frac{1}{2}x^2 + 0\cdot x^3 + \cdots) + b_0(x^3 + \cdots)$

$z = a_0(x + \frac{1}{2}x^2 + \frac{1}{6}x^3 + \cdots) + b_0(1 + 0\cdot x + 0\cdot x^2 + 0\cdot x^3 + \cdots)$

2. $y = a_0(1 + x + \frac{3}{2}x^2 + \frac{4}{3}x^3 + \cdots) + b_0(x + x^2 + x^3 + \cdots)$

$z = a_0(x + x^2 + \frac{5}{6}x^3 + \cdots) + b_0(1 + x + x^2 + \frac{2}{3}x^3 + \cdots)$

3. $y = a_0(1 + x^2 + \frac{1}{3}x^3 + \cdots) + b_0(x + \frac{1}{2}x^3 + \cdots)$

$z = a_0(2x - x^2 + x^3 + \cdots) + b_0(1 - x + \frac{3}{2}x^2 - \frac{1}{2}x^3 + \cdots)$

5. $y = a_0 + a_4x^4$, $z = -2a_0 + 2a_4x^4$ (a_0, a_4 arbitrary)

6. $\begin{vmatrix} p_0 - k & q_0 \\ r_0 & s_0 - k \end{vmatrix} \equiv k^2 - (p_0 + s_0)k + p_0s_0 - r_0q_0 = 0$

7. $k = 2 \pm \sqrt{3}$ 8. $k = 0, 4$ 9. $k = 0, 1$

SECTION 5-8

1. $y = x + \frac{1}{2}x^2 + \frac{3}{2}x^3 + \frac{9}{8}x^4 + \cdots$, $z = 2x + \frac{3}{4}x^2 + \frac{1}{6}x^3 + \frac{3}{8}x^4 + \cdots$

2. $y = 2x + x^2 + \frac{1}{3}x^4 + \frac{1}{5}x^5 + \cdots$, $z = x + \frac{4}{3}x^3 + x^4 + \frac{1}{5}x^5 + \cdots$

3. $y = -x + \frac{2}{3}x^3 + \frac{1}{8}x^4 - \frac{2}{15}x^5 + \cdots$, $z = 2x + \frac{1}{2}x^2 - \frac{2}{3}x^3 - \frac{1}{8}x^4 + \cdots$

4. $y = 2 + 5(x - 1) + \frac{9}{2}(x - 1)^2 + 5(x - 1)^3 + \cdots$,

$z = 4 + 9(x - 1) + 15(x - 1)^2 + \frac{58}{3}(x - 1)^3 + \cdots$

MISCELLANEOUS EXERCISES, CHAPTER 5

1. $2(x^2 - x)yy' + 2(x^2 - x)zz' + y^2 - y^3 = 0$
   $3(x - 1)y^2 y' + 2(x - 1)zz' + 2(y^2 - y^3) = 0$

2. $3y' = 4y - z, \quad 3z' = -2y + 5z$

3. $y' = 2y, \quad z' = 3y + 2z$

6. $y_1 = 2A_1 + A_2 e^{5x}, \quad y_2 = -A_1 + 2A_2 e^{5x}$

7. $x = A_1 e^{2t} + A_2 e^{-t}, \; y = A_1 e^{2t} + A_3 e^{-t}, \; z = A_1 e^{2t} - (A_2 + A_3)e^{-t}$

8. $y_1 = A_1 e^{3x} + A_2 e^{2x}, \; y_2 = A_1 e^{3x} + 2A_2 e^{2x} + e^x$

9. $y_1 = 2A_1 e^{2x} + 2A_2 e^{-2x} - x + \frac{1}{2}, \; y_2 = A_1 e^{2x} - A_2 e^{-2x} + \frac{1}{2}x - \frac{1}{4}$

10. $y = \frac{11}{2}e^{x/3} - \frac{9}{2}e^{-x/3} - 6x, \quad z = -11e^{x/3} + \frac{9}{2}e^{-x/3} + \frac{1}{2}e^x + 9x + 9$

11. $y = bA_1 + A_2 e^{(a+\lambda b)x}, \quad z = -aA_1 + \lambda A_2 e^{(a+\lambda b)x}, \;$ if $\; a + \lambda b \neq 0$
    $y = bA_1 x + bA_2, \quad\quad z = -aA_1 x + A_1 - aA_2, \;$ if $\; a + \lambda b = 0$

12. $y_1 = 3e^{3x} - 2e^{2x}, \quad y_2 = 3e^{3x} - 4e^{2x} + e^x$

13. (a) $y_1 = 0, \quad y_2 = e^x,$ \qquad\qquad (b) $y_1 = e^x, \; y_2 = 2xe^x,$
    (c) $y = e^x, \quad y_2 = (2x + 1)e^x$

14. $\begin{cases} y = e^{\int p\,dx}[c_1 \cos (\int q\,dx) - c_2 \sin (\int q\,dx)] \\ z = e^{\int p\,dx}[c_2 \cos (\int q\,dx) + c_1 \sin (\int q\,dx)] \end{cases}$

15. $k = \frac{1}{2}(3 \pm \sqrt{5}),$ \qquad\qquad 16. $k = -1, 2$

17. $y = a_0 + \frac{1}{2}b_0 x^2 + 0 \cdot x^3 + \cdots, \quad z = b_0 + \frac{1}{3}a_0 x^3 + \cdots$

18. $\begin{cases} y = a_0(1 + x^2 + \frac{1}{3}x^3 + \cdots) + b_0(x + x^2 + \frac{7}{6}x^3 + \cdots) \\ z = a_0(x + x^2 + x^3 + \cdots) + b_0(1 + 2x + \frac{5}{2}x^2 + 2x^3 + \cdots) \end{cases}$

19. $y = 2x + x^2 + \frac{1}{3}x^3 + \frac{1}{3}x^4 + \cdots, \; z = x + x^2 + \frac{4}{3}x^3 + x^4 + \cdots$

20. $y = 2x + \frac{1}{2}x^2 + \frac{1}{3}x^3 + \frac{1}{2}x^4 + \cdots, \; z = x + x^2 + \frac{2}{3}x^3 + \frac{5}{8}x^4 + \cdots$

21. $y = 1 + 4(x - 1) + \frac{5}{2}(x - 1)^2 + \frac{7}{3}(x - 1)^3 + \cdots,$
    $z = 3 + 5(x - 1) + 7(x - 1)^2 + \frac{28}{3}(x - 1)^3 + \cdots$

22. $y = 2 + 2(x - 1) + 2(x - 1)^2 + \frac{4}{3}(x - 1)^3 + \cdots,$
    $z = 1 + 3(x - 1) + 4(x - 1)^2 + \frac{16}{3}(x - 1)^3 + \cdots$

CHAPTER 6

SECTION 6–1

2.

$x =$	0.1	0.2	0.5
$y_1(x) =$	1.0	1.0	1.0
$y_2(x) =$	1.1	1.2	1.5
$y_3(x) =$	1.09	1.16	1.25
$y_4(x) =$	1.09133	1.17067	1.41667
$y_5(x) =$	1.09108	1.16667	1.26042
$y_6(x) =$	1.09114	1.16837	1.42708

3. $k = 1: 0.5$; $k = 2: 0.515625$; $k = 3: 0.516183$;   4. 0.516203

5. (a) $0.1, 0.10033, 0.10033066$

   (b) $0.5, 0.5417, 0.54378, 0.54405$

6. (a) $n \geq \dfrac{2}{\log 1/x}$ (b) $n \geq 2$ (c) $n \geq 7$ (d) $n \geq 44$

SECTION 6–2

1. From Eq. (3′): $\tilde{y}_1 = \pi/4 = 0.785$;
   from Eq. (5): $\tilde{y}_1 = \frac{1}{8}\pi[2 + (\pi/4)^2] = 1.026$

2. From (I): $y_1 = 0.1$, $y_2 = 0.218$, $y_3 = 0.354$, $y_4 = 0.508$, $y_5 = 0.681$;
   from (II): $y_1 = 0.109$, $y_2 = 0.238$, $y_3 = 0.386$, $y_4 = 0.555$, $y_5 = 0.744$;
   exact: $y(0.1) = 0.11$, $y(0.2) = 0.24$, $y(0.3) = 0.39$, $y(0.4) = 0.56$,
   $y(0.5) = 0.75$

3. (a) $y_1 = 0.25$, $y_2 = 0.504$, $y_3 = 0.786$, $y_4 = 1.152$
   (b) $y_1 = 0.252$, $y_2 = 0.520$, $y_3 = 0.848$, $y_4 = 1.355$

4. (a) $y_1 = 0.1$, $y_2 = 0.2$, $y_3 = 0.301$, $y_4 = 0.404$, $y_5 = 0.511$
   (b) $y_1 = 0.1$, $y_2 = 0.201$, $y_3 = 0.303$, $y_4 = 0.408$, $y_5 = 0.518$

SECTION 6–3

1. Set $c_1 = -(x + x_0)/2$ in Eq. (4).

4. $R(x_n, h) = \frac{1}{2} \displaystyle\int_{x_n}^{x_n+h} [(\xi - x_n)^2 - (\xi - x_n)h] y'''(\xi)\, d\xi$

      $= -\frac{1}{12}h^3 y'''(x_n + \theta h)$ for some θ in $0 < \theta < 1$

SECTION 6–4

1. $y_n''' = \left[\dfrac{\partial^2 F}{\partial x^2} + 2 \dfrac{\partial^2 F}{\partial x\, \partial y} F + \dfrac{\partial^2 F}{\partial y^2} F^2 + \dfrac{\partial F}{\partial x}\dfrac{\partial F}{\partial y} + \left(\dfrac{\partial F}{\partial y}\right)^2 F \right]_{x_n}$

2. (a) $1 + H + \frac{1}{2}H^2$ (b) $2 + \frac{5}{2}H + 2H^2 + H^3$

SECTION 6–6

1. $y(\frac{3}{8}) \approx 2.02$

SECTION 6–7

1. By iteration: $x = 1.21$; exact solution: $x = \frac{1}{2}(1 \pm \sqrt{2}) \approx 1.207, -0.207$

2. 0.83

3. $x_n = 2^{1+1/2+1/4+\cdots+1/2^n} = 2^{2-2^{-n}}$; $\lim_{n\to\infty} x_n = 4$

4. $x_n = 1 + \alpha + \alpha^2 + \cdots + \alpha^n$

SECTION 6–8

1. $y_1(x) = x^2/2$, $y_2(x) = x^2/2 + x^5/20$,
   $y_3 = x^2/2 + x^5/20 + x^8/160 + x^{11}/4400$

3. $y_1(x) = -1 + 3x^2$, $y_2(x) = \frac{1}{2} + \frac{3}{2}x^4$

4. $y_1(x) = x$, $y_2(x) = x + (x^4/4)$,
   $y_3(x) = x + (x^4/4) + (x^7/14) + (x^{10}/160)$

5. (a) $y_1(x) = 1 + x + \frac{1}{2}x^2$, $y_2(x) = 1 + x + \frac{3}{2}x^2 + \frac{2}{3}x^3 + \frac{1}{4}x^4 + \frac{1}{20}x^5$
   (b) $y_1(x) = 1 + x + \frac{3}{2}x^2 + \frac{1}{3}x^3$,
   $y_2(x) = 1 + x + \frac{3}{2}x^2 + \frac{4}{3}x^3 + \frac{11}{12}x^4 + \frac{7}{12}x^5 + \frac{1}{6}x^6 + \frac{1}{63}x^7$

6. $y_1(x) = 1 + x + \frac{2}{3}x^3 + \frac{1}{5}x^5$
   $y_2(x) = 1 + x + x^2 + \frac{1}{3}x^3 + \frac{1}{3}x^4 + \frac{4}{15}x^5 + \frac{1}{15}x^6 + \frac{38}{315}x^7 + \frac{4}{135}x^9$
   $\qquad + \frac{1}{275}x^{11}$

SECTION 6–9

2. (a) $M = 1$

MISCELLANEOUS EXERCISES, CHAPTER 6

1. (a) 0.1,   0.105,   0.1049875,   0.1049865
   (b) 0.5,   0.625,   0.6172,   0.614075

3. h, $h + \frac{1}{2}h^2 \cos h$

6. $y_2 = 1.42$

7. $y_1(x) = 1 + 2x + \frac{1}{2}x^2$
   $y_2(x) = 1 + 2x + \frac{1}{2}x^2 + \frac{4}{3}x^3 + \frac{5}{4}x^4 + \frac{2}{5}x^5 + \frac{1}{24}x^6$

8. $y_1(x) = 1$, $y_2(x) = 1 + x$, $y_3(x) = 1 + x + \frac{1}{2}x^2$
   $y_4(x) = 1 + x + \frac{1}{2}x^2 + \frac{1}{6}x^3$

9. $y_1(x) = \sin x = x - \frac{1}{6}x^3 + \frac{1}{120}x^5 + \cdots$
   $y_2(x) = \int_0^x \cos (\sin t) \, dt = x - \frac{1}{6}x^3 + \frac{1}{24}x^5 + \cdots$
   $y = 2 \tan^{-1} (e^x) - \frac{1}{2}\pi$

10. $|x| < 1$

CHAPTER 7

SECTION 7–1

3. $A_n = (1 + \frac{1}{100}p) A_{n-1}$

4. $n(n-1)a_n = a_{n-2}$, $n = 2, 3, \ldots$

5. $a_2 = \frac{1}{2}a_0$; $n(n-1)a_n = a_{n-2} + a_{n-3}$, $n = 3, 4, 5, \ldots$

6. $(n^2 - n)a_n = (n-4)a_{n-2}$, $n = 2, 3, \ldots$

SECTION 7-2

1. $y_n = 2^n y_0$
2. $y_n = (n-1)! y_1$
3. $y_n = \dfrac{1}{(n-1)!} y_1$

4. $y_n = a^n y_0 + b \dfrac{1-a^n}{1-a}$, if $a \neq 1$; $y_n = y_0 + nb$, if $a = 1$

5. $y_1 = ay_0$; $y_n = a^n y_0 + b \sum_{j=1}^{n-1} ja^{n-j-1}$, $n = 2, 3, \ldots$

6. $y_n = y^{1/2^n}$

7. $y_{n+1} = ey_n + n(1-e) + 1$

8. $(y_{n+1} - y_n)^2 + n(y_{n+1} - y_n) - y_n = 0$

9. $y_n = \dfrac{1-n}{y_{n+1} - 2y_n} 2^n + \dfrac{n}{1-n}(y_{n+1} - 2y_n)$

11. $C_{n+1} = C_n + \dfrac{b_n}{u_{n+1}}$; $C_0 = \dfrac{y_0}{u_0}$;

$y_n = u_n \left[\dfrac{y_0}{u_0} + \sum_{j=0}^{n-1} \dfrac{b_j}{u_{j+1}} \right]$, $n = 1, 2, \ldots$

12. $A = -\frac{1}{4}$, $B = 0$, $C = \frac{1}{16}$

SECTION 7-3

1. $y_n = c_1 2^n + c_2 2^{-n}$
2. $y_n = c_1 2^n + c_2 (-1)^n$

3. $y_n = c_1 \cos \frac{1}{3}n\pi + c_2 \sin \frac{1}{3}n\pi$

4. $y_n = 2^{n/2}(c_1 \cos \frac{1}{4}n\pi + c_2 \sin \frac{1}{4}n\pi)$

5. $y_n = \dfrac{5 - \sqrt{5}}{10}\left(\dfrac{1 + \sqrt{5}}{2}\right)^n + \dfrac{5 + \sqrt{5}}{10}\left(\dfrac{1 - \sqrt{5}}{2}\right)^n$

7. (a) $y_{n+2} - 5y_{n+1} + 6y_n = 0$
   (b) $y_{n+2} - 4y_{n+1} + 4y_n = 0$
   (c) $y_{n+2} - 2\cos\alpha \, y_{n+1} + y_n = 0$

8. (a) $n(n+1)y_{n+2} - 2n(n+2)y_{n+1} + (n+1)(n+2)y_n = 0$

   (b) $\begin{vmatrix} y_n & f(n) & g(n) \\ y_{n+1} & f(n+1) & g(n+1) \\ y_{n+2} & f(n+2) & g(n+2) \end{vmatrix} = 0$

SECTION 7-4

2. $y_n = c_1 + c_2 \cos \frac{1}{2}n\pi + c_3 \sin \frac{1}{2}n\pi$

3. $y_n = c_1 2^n + c_2 3^n + c_3 (-2)^n$

4. $y_{n+3} + 3y_{n+2} + 3y_{n+1} + y_n = 0$

5. $y_n = (A_1 \cos \frac{1}{2}n\pi + A_2 \sin \frac{1}{2}n\pi)7^{n/2}$,

$z_n = \frac{1}{4}[(A_1 - A_2\sqrt{7}) \cos \frac{1}{2}n\pi + (A_1\sqrt{7} + A_2) \sin \frac{1}{2}n\pi]7^{n/2}$

6. $y_n = A_1$, $z_n = -3A_1 + B_2 2^n$

7. $y_n = A_1 5^{n/2} + A_2(-1)^n 5^{n/2}$,

$z_n = \frac{1}{2}(\sqrt{5} - 1)A_1 5^{n/2} - \frac{1}{2}(\sqrt{5} + 1)A_2(-1)^n 5^{n/2}$

SECTION 7-5

1. $y_{n,p} = 3 + \frac{3}{2}n + \frac{1}{2}n^2$

2. $y_{n,p} = \dfrac{q^n}{q^2 - \sqrt{2}\,q + 1}$, if $q^2 - \sqrt{2}\,q + 1 \neq 0$

3. $y_{n,p} = \dfrac{q^n}{q^2 - \frac{5}{2}q + 1}$, if $q \neq \frac{1}{2}, q \neq 2$

4. $y_{n,p} = C_{1,n}2^n + C_{2,n}3^n$,

where $C_{1,n} = \begin{cases} c_1, & \text{for } n = 0, 1 \\ c_1 - \displaystyle\sum_{j=1}^{n-1} \frac{j^k}{2^{j+1}}, & \text{for } n = 2, 3, \ldots \end{cases}$

and $C_{2,n} = \begin{cases} c_2, & \text{for } n = 0, 1 \\ c_2 + \displaystyle\sum_{j=1}^{n-1} \frac{j^k}{3^{j+1}}, & \text{for } n = 2, 3, \ldots \end{cases}$

5. If $\beta_1 \neq \beta_2, \beta_1\beta_2 \neq 0$: $y_{n,p} = C_{1,n}\beta_1^n + C_{2,n}\beta_2^n$,

where $C_{1,n} = \begin{cases} c_1, & \text{for } n = 0 \\ c_1 + \dfrac{1}{\beta_1 - \beta_2}\dfrac{1}{\beta_1}\displaystyle\sum_{j=0}^{n-1} \frac{1}{j!\beta_1^j}, & \text{for } n = 1, 2, \ldots \end{cases}$

and $C_{2,n} = \begin{cases} c_2, & \text{for } n = 0 \\ c_2 + \dfrac{1}{\beta_2 - \beta_1}\dfrac{1}{\beta_2}\displaystyle\sum_{j=0}^{n-1} \frac{1}{j!\beta_2^j}, & \text{for } n = 1, 2, \ldots \end{cases}$

If $\beta_1 = \beta_2 \neq 0$: $y_{n,p} = (C_{1,n} + nC_{2,n})\beta_1^n$,

where $C_{1,n} = \begin{cases} c_1, & \text{for } n = 0 \\ c_1 - \dfrac{1}{\beta_1^2} \displaystyle\sum_{j=0}^{n-1} \dfrac{j+1}{j!\beta_1^j}, & \text{for } n = 1, 2, \ldots \end{cases}$

and $C_{2,n} = \begin{cases} c_2, & \text{for } n = 0 \\ c_2 + \dfrac{1}{\beta_1^2} \displaystyle\sum_{j=0}^{n-1} \dfrac{1}{j!\beta_1^j}, & \text{for } n = 1, 2, \ldots \end{cases}$

6. $D_{n+1} - b_n \dfrac{u_n}{u_{n+2}} D_n = 0$

7. $D_{n+1} - D_n = 0$, $D_n = d_0$; $C_{n+1} - C_n = d_0$, $C_n = c_0 + n\,d_0$;
   $y_n = C_n u_n = (c_0 + n\,d_0)\beta^n$

8. $y_n = C_n = \begin{cases} C_0, & \text{for } n = 0 \\ C_0 + \sum_{j=0}^{n-1} D_j, & \text{for } n = 1, 2, \ldots, \end{cases}$

   where $D_j = \begin{cases} D_0, & \text{for } j = 1 \\ (-1)^j D_0 \prod_{k=0}^{j-1} \alpha_k, & \text{for } j = 1, 2, \ldots \end{cases}$

9. $(C_{1,n+1} - C_{1,n})u_{1,n+1} + (C_{2,n+1} - C_{2,n})u_{2,n+1} = f_n$,
   $(C_{1,n+1} - C_{1,n})v_{1,n+1} + (C_{2,n+1} - C_{2,n})v_{2,n+1} = g_n$

SECTION 7–6

1. $y_{n+1} - \dfrac{2 + hA}{2 - hA} y_n = 0$

2. $y_{n+1} = \dfrac{y_n}{1 - Ahy_n}$

3. $y_n = y_0(1 + h^2)^{n/2} \cos(n \tan^{-1} h)$, $z_n = -y_0(1 + h^2)^{n/2} \sin(n \tan^{-1} h)$

4. Approximating difference equation problem

$$\left.\begin{array}{l} y_{n+1} = \cos\phi\, y_n + \sin\phi\, z_n, \\ z_{n+1} = -\sin\phi\, y_n + \cos\phi\, z_n, \end{array}\right\} y_0 \text{ arbitrary, } z_0 = 0$$

Solution: $y_n = y_0 \cos n\phi$, $z_n = -y_0 \sin n\phi$, where $\phi = \cos^{-1}(4 - h^2)/(4 + h^2)$

MISCELLANEOUS EXERCISES, CHAPTER 7

1. $na_n - (n - 1)(n - 2)a_{n-1} - 3a_{n-2} = 0$, $n = 2, 3, \ldots$
   a_0 arbitrary, $a_1 = 0$

3. $ny_{n+1} - (n + 1)y_n = n(n + 1)$

5. $y_n = y_0^{1/3^n}$

6. $y_n = (c_1 + c_2 n)2^n$

7. $y_n = c_1 + c_2 5^n$

8. $y_n = (c_1 \cos \frac{1}{6}n\pi + c_2 \sin \frac{1}{6}n\pi)3^{n/2}$

9. $y_n = (c_1 + c_2 n)2^n + n^2 + 7n + 15$

10. $y_n = c_1 - \frac{1}{2}n(n-1) + \left(c_2 + \sum_{j=1}^{n-1} \frac{j}{2j+1}\right)2^n, \quad n = 2, 3, \dots$

   $y_0 = c_1 + c_2, \quad y_1 = c_1 + 2c_2$

11. $q_n(t) = (\lambda t)^n/n!$ 12. $p_n(t) = (\lambda t)^n e^{-\lambda t}/n!$

13. $y_n = 3A_1 2^n + A_2 4^n, \quad z_n = -A_1 2^n - A_2 4^n$

14. (a) $y = \frac{1}{12}n^2 + c_1 + c_2(-1)^n + c_3\omega^n$
   $+ c_4(-1)^n\omega^n + c_5\omega^{2n} + c_6(-1)^n\omega^{2n}$ where $\omega = (-1+i\sqrt{3})/2$

   (b) $c_1 = -\frac{7}{72}, \quad c_2 = -\frac{1}{8}, \quad c_3 = \frac{1}{9}, \quad c_4 = 0, \quad c_5 = \frac{1}{9}, \quad c_6 = 0,$
   $y_n = \frac{1}{12}n^2 - \frac{7}{72} - \frac{1}{8}(-1)^n + \frac{1}{9}(\omega^n + \omega^{2n})$

15. $a_0 = a_1 = 0, \quad a_2 = 1;$
   $a_{n+3} - a_{n+2} - a_{n+1} + a_n = 0, \quad n = 0, 1, 2, \dots$

16. $a_n = \frac{1}{2}[n - \frac{1}{2} + (-1)^n\frac{1}{2}], \quad n = 0, 1, 2, \dots$

18. $a_0 = a_1 = a_2 = 0, \quad a_3 = a_4 = 1, \quad a_5 = 2;$
   $a_{n+6} - a_{n+5} - a_{n+4} + a_{n+2} + a_{n+1} - a_n = 0, \quad n = 0, 1, 2, \dots$

19. $a_n = \frac{1}{12}n^2 - \frac{7}{72} - \frac{1}{8}(-1)^n + \frac{1}{9}(\omega^n + \omega^{2n}), \quad n = 0, 1, 2, \dots$

22. (b) $a_n = c_1 n^3 + c_2 n^2 + c_3 n + c_4 + (-1)^n c_5 n$
   $+ (-1)^n c_6 + i^n c_7 + (-i)^n c_8 + \omega^n c_9 + \omega^{2n} c_{10}$

CHAPTER 8

SECTION 8–1

1. $z = x \sin y + f(x)$ 2. $z = \frac{1}{2}x^2 \cos y + f(y)$

3. $z = -y + e^x f(y)$ 4. $z = \dfrac{\sin (xy)}{xy} + \dfrac{f(x)}{y}$

5. $z = \frac{1}{2}x^2 + xf(y) + g(y)$ 6. $z = f(x)e^y + g(x)e^{-y}$

7. $z = f(y)x^{(1+\sqrt{5})/2} + g(y)x^{(1-\sqrt{5})/2}$ 8. $z = ye^{2x} + f(x) + g(y)$

SECTION 8–2

1. $\dfrac{\partial z}{\partial x} + 2x\dfrac{\partial z}{\partial y} = 0$ 2. $\dfrac{\partial z}{\partial x} + 2x\dfrac{\partial z}{\partial y} = 0$

3. $2x\dfrac{\partial z}{\partial x} + y\dfrac{\partial z}{\partial y} = z$ 4. $x\dfrac{\partial z}{\partial y} - y\dfrac{\partial z}{\partial x} = 0$

5. $yz\dfrac{\partial z}{\partial x} - xz\dfrac{\partial z}{\partial y} - xy = 0$ 6. $2z\dfrac{\partial z}{\partial x} + (x - z)\dfrac{\partial z}{\partial y} + 2x = 0$

SECTION 8–3

1. $f(x^2 + y^2, y^2 + z^2) = 0$ 2. $z = f(x + y^2)$

3. $f(x + y^2, 3xy + 2y^3 + 3z) = 0$ 4. $f(x^2 - y, x^3 - 3xy + 3z) = 0$

5. $f(x - z, 2y - z^2) = 0$ 7. $f[e^{-3x}(y + z), e^{3x}(z - 2y)] = 0$

8. $f[(2y + z)/x^4, 2y - z] = 0$

SECTION 8–4

1. $z = 1 + \sqrt{(x + y^2)/2}$ 2. $z = \cos(1 + \sqrt{x - y})$

3. $z = y^3$ 4. $z = xy^2$

5. $z = f(x + y^2)$ where $f(u)$ is any function for which $f(2) = 3$; for example, $f(u) = u + 1$ or $f(u) = \frac{3}{2}u$ or $f(u) = 3\cos(u - 2)$

6. $(A_1 - B_1)(z - C_0) = C_1(x - y - A_0 + B_0)$

7. $z^2 = x^2 + 1 - 2(x^2 + y^2)^{1/2}$

SECTION 8–7

1. (a) $T(x, t) = T_1 \sin(\pi x/L)e^{-\lambda(\pi^2/L^2)t} + T_3 \sin(3\pi x/L)e^{-\lambda(\pi^2/L^2)9t}$

(b) $T(x, t) = \dfrac{32T_1}{\pi^3} \displaystyle\sum_{n=1,3,5,\cdots} \dfrac{1}{n^3} \sin\dfrac{n\pi x}{L} e^{-(n^2\pi^2\lambda/L^2)t}$

(c) $T(x, t) = \dfrac{2T_1}{\pi} \displaystyle\sum_{n=1}^{\infty} \dfrac{1}{n}\left[\cos\dfrac{n\pi x_1}{L} - \cos\dfrac{n\pi x_2}{L}\right]\sin\dfrac{n\pi x}{L} e^{-\lambda(n^2\pi^2/L^2)t}$

2. $T(x, t) = \displaystyle\sum_{n=1}^{\infty} C_n \sin\dfrac{n\pi x}{L} e^{-\lambda(\pi^2/L^2)n^2 t} + A + (B - A)\dfrac{x}{L}$,

where $C_n = \dfrac{2}{L}\displaystyle\int_0^L T_0(x)\sin\dfrac{n\pi x}{L}\,dx + \dfrac{2}{n\pi}[(-1)^n B - A]$

4. $T(x, t) = \frac{1}{2}T_1[1 - \cos(2\pi x/L)e^{-\lambda(4\pi^2/L^2)t}]$

6. $T(x, t) = \displaystyle\sum_{n=0}^{\infty} C_n \cos\dfrac{n\pi x}{L} e^{-\lambda(\pi^2/L^2)n^2 t}$

where $C_0 = \dfrac{1}{L}\displaystyle\int_0^L T_0(x)\,dx$, $C_n = \dfrac{2}{L}\displaystyle\int_0^L T_0(x)\cos\dfrac{n\pi x}{L}\,dx$.

SECTION 8–9

1. (a) $T(r, \theta) = \frac{1}{2}T_0\left(1 + \dfrac{r}{a}\cos\theta\right)$

(b) $T(r, \theta) = \frac{1}{2}T_0 \left(1 + \frac{3}{4}\frac{r}{a}\cos\theta + \frac{1}{4}\frac{r^3}{a^3}\cos 3\theta\right)$

2. (a) $T(r, \theta) = a_0 + Ar\cos\theta$

    (b) $T(r, \theta) = a_0 + (A + \frac{3}{4}B)r\cos\theta + \frac{1}{12}B(r^3/a^2)\cos 3\theta$

3. $T(r, \theta) = C_m(a/r)^m \cos m\theta$

4. A modified Bessel differential equation, namely,

$$r^2 g''_{m,n}(r) + r g'_{m,n}(r) - \left(\frac{m^2\pi^2}{L^2}r^2 + n^2\right)g_{m,n}(r) = 0.$$

Its general solution is of the form

$$g_{m,n}(r) = c_1 I_n\left(\frac{m\pi}{L}r\right) + c_2 K_n\left(\frac{m\pi}{L}r\right),$$

where c_1 and c_2 are arbitrary constants, and I_n and K_n are modified Bessel functions of order n, of the first and second kind, respectively. (Since the function K_n has a singularity at the origin, the constant c_2 must be taken to be zero for solid cylinders.)

5. (a) $T(r, \theta, z) = \dfrac{T_0}{I_0(\pi a/L)}I_0\left(\dfrac{\pi r}{L}\right)\sin\dfrac{\pi z}{L}$

$$= \frac{T_0}{I_0(\pi a/L)}\sin\frac{\pi z}{L}\sum_{\nu=0}^{\infty}\frac{1}{(\nu!)^2}\left(\frac{\pi r}{2L}\right)^{2\nu}$$

    (b) $T(r, \theta, z) = \frac{1}{2}T_0\left[\dfrac{I_0(\pi r/L)}{I_0(\pi a/L)} + \dfrac{I_1(\pi r/L)\cos\theta}{I_1(\pi a/L)}\right]\sin\dfrac{\pi z}{L}$

6. (a) $A_0 = \dfrac{1}{P}$, $A_n = \dfrac{\sin 2n\pi Q/P}{n\pi Q}$, $B_n = \dfrac{1 - \cos 2n\pi Q/P}{n\pi Q}$

    (b) $A_0 = \dfrac{1}{P}$, $A_n = \dfrac{1}{n\pi Q}\left[\sin\dfrac{2n\pi(R + Q)}{P} - \sin\dfrac{2n\pi R}{P}\right]$

    $B_n = \dfrac{-1}{n\pi Q}\left[\cos\dfrac{2n\pi(R + Q)}{P} - \cos\dfrac{2n\pi R}{P}\right]$

    (c) $A_0 = \dfrac{2}{\pi}$, $B_n = \dfrac{\sin(2n - 1)\pi}{(2n - 1)\pi} - \dfrac{\sin(2n + 1)\pi}{(2n + 1)\pi}$,

    $A_n = \dfrac{1 - \cos(2n + 1)\pi}{(2n + 1)\pi} - \dfrac{1 - \cos(2n - 1)\pi}{(2n - 1)\pi}$

    (d) $A_0 = \dfrac{P}{4}$, $A_n = \dfrac{P(1 - \cos n\pi)}{n^2\pi^2}$, $B_n = \dfrac{P(1 - \cos n\pi)}{2n\pi}$

SECTION 8–10

1. $T(r, t) = AJ_0(k_1 r)e^{-k_1^2\lambda t} + BJ_0(k_2 r)e^{-k_2^2\lambda t}$

MISCELLANEOUS EXERCISES, CHAPTER 8

1. $z = \frac{1}{2}x^2 e^y + f(y)$

2. $z = xe^y + f(x)$

3. $xz + e^z + \frac{1}{3}x^3 = f(y)$

4. $ze^{x^3} = \int e^{x^3}\,dx + f(y)$

5. $z = f\left(\dfrac{y-4}{y-1}e^{3x}\right)$

6. $z = yf(ye^x)$

7. $f\left(\dfrac{x}{y}, \dfrac{y}{z}\right) = 0$

8. $f(2x^2 - y^2, z + 2x^3 - xy^2 - \frac{1}{2}x^2) = 0$

9. $f(y/x, 2z - x^2) = 0$

10. $z = \frac{1}{6}x^3 + \frac{1}{2}x^2 y + xf(y) + g(y)$

11. $z = \frac{1}{2}x^3 y^4 + f(x) + g(y)$

12. $z = f(x)\ln|y| + g(x)$

13. $z = f(x)e^{xy} + g(x)e^{2xy}$

14. $\dfrac{\partial z}{\partial x} - 2x\dfrac{\partial z}{\partial y} = 0$

15. $x\dfrac{\partial z}{\partial x} - (2x + y)\dfrac{\partial z}{\partial y} = 0$

16. $e^y\dfrac{\partial z}{\partial x} = \dfrac{\partial z}{\partial y}$

17. $xz\dfrac{\partial z}{\partial x} - yz\dfrac{\partial z}{\partial y} + x^2 = 0$

18. $x\dfrac{\partial z}{\partial x} + y\dfrac{\partial z}{\partial y} + z = 0$

19. $2xy\dfrac{\partial z}{\partial x} - x\dfrac{\partial z}{\partial y} - 2yz = 0$

20. $2x\dfrac{\partial z}{\partial x} - y\dfrac{\partial z}{\partial y} = 2z$

21. $3y^2\dfrac{\partial z}{\partial x} - 2x\dfrac{\partial z}{\partial y} = 3y^4 - 4x^2 y^2$

22. $\dfrac{\partial z}{\partial x} - \dfrac{\partial z}{\partial y} = 0$

23. $z = y^4 e^{3x}$

24. $z = x(x + y^2)\cos\sqrt{x + y^2}$

25. $z = xy - \frac{1}{3}x^3 + 4x^2 - 4y - 3$

26. $\dfrac{\partial z}{\partial x}\dfrac{\partial z}{\partial y} = z$

27. $\sqrt{3}\left(x\dfrac{\partial z}{\partial x} + y\dfrac{\partial z}{\partial y}\right) = \left(\dfrac{\partial z}{\partial x}\right)^{3/2}$

28. $a^2\dfrac{\partial^2 z}{\partial x^2} = \dfrac{\partial^2 z}{\partial y^2}$

29. $a^2 x\dfrac{\partial^2 z}{\partial x^2} - a^2\dfrac{\partial z}{\partial x} - 4x^3\dfrac{\partial^2 z}{\partial y^2} = 0$

30. $z = \dfrac{x}{a}(b - \sin y) + \sin y$

31. $z = e^{(1+k)y}(Ae^{\sqrt{k}x} + Be^{-\sqrt{k}x})$

32. (a) $z = \sin nx(A_n e^{ny} + B_n e^{-ny})$

    (b) $z = \sin nx\, y^{1/2}(A_n y^{\sqrt{1/4+n^2}} + B_n y^{-\sqrt{1/4+n^2}})$

33. $u = \sum U_n \sin nx, \quad \pi\lambda n^3 U_n = 2k(1 - \cos n\pi)(e^{-\lambda n^2 t} - 1)$

INDEX

NOTES

NOTES

NOTES

NOTES

NOTES

NOTES